The Setmakers

A HISTORY OF THE RADIO AND TELEVISION INDUSTRY

BREMA
Landseer House, 19 Charing Cross Road,
London WC2H OES

Copyright © BREMA 1991
World copyright reserved
ISBN 0 9517042 0 6

Designed by *Aztec Press* using QuarkXpress
Set in Bookman
Index by *Paul Nash*
Jacket illustrations by
RDH Artists
Reproduced, printed and bound, in the UK by
Jarrold Printing
Norwich

The Setmakers

A HISTORY OF THE RADIO AND TELEVISION INDUSTRY

Foreword by Lord Chapple of Hoxton,
President of BREMA

KEITH GEDDES, OBE, MA, CEng(MIEE)

IN COLLABORATION WITH

GORDON BUSSEY, ARHistS

The British Radio & Electronic Equipment Manufacturers' Association

ACKNOWLEDGEMENTS

Of the many people who have contributed to this book, pride of place must go to my collaborator, Gordon Bussey. It is through his dilligence and resourcefulness that I have been able to contact many of the people listed below, and from his unrivalled collection of articles, personal memoirs and ephemera that much information not previously published has been gleaned, while at every turn I have been able to draw upon his wise counsel, his encyclopaedic knowledge of vintage radio and television, and his ability to lay hands on the most obscure document and despatch a photocopy by the next post. Indeed, the book could not have been written without him. His collection has provided many of the pictures, and he has taken great pains to ensure that they have been worthily reproduced. Finally, he has managed the production of the book at every stage.

We have received help, jointly or individually, from the following people, and we wish to record our gratitiude for the generosity and enthusiasm with which they have responded to our often considerable calls upon their time, whether by writing to us, submitting to endless telephone calls, granting interviews, or looking out pictures and documents to lend us.
Percy Adams, Denise Adeane, Linda Anderson, Walter Anderson, John Archer,
Alan Bamford, Zbigniew Banks, Bill Bayliff, Alan Bednall, Maurice Bennett, J. Bennigsen, H Berghman, Edward Bickham, Edwin Birch, Tony Bertenshaw, I Blanken, Sir Kenneth Bond, Mike Bowers, C J Bowry, John Brace, Christine Brice, Len Briggs, Ernest Brown, Roy Browning, M van Bruggen, Michael Burnham, Pat Burnham, Les Burrage, Norman Butler, Douglas Byrne,
Alan Carter, Bill Caten, Ray Chance, Percy Chapman, E A Clark, Ron Clark, David Cochrane, B Colcough, Bernard Cole, Mary Cole, D Cooper, Ted Cope, Patricia Corby, John Coupé, A Cullas, Dennis Curry, Michael Curry,
Bill Dalziel, John Davies, Derek Dawson, Robin Day, Peter Degan, Geoffrey Dixon-Nuttall, Norman Doherty, Ted Dunstall, A A Dyson,
Ruth Edge, George Edwards, Maurice Eley, Angela Eserin, Walter Ficker, D Q Fuller,
G.R.M. Garratt, James Gildea, Peter Gillibrand, Ted Glaisher, Tom Going, John Grant, Reg Gray, F V Green, Jimmie Griffiths, Les Griggs,
Eric Hanson, Bob Harvey, Dennis Harvey, Robert Hawes, Frank Hawley, Jack Hester, David Hewitt, Cyril Hirshman, Margaret Holmes, Wally Hull, Jack Hum, Bernard Huntbatch, Julie Hutchings,
Norman Jackson, C F M Jansen, George Jessop, Brian Johnson, G Johnson, Alec Jones, David Jones, Keith Jones, Sid Jones,
Trevor Kemp, Fred Keys, Dennis Knight,
Norman Leaks, W N G Lee, Pat Leggatt, John Lentakis, Richard Lewis, Dennis Lisney, Jim Lodge, Joan Long, Tom Ludlow, Hugh Lynn,
Charles McClelland, Don McLean, Louis MacDonald, Colin MacGregor, J C MacKellar, J E Malin,
Michael Mason, Norman Manners, Ernie Marsden, Bob Meens, Ivan Milliner, K Mullard, E Brian Munt, Peter Neave, Dickie Norman,
Bernard O'Kane, John O'Neill, Laurence Orchard, A Otten, David Oxland,
Frank Pack, David Page, W Pannell, Cecil Payne, G Pennington, W S Percival, Sid Perry, Michael Petty, Chris Pickard, E J Power, Alfred Priestley, M Puran, Dick Purdy,
C G B Quincey,
Stanley Radford, Nigel Rigler, Maurice Roach, Dick Roberts, Ian Robertson, Roy Rodwell, Bernard Rogers, Derek Roper, Alan Rose, Jim Ross, Roy Sanderson, Robert Scott, Hilda Shaw, Walter Sicker, Joshua Sieger, Charlie Sjöberg, Henry Skinner, P. Smith, E W Snell, Bill Spalding, K S S Spencer, Patricia Spencer, Fred Stanhope, Lord Strathcarron, John Street, Oliver Sutton, Dennis Swadling, D Swannack,
Ray Talks, Bill Taylor, Angela Tidmarsh, Keith Thrower, Doug Topping, Norman Townsend, W Townsly, Peter Threlfall, E R Turner,
Kurt Vesely,
Edward Wall, P Warlow, B Watkins, Alan Watling, Jessie Webb, Gerald Wells, Sid Westwood, Arthur Wherrell, Bill White, Christine Whitlock, Daphne Whitmore, R C G Williams, Derek Willmott, Anne Wilson, Jack Wilson, Cliff Wimpenny, Lord Weinstock, Charles Wright, Wally Wright, Peter Wyatt, Walter York.

Gordon Bussey has received invaluable help from photographer Richard Williams, and from the library staff at Philips Research Laboratories.

Gordon and I wish also to thank the following organisations:
Archives BREMA Archives; Communications & Electronics Museum Trust; EMI Music Archives; Ferranti International Signal plc, Archives Department; Hirst Research Centre; Mullard Archives, now Philips Components Ltd, Archives Department; Philips International BV, Archives Department; The Plessey Company plc, Archives Department; Southend Museum Service; The Vintage Wireless Museum.
Companies Alba Radio Ltd; Aiwa (UK) Ltd; Dynatron Radio Ltd; Ferguson Ltd; General Electric Company Ltd; GEC Marconi Ltd; Hitachi Sales (UK) Ltd; JVC (UK) Ltd; Mitsubishi Electric (UK)Ltd; NEC (UK) Ltd; Panasonic (UK)Ltd; Philips Electronic & Associated Industries Ltd; Pye Ltd; Roberts Radio Co Ltd; Sanyo Marubeni (UK) Ltd; Sharp Electronics; Sony (UK) Ltd; Tatung (UK)Ltd; Thorn EMI plc; Toshiba (UK) Ltd.
Libraries Bodleian Library, Cambridge Collection, Greenwich Library, Quadrant Picture Library, Science Museum Library, Suffolk Central Library, Victoria & Albert Museum Library, Welwyn Garden City Library.
Publications British Vintage Wireless Society Bulletin, Electrical & Radio Trading, Electronic World, successor to Wireless World.
Miscellaneous Ekco Social & Sports Club.

Keith Geddes, 1990

The 1980s have seen a revival in the fortunes of Britain's setmaking industry after a major restructuring, and in 1988 we at BREMA decided that its story ought to be set down while its early days were still within living memory. This absorbing book is the outcome of that decision.

A constant theme running through it is the interdependence of setmaking and broadcasting. Whether it is the BBC in the 1920s making changes that will commit crystal-set listeners to buying valve receivers, or the BBC and the IBA jointly launching teletext in the 1970s, the broadcasters' plans for progress can succeed only if setmakers come up with the right products at affordable prices. For their part, setmakers depend on the broadcasters' making their new developments attractive, so that people will buy those products; in 1964 sales of the new dual-standard television sets were depressed by public indifference to BBC2, launched as Britain's only 625-line channel.

Initially, the interdependence was total — broadcasting to a nation without receivers would have been as futile as tuning receivers across an empty waveband — and reading the first chapter I am struck by how well Britain managed to break that vicious circle. A group of leading electrical and wireless-telegraphy manufacturers, eager to exploit a promising new line of business, negotiated with an all-powerful, unenthusiastic Post Office. It was not, one might have thought, a very promising approach, yet by hammering out the constitution of the British Broadcasting Company, and by appointing John Reith as its General Manager, the manufacturers founded one of twentieth-century Britain's most admired institutions; the Company became the Corporation in 1927. Similarly, it was a setmaker that made a crucial contribution to high-definition television by developing the Emitron camera, and by 1937 Britain was showing the world that television was a practical entertainment medium, even if still far beyond most people's pockets.

Before the industry had fully come to terms with television the war took it into the even more challenging realm of radar, and also gave it a major role in updating the Services' radio-communication equipment. It acquitted itself with distinction, and the return of peacetime brought fifteen years of growth and prosperity, replacement of the nation's stock of aged radio receivers dovetailing into the expansion of television.

Up to 1960, in fact, this book chronicles mainly success, with some failures by way of contrast, but then for almost twenty years the balance is reversed. The television market suddenly declined, and over-capacity condemned leading setmakers to take-over, while imported transistor portables practically annihilated radio manufacture. Colour generated a brief boom in the early 1970s but there were chastening reverses to be endured before Britain finally attained a profitable setmaking industry performing to world quality standards — though, like its overseas counterparts, it is almost entirely owned by multinationals, most of which are Japanese.

Through it all, the setmakers have continued to collaborate actively with the broadcasters. They deserve much credit for their part in planning and implementing the difficult transition from 405-line monochrome television to 625-line colour, and more recently in exploiting a number of major technical developments that the broadcasters have devised. As a trade unionist I am proud that, by their enlightened approach to industrial relations, management and unions have together contributed greatly to the industry's revitalization. Today's professional managers may give rise to fewer anecdotes than Keith Geddes and Gordon Bussey have gathered concerning the autocratic bosses of the past, but I suspect that on the whole these colourful characters are more rewarding to read about than they were to work for.

Before I leave you to enjoy this book, I must tell you that there is another one waiting to be written, I hope, though as yet it is no more than a tentative notion. In the 1950s, long-playing records and VHF broadcasting laid the foundations of a high-fidelity audio industry, mainly consisting of small companies, which has been one of post-war Britain's notable successes. Its story is well worth telling but it could not have received its just deserts within the confines of this present book and indeed merits a book of its own. The Hi Fi industry's trade association, The Federation of British Audio, has lodged with BREMA ever since being founded in 1965 and joined BREMA as a Special Member in 1980, so we have at Landseer House a mass of relevant documentation to draw upon. I do hope that this book, *The Setmakers*, will inspire a sequel for the British Hi Fi makers.

Lord Chapple of Hoxton, President of BREMA

1 • *An Industry in Embryo*

Prelude to Broadcasting

When broadcasting began, early in the 1920s, radio communication had been established for over twenty years, as 'wireless telegraphy': a means of sending Morse code that was used mostly where wires and cables were not available, as when ships were involved. Speech transmission was impracticable; 'spark' transmitters predominated, and attempting to impress speech onto their coarsely structured waves was like trying to print a newspaper on a roll of staircarpet.

However, transmitters did exist that radiated continuous waves, and as early as 1906 R A Fessenden, a Canadian engineer working in America, transmitted several programmes of speech and music from Brant Rock, Massachusetts, using a special high-frequency alternator to generate an 80kHz wave.[1] Unsuspecting ships' operators who picked up the signals were astounded to hear voices and instruments over their headphones, and Fessenden deserves his place in the history books as the first broadcaster. But with the technology of that period, broadcasting was well short of practicability; to take just one example, if you got too close to Fessenden's microphone it scorched your lips.

'Radio telephony' became practicable through the perfecting of the thermionic valve during the 1914–18 war. The presence of residual gases made early valves unreliable and short-lived, but in 1913 an American scientist, Irving Langmuir, described how to achieve a near-perfect vacuum, and early in the war French military scientists applied his techniques to producing a successful three-electrode ('triode') valve that came to be known as the 'R' valve. In some ways resembling a light-bulb, it was mass-produced in electric-lamp factories, and by 1918 one French factory was making 1,000 valves a day.[2] From 1916 the valve was also made in Britain, at the Ediswan, BTH and Osram lamp factories.[3] When the war ended large stocks of R valves were disposed of through the 'surplus' market and became the mainstay of amateur experimenters' receivers.

Two people are on record as having foreseen before the end of the war that radio telephony could enable entertainment to be dispensed to the general public. In America David Sarnoff, later to head the Radio Corporation of America, envisaged a transmitter radiating a variety of programmes to receivers that would be "...designed in the form of a simple 'Radio Music Box', and arranged for several different wavelengths...".[4] Arthur Burrows, to be involved in British broadcasting from its earliest preliminaries, made a similar prophecy, and was apprehensive that intervals in the programme might be "filled with audible advertisements ... on behalf of somebody's soap or tomato ketchup."[5]

The microphone entertains

The Marconi Company, which dominated the British radio industry, was steeped in a tradition of point-to-point communication for utilitarian purposes, and the concept of broadcasting came more easily to amateur radio enthusiasts. As war-time restrictions were relaxed, pre-war amateurs were joined by men who had encountered radio in the services and now took it up as a hobby; radio telephony began to take over from wireless telegraphy as the main interest.[6] Amateurs had to be licensed by the Post Office, who had absolute control over radio communication. Licences to operate receivers were

Marconi's Wireless Telegraph Company were considerable manufacturers well before WW1, but in a tradition far removed from that of mass-produced consumer products:

Machine shop at Marconi Works, Dalston, London, in 1905

Power Test Room at Chelmsford, 1912

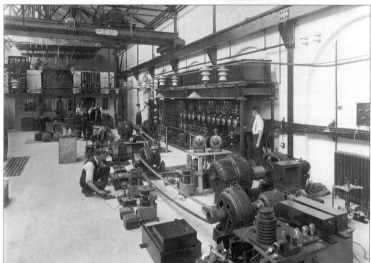

granted fairly freely but transmitters, restricted to a power of ten watts, could be operated only by those who could "satisfy the Post Office that their qualifications, apparatus, knowledge of the subject and objects, are sufficiently good to justify the grant." Those objects, the Post Office told them, should be "scientific research or...general public utility",[7] and music should be transmitted only for test purposes. But it was only natural for the more extrovert to enliven their transmissions by reading out amusing newspaper articles and playing gramophone records or even musical instruments, to the delight of their listeners.

In the field of professional radio communication, too, entertainment was beginning to be transmitted, though not yet with broadcasting in view. Early in 1920 the Marconi Company began transmitting speech from Chelmsford on 2,750 metres, to test the long-distance propagation of radio telephony. When the engineers tired of reading from Bradshaw's railway timetable and substituted records,

*Carpenters' shop at
Chelmsford, 1912*

and recitals by local musicians, reports of reception increased dramatically, both from amateurs and from ships' operators. The newspaper proprietor Lord Northcliffe saw a unique opportunity for publicity, and sponsored the transmission of a 30-minute recital by Dame Nellie Melba on 15 June, giving it heavy coverage in his *Daily Mail.* This event generated great interest, with reception reported from all over Europe, and further transmissions of music from Chelmsford took place throughout the summer. Though their overt purpose remained the promotion of radio telephony for point-to-point communication, it is safe to assume that by this time Arthur Burrows, now Marconi's Publicity Manager, was not the only person in the company with a vision of broadcasting.

Keeping the ether undefiled
As the transmissions continued into the autumn, however, they were increasingly criticized, particularly by high-ranking officers in the armed forces, for interfering with legitimate services. A newspaper article related how the pilot of a Vickers Vimy "...was crossing the channel in a thick fog and was trying to obtain weather and landing reports from Lympne. All he could hear was a musical evening." No doubt the critics were in part expressing a priggish objection to the very idea of using high technology for mere entertainment, but congestion of the radio spectrum was a valid cause for concern. The spectrum is an inherently limited natural resource, and of the many thousands of megahertz in use today only the lowest one or two could be exploited with the technology of 1920; moreover, transmitters had to be widely separated in frequency because of the poor selectivity of

contemporary receivers. The Post Office was obliged to act. It had authorized each transmission from Chelmsford individually, as a demonstration; it now stopped issuing authorizations, and granted only a handful during the whole of 1921. This was a severe blow to the amateurs, who relied upon high-quality transmissions of known power and wavelength, in order to check and calibrate their equipment.

Broadcasts with no purpose other than entertainment were made by a Dutch station, PCGG, which could be picked up in many parts of Britain despite technical eccentricities that prevented its use for calibration purposes. The station was run by one Hans Idzerda to promote sales of his company's crystal sets and components, and from April 1920 it radiated regular concerts on Sunday afternoons and on Monday and Thursday evenings, with the Dutch announcements repeated in French and English.[8] A number of telegraphic signals of general interest were also available at this period. Time signals had been radiated from the Eiffel Tower since 1910, and were also available from Lyons and from Nauen, near Berlin; for those able to read Morse, there were news transmissions by the principal press agencies, and meteorological reports and weather forecasts from the Marconi station at Poldhu, in Cornwall.

In March 1921 there were 150 amateurs licensed to transmit and

another 4,000 to receive only.[7] What was to be heard over the air undoubtedly enhanced the pleasure of experimenting, but it fell a long way short of being viable as entertainment, and there was little demand for ready-made receivers. The first valve receiver offered to the public, in fact, was not intended primarily for entertainment. It was made by a major electrical manufacturer, the British Thomson-Houston Company (BTH). One of their engineers, R C Clinker, was a horological expert who in 1912 had built a crystal set to receive the Eiffel Tower time signals, and in 1915 had made what has been claimed to be Britain's first high-vacuum triode.[9] After the war Clinker replaced his crystal set with a simple two-valve portable receiver, which was marketed from early in 1920. A brochure dated February 1921 lists its possible applications. In addition to the reception of time signals, these included instructional purposes in Technical Colleges and the generation of radio-frequency oscillations for laboratory use.

Complete receivers were also available during 1921 from Burnham and Co. and from L McMichael Ltd — both early entrants to the wireless business through the enterprise of well-to-do enthusiasts whose voices and call-signs were familiar to amateurs in the London area. Burnham and Co's main business was the manufacture of enamelled advertising signs, but the founder's eldest son, Walter Witt Burnham, had become interested in wireless, and in 1918 his father had reluctantly agreed to his opening a radio department, although considering it a frivolous distraction. The company's premises were at Deptford, in south-east London, so Walter coined the name 'Burndept' for his components and receivers. Leslie McMichael, trained as an electrical engineer but at one time earning his living as a laundry manager,[10] had been at the heart of the amateur radio movement since 1913, when he was a founder of the London Wireless Club. This was soon renamed the Wireless Society of London, and in 1922 merged with the other societies to become the Radio Society of Great Britain (RSGB). McMichael served in the Wireless Instructional Section of the Royal Flying Corps during the war, formed a private company, L McMichael Ltd, in 1920, and sold war-surplus equipment to experimenters from a stall outside his home in West Hampstead.[11, 12]

Dawn in the west
Meanwhile, in the more permissive climate of the United States, broadcasting had already begun. An engineer at Westinghouse's Pittsburgh plant, Dr Frank Conrad, who operated an amateur transmitter in his garage, would sometimes leave a phonograph playing in front of the microphone while he made adjustments. Other amateurs wrote asking for more, and he began regular recitals. This far the story could equally well have taken place in Britain, but only this far. On 29 September 1920 a local department store advertised receivers to pick up Conrad's 'Air Concerts' and sold out its stock in two weeks, whereupon Westinghouse's vice-president, Harry P Davis, encouraged Conrad to build for the Company a larger transmitter, which was allocated the callsign KDKA. At the same time, receivers capable of being operated by the non-technical were designed and built. On 2 November, within six weeks of the department store's advertisement, KDKA began broadcasting, giving the results of the presidential election, and entered history alongside the Dutch station PCGG, each claimed by its supporters to have been the world's first non-experimental broadcasting station. KDKA's success initiated a

chain reaction, and by 1922 American broadcasting was exploding into a chaos of interfering stations.

Throughout 1921 Britain lay under the Post Office's almost total ban on radio-telephony broadcasts. However, the amateurs now proved themselves an effective pressure group; though a number of them were, like Burnham and McMichael, commercially involved in radio, collectively they were considered as having no commercial axe to grind. In December, sixty-four wireless societies representing amateurs from all parts of Great Britain submitted to the Post Office a petition nicely calculated to achieve its end without offending official susceptibilities.[13] In the midst of proclaiming amateur radio's scientific, educational, economic and strategic importance, it slipped in the admission that to keep members interested "it is necessary to make the occupation interesting and even entertaining; hence the need for wireless telephonic speech and even music." As a result, the Post Office allowed the Marconi Company to include fifteen minutes of telephony in the weekly half-hour already being radiated as a calibration transmission for amateurs but hitherto restricted to Morse. However, for three minutes in every ten the engineers still had to suspend transmission and listen on their own wavelength, so that they could be instructed to close down if they were interfering with a government or commercial station.

Common sense and compromise
The spring of 1922 brought a dramatic change in official attitude. Quite suddenly the question was not whether a weekly fifteen minutes of telephony could be allowed, but how a full-time nationwide broadcasting service could best be brought about. News was reaching Britain of spectacular growth in America, creating a seemingly insatiable demand for receivers and components. British companies were understandably eager to promote a similar bonanza here, and by the end of May the Post Office had received 23 applications for permission to start broadcasting.[14] In the face of this pressure, and of a growing public awareness that Britain was being left behind, a negative official policy would no longer serve. It was time for Britain to show the world how to organize broadcasting in an orderly manner.

On 18 May the Post Office met representatives of eighteen companies, and told them to come up with proposals for a co-operative

Oxford Street in 1926, showing the aerial of 2LO on the roof of Selfridges, to which it had been transferred from Marconi House in 1925

scheme for broadcasting, or at most two such schemes; all the companies were in either the wireless or the electrical business, the Post Office having already decided not to allow broadcasting by other organizations such as newspapers and retail stores. A few days later the companies appointed a small committee to take part in the subsequent negotiations, comprising representatives of six major companies and one minor one, the latter included at the Post Office's suggestion to represent the interests of all the smaller firms. The 'big six' were the Marconi Company, Metropolitan-Vickers, Western Electric, GEC, BTH and the Radio Communication Company, this last being entirely engaged in marine radio. The minor company chosen was Burndept Limited — Burnham & Co's radio department now hived off as a separate company — represented by its Chief Engineer and Works Director, Lt-Com C Frank Phillips. Witt Burnham's early entry into the receiver business had secured him a seat at the top table.

HRH The Duke of York's wireless set, 1923

For five months, while press and parliament grumbled at the delay, Post Office and committee struggled to reconcile conflicting interests. The Marconi Company wished to build all the transmitters itself and was unwilling to license competitors to use any of its 152 patents; the manufacturers were only prepared to guarantee a service for two years, but the Post Office wanted five; there was haggling over how broadcasting was to be paid for. It was not until 18 October that matters were sufficiently settled for a meeting to be held at which firm proposals were put to the industry for approval. The wireless industry had already expanded in anticipation of broadcasting, and over 200 firms sent representatives.

A company to be known as the British Broadcasting Company (BBC) was to be set up, having eight stations (six with Marconi transmitters) located in the main centres of population. Capital would mostly be subscribed by the 'big six' who would also provide further funding if necessary, but any bona fide British manufacturer or retailer could become a member of the Company by purchasing one or more £1 shares; (by May 1923, membership reached 564).[15] Listeners would buy an annual licence costing 10s (50p) and only permitting the use of receivers made by members of the BBC; the receivers were to carry a distinctive label. Half the licence-fee would go to the BBC, and receivers would carry two tariffs. One, charged upon the receiver's various components, would go to the BBC; the other, amounting to 12s 6d (62.5p) on each valve-holder, would go to the Marconi Company as a royalty, in return for allowing their patents to be used. To protect the infant industry from imports, against which British goods would have been uncompetitive at current exchange rates, members of the BBC would be confined to British-made apparatus for a period of two years.[16] The BBC was not intended to be a direct source of profit to its shareholders, so the annual dividend was fixed at 7.5% and no capital gain was allowed.

The proposals were agreed, and on 14 November 1922 the BBC went on the air from 2LO in London, to be joined the next day by 2ZY in Manchester and 5IT in Birmingham. By the following October all eight of the planned stations were in operation, each producing its own programmes, and about half the population could pick up a signal strong enough to operate a crystal set. By the end of 1924 the figure was up to 70%, with the opening of a ninth 'main' station, in Belfast, and also of 11 low-power 'relay' transmitters serving large towns not covered by the 'main' stations. In July 1925 the BBC opened a high-powered long-wave transmitter at Daventry, itself covering 55% of the population of Great Britain, and bringing 85% of the population within 'crystal range' of at least one transmitter.

A Start to Setmaking

In 1935 Wireless World remarked that "the radio industry" was a fairly recent term, and that in the early days of broadcasting one always spoke, with some justification, of "the wireless trade".[17] Initially that trade was largely in components and home-construction kits, but it is convenient to consider ready-built receivers first.

The crystal and the valve

Although valve receivers played a more prominent role in the story of the emergent radio industry, crystal sets were to outnumber them until 1927, and to that extent may be said to have dominated the early years of broadcasting. A good one could be bought for £2 or £3, or easily built at home for less, and cost nothing to run; a good valve set cost upwards of £15 and needed a new high-tension (HT) battery to be bought every few months, as well as weekly recharging of the two or three lead–acid accumulators that provided the low-tension (LT)

AERIAL TYPES

1.—Two-wire Inverted **L**-type Aerial. 2.—Counterpoise Earth. 3.—Aerial for Use in Restricted Space. 4.—Simply-erected Two-wire Aerial. 5.—Dispensing with the Aerial Mast. 6.—Double-wire **T**-type Aerial. 7.—"Birdcage" Aerial. 8.—An Imposing Aerial Layout. 9.—Single-wire **T**-type Aerial. 10.—Efficient Cage Aerial. 11.—Simple Double-wire **T**-type Aerial. 12.—Plain Single-wire Aerial.

current heating the valves. The valves themselves, moreover, required fairly frequent replacement; the life expectancy of an R valve was only 100 hours.[18] Thus for the less affluent majority it was a crystal set or nothing. Since the set contained no source of energy, the only power available to operate its headphones was that minute fraction of the transmitted energy intercepted by its aerial, and even with 100' of wire rigged as a 70' horizontal top and a 30' downlead (the maximum dimensions permitted) satisfactory reception was possible only within 15–20 miles of a high-power transmitter. Yet until it provided a community with a signal adequate for crystal-set reception the BBC derived little income from it, and was failing the poorer sections of its population.

Under favourable conditions a crystal set could operate two or three pairs of headphones, but it was difficult to combine 'listening in' with conversation. The set consisted typically of a tuned circuit connected to the aerial and a metal-to-mineral contact that allowed current to pass through it in one direction but not in the other, thereby recovering the radio wave's audio content. In most models this crucial, but unstable, contact was achieved by the tip of a springy metal 'cat's whisker' pressing against a fragment of crystalline mineral, and achieving the best performance depended upon applying the right pressure to the right spot; fiddling with the cat's whisker might improve the contact, but at the cost of temporarily losing the programme.

The valve receiver was free of this quirk, and had further advantages over the crystal set: it could operate a loudspeaker, it could amplify weak signals and it could separate stations better. Thus, as well as bringing broadcasting to those not within crystal-set range of a transmitter, in many areas it offered a choice of programmes, since the BBC's main stations originated almost all their own material. And, wherever one lived, the valve receiver offered the exotic prospect of exploring Europe from one's fireside, at a time when many people had never heard a foreign language spoken, and familiarity had not yet dulled the impact of a Parisian accordion or a Tyrolean band.

But there were penalties besides price to be paid. Receiver and loudspeaker usually produced more distortion than crystal set and headphones did, while sensitivity and selectivity almost always relied on using a 'reaction' control to feed back part of a valve's output to its input. Increasing the amount fed back improved performance, inevitably tempting the user to cross the threshold at which the valve's amplification became literally infinite, thereby converting the valve from an amplifier to an oscillator and the set from a receiver to a transmitter. This produced howling noises in other receivers tuned to the same station, possibly for a mile or more around. Oscillation became sufficient of a nuisance to cause the BBC's ebullient Chief Engineer, P P Eckersley, to come on the air: "Is this fair? Is this British? Don't oscillate. Please don't oscillate. Don't do it."[19] The problem had, in fact, been anticipated before broadcasting began, and initially a specimen of each model made by a BBC company had to be sent to Post Office headquarters for approval, to ensure that any reaction employed was incapable of producing oscillation in the aerial circuit; if approved, the pattern set was sealed and returned to the manufacturer, who had to preserve it intact and obtain sanction for any change in design. Inevitably this restriction compromised performance and, moreover, could not be imposed on home-

constructed sets, so it was quietly dropped.

The listener who was content to hear only his local station and could receive it satisfactorily on a crystal set could obtain loudspeaker reception by adding a low-frequency amplifier, which was much more docile than circuits using valves at radio frequencies; alternatively 'valve–crystal' receivers were available, offering this combination in a single unit.

Lads in small back rooms

Early receivers, whether crystal or valve, were rudimentary, and the beginning of broadcasting caused many back-street factories to spring up, where a few hands assembled bought-in components. There was an extreme example of this in Leeds,[20] where the spectacular demand created in 1924 by the opening of a local transmitter sent a young entrepreneur off on a trip to London to establish sources of parts for the manufacture of crystal sets in a small workroom behind his electrical shop. With a partner and two or three youths he made sets up to sell at 30s (£1.50) including aerial and headphones, while

Boys winding coils at Ediswan's Ponders End factory in 1926

customers queued up to buy sets as they were completed. Fifty sets a day were produced and each yielded a gross profit of 10s (50p), enabling the partners to finance a well-stocked components business serving home constructors. But after a year or so the market became saturated, demand suddenly collapsed, and they were glad to get rid of their stock, for about a quarter of what it had cost them, to people similarly exploiting a newly opened transmitter in the East Midlands.

At this period, 'cottage industry' conditions were not confined to obscure firms. Ediswan, primarily lampmakers, diversified into wireless via valve-making, and the reminiscences[21] of one who joined their labour force as a fourteen-year-old in 1923 suggest a cheerfully disorganized operation. In the small workshop where a dozen or so lads wound bobbins for headphones and loudspeakers the basic rate was 3d (1.25p) per hour, supplemented by a bonus scheme designed to produce a target output but no more. Among their duties was lubricating the crude little winding machines, belt-driven from fan-motors, and someone discovered that adding a little paraffin to the thickish oil provided for the purpose doubled the speed. As a result, they could complete their weekly quota of work well before the week-end, leaving plenty of time for visiting the toilets to smoke Woodbines and talk about girls.

Wireless for the wealthy

Burndept Ltd were the 'Rolls Royce' of early wireless manufacturers. Witt Burnham established this private company as a separate entity in March 1922, giving Burnham & Co 5,000 of its 20,000 £1 shares in return for the goodwill and existing contracts of their former wireless department, and himself receiving 500 shares for the rights to his patents and registered designs.[22] His value to the company, however, was not primarily as a technical man but as a prominent personality in the trade and a director of the BBC, using his many contacts and his flair for publicity to keep Burndept always in the news. On three occasions he made wagers with the Secretary of the American amateurs' organization that some feat of transatlantic communication would not be achieved.[23] He always lost, but he gained valuable publicity when first a top hat, then a walking stick, then a clock, were sent across the Atlantic as forfeited stakes.

Not for Witt Burnham a run-down factory in an industrial area. 'Aerial Works' was a former furniture depository in fashionable Blackheath, conveniently near his home, and there was a London showroom in Bedford Street, near the Strand. By the autumn of 1922 more space was needed and the company acquired Eastnor House, a Regency mansion fallen on hard times, overlooking Blackheath Common and close to Aerial Works. As expansion continued, head-office staff moved up to Bedford Street and extra buildings were put up at both Blackheath sites. Provincial branches were opened, considerable export business was done and a Canadian subsidiary created. Meanwhile, capital was increased to £50,000, with shares sold at a 37.5% premium,[24] and in the company's first two years of operation, dividends were respectively 25% and 20%.[25]

When the Science Museum decided, in 1923, that it ought to have a broadcast receiver in its collection, a top-of-the-range Burndept was chosen. Such high-performance sets, available from a number of manufacturers, were not for the faint-hearted, and Burndept provided two closely printed pages of operating instructions. Valves' filament currents and electrode voltages had to be adjusted, several circuits tuned and reaction optimized, many of these operations being interdependent; strong signals overloaded the receiver unless whole sections were switched out of circuit. But Burndept's 1924–25 catalogue includes the Ethophone III (Mark III), described as "remarkable for its extreme simplicity of operation...the ideal family

The captioning of this 1923 picture from the Illustrated London News *was a major gaffe. As a director of the BBC, Witt Burnham could not have it thought that he was using the connection to promote his products, and made his Publicity Manager apologize to John Reith, who was very sympathetic*

"HULLO THE BRITISH ISLES!" THE PERFECT "RADIO" VOICE.
Our illustration is of Mr. Arthur R. Burrows, Director of Broadcast programmes, who has the rare gift of voice and temperament especially suited to broadcasting. His announcements from the London Broadcasting Station are appreciated by thousands of listeners all over the British Isles. Our photograph shows Mr. Burrows with his "Ethophone V." receiver, listening to a broadcast performance.—[*Photograph by Foulsham and Banfield, Ltd.*]

A corner of Witt Burnham's amateur-radio station 2FQ in 1921

Burndept's factory in fashionable Blackheath, 1922

When the celebrated diva
Tetrazzini visited London in
1922 she bought a
Burndept receiver at the
All-British Wireless
exhibition at the
Horticultural Hall. In 1925,
Witt Burnham had an
Ethophone V installed in her
suite at the Savoy Hotel

Burndept publicity stunt,
1923

By distributing these
postcards, Burndept
combined publicity for
themselves with Listener
Research for the BBC

Ethophone V. Portable Model
For the Holidays

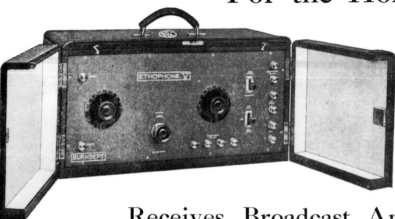

Receives Broadcast Anywhere

THE Ethophone V. receives broadcast anywhere— take it anywhere. Take it motoring, on the river, to the seaside, wherever you go for a weekend or holiday.

The Ethophone V. is specially designed to give simplicity of control, and is fully licensed under Marconi patents and bears the stamp of the British Broadcast Company.

Write for our Catalogues and pamphlets which will be forwarded post free.

All trade enquiries to be addressed to the Works.

No. 507. Model L. The Ethophone V. in real morocco leather portable case, as illustrated, complete with H.T. Battery Valves, and Coils to cover the wavelength range of all British Broadcast Stations ... ... **43** guineas.

No. 507. As above, but in oak cabinet of high-class finish ... **38** guineas.

BURNDEPT LTD. London Office & Showrooms: 15, BEDFORD STREET, STRAND, W.C.2.

City Depot: 79, Mark Lane, E.C.　　　　　　Aerial & Eastnor Works, Blackheath, S.E.3.

CANADIAN OFFICES: 172, King Street West, TORONTO.

In pre-war years vans decked out as radios were a popular form of publicity. This 1923 model was one of the first

PERSONALITIES AT THE ALL-BRITISH WIRELESS EXHIBITION, WHICH OPENED YESTERDAY. BY OUR ARTIST.

receiver for those whose interest lies in perfect reception of the programme sent out from the nearest broadcast station...rather than in the scientific achievement of listening to one or other of the more distant stations." While acknowledging the emergence of this market, Burndept continued to cater for the affluent experimenter. The opulent Ethophone Grand ("Cabinet by Broadwood") at an all-up price of around £120 could be temporarily simplified for use by the novice, but was primarily "an instrument fitted with every possible control, and therefore suitable in every way for the expert user. Do not forget that you will not always require simplicity...".

Burndept had the receiver industry's first advertising manager, appointed in 1922, before BBC transmissions had even begun. One day Frank Murphy, later to found Murphy Radio but then running an advertising agency, chanced to meet a young advertising man he knew, N Dundas Bryce. Murphy suggested that he should try the as-yet untrodden field of radio, and introduced him to Witt Burnham, who engaged him.[26] Bryce soon discovered his new employer's love of publicity stunts when, on one of his first visits to Blackheath, he found Burnham picking up a broadcast from The Hague by Adelina Patti and relaying it by loudspeakers on the roof of Eastnor House to public and press gathered on the common. Early Burndept receivers looked like laboratory instruments, but the Ethophone V, introduced in 1923, had its valves totally enclosed and was much more presentable. Bryce placed them with society photographers for use as studio props and, less credibly, had an allegedly portable version photographed on board punts and houseboats, cruisers and yachts, at suitably fashionable locations. A set was also pushed around Blackheath on a handcart, playing loudly. This provoked a man with a barrel organ and a donkey to remark that he was wasting his time; could he perhaps take the set round instead? Bryce and Burnham took up the suggestion and paid him a weekly wage to tour London and the provinces, where Burndept agents clamoured for their particular towns to be visited.

McMichael makes his preparations

From the early months of 1922 Leslie McMichael, hitherto trading from his home and from a stall pitched outside it, strove to be ready for the anticipated broadcasting boom. One of those supplying him with both receivers and components was Benjamin Hesketh, BSc, who ran a small business in Chalvey, near Slough; boys from Eton College bought components from him, and ebonite panels that they would bring back to be engraved at 1½d (0.6p) per letter. Hesketh's company made, to his own novel and advanced designs, many of the components he sold and used in his receivers. McMichael evidently saw in his talents the basis for a successful partnership, for the two companies merged, producing receivers under the trade mark 'MH' (McMichael Hesketh) though still trading as L McMichael Ltd. Initially, their factory was only a timber and corrugated-iron shed in Wexham Road, Slough, but they were shortly able to acquire two acres of the site on which it stood, giving them ample room for expansion. By the time the first All-British Wireless Exhibition opened at the Horticultural Hall on 30 September 1922 they were able to show receivers with 1, 2, 3 or 4 valves, and *Wireless World* gave their exhibit more space than any other. Like Burnham, McMichael adopted a high profile by siting his head office and showrooms in the Strand area.[11, 27]

McMichael delivery van, 1923

Benjamin Hesketh (left) and Leslie McMichael operating 'Radio Coach 6ZZ' on a Scottish express from Kings Cross, 5 July 1924

Instrument-maker turns setmaker
Pye, located in Cambridge, had the distinction of making scientific instruments for various departments of the university.[28] In 1896 William George Pye had started a part-time business while employed as an instrument-maker at the Cavendish Laboratory, and by 1914 W G Pye & Co employed 40 people and manufactured a range of

W G Pye & Co factory at Church Path, Chesterton, 1923

Pye 500-series receivers in production, 1923

instruments for teaching and research. The war created a strong military demand for precision instruments, and the work-force was increased to 100, but peacetime brought a potentially disastrous fall in business. Wireless seemed a promising means of extending the company's activities, and the first venture was a unit system of valve panels, intended for educational use but also bought by amateurs. This product caught the attention of Edward (later Sir Edward) Appleton, who became a technical adviser to the company and was also tutor to W G Pye's son Harold, then a science student at St John's College.

With the advent of broadcasting, a series of 2-, 3- and 4-valve receivers was produced, every inch the laboratory instrument. Where Pye's engineers found commercial components unsatisfactory, they designed their own. Thus they made resistors from blotting paper soaked in indian ink then gently baked as a pile of discs compressed in an ebonite tube; these were less unstable than commercial resistors consisting of a single strip of such material, or even of a pencil line drawn on paper.[29] Their tuning coils had low self-capacity and gave exceptionally sharp tuning. The qualified electrical engineer who reviewed the 1923 wireless exhibition for *Popular Wireless* was enthusiastic: "Like the sets, the coils are splendidly made, and will recommend themselves to all who know a good thing when they see it. We were most favourably impressed with these exhibits...". Alas this was not the verdict of the cycle dealers, electrical retailers and garage proprietors to whom Harold Pye, newly graduated, demonstrated the sets. In five weeks 'on the road' he did not sell one. More conscientious than many of their competitors, Pye had fully complied with the Post Office ruling that receivers must not be capable of radiating oscillation from the aerial, and this had made them fatally insensitive. Against some opposition, Harold was able to have the series dropped, and with Appleton's help designed a new range of receivers in 1924. These were well up to current standards, and the wireless side of the company began to prosper.

Largely lacklustre
Meanwhile, what of the 'big six', who had set up the BBC in order to make profits from receivers? A year after broadcasting began, a technical journalist reviewing a major wireless exhibition wrote:

> "Some of the larger companies are merely dabbling. There seems to be no imagination or originality being exercised; they are making petty little efforts to see whether wireless is really worth going in for; they will probably in the end decide that it is not, and the fault will be their own"[80]

The analysis is perceptive, and the prophecy was to prove correct. Of the 'big six', only GEC had any background in consumer products, and their 'Gecophone' receivers were widely distributed and well-regarded. But to judge from the numbers surviving in collections, neither Metro-Vick's 'Cosmos' nor BTH's 'Radiola' receivers were among the early valve receivers produced in quantity, though Radiola crystal sets were notably successful and Metro-Vick's research department quickly established a leading position in valve development. In both companies, receiver manufacture was a relatively minor diversification which had to fit as best it could into a predominantly 'heavy-electrical' culture. The Radio Communication Company and Western Electric (whose British arm from 1925 was Standard Telephones and Cables) both had their successes with components, but neither became significant as a setmaker.

The Marconi Company, which had broadcast music almost three years before the BBC, seems to have been unprepared for this totally new line of business. P P Eckersley, who before joining the BBC was at the centre of Marconi's broadcasting activities, later revealed that owing to considerable indecision in head office the engineers who were to design the first 'Marconiphone', the two-valve 'V2', got their first knowledge of the requirements of performance from a full front-page advertisement in the *Daily Mail*.[31] Since soon after the war, Marconis had made some non-industrial receivers, principally for the amateur market, at the Soho premises of The Marconi Scientific Instrument Co, but in 1922 a 'Marconiphone' department was set up at Chelmsford. A publicity document of 1923 says of the receivers "Upwards of 1,500

work people are constantly employed on their manufacture." However, it is likely that most of them did not work at Chelmsford but at Dagenham, where The Sterling Telephone and Electric Company had its factory, employing over 2,000 people.[32] At that time Sterling was

one of Marconi's 'Associated Companies'[33] but in August 1925 was taken over by Marconiphone,[34] who moved their headquarters to Sterling's premises in Tottenham Court Road and thereafter had almost all their receivers made at Dagenham.

Between 1922 and 1925 Marconiphone sets were also made in considerable numbers by a small and struggling firm of jobbing engineers, which initially occupied a converted laundry in Holloway. That firm was Plessey, and the episode had far-reaching consequences.

Contractors to the trade[35]

Plessey had been founded in 1917 as a private company, taking over the business and premises of an unsuccessful firm making pianoforte actions, the better to exploit the production-engineering talents of one of the employees, W O Heyne. Though Bill Heyne had lived in Britain since early childhood he was German by birth and had been interned until late in 1916, then obliged to take work well below his capability. In 1921 an American, B G Clark, who was in the shoe business, got Plessey to manufacture tools for producing tags and eyelets. He was sufficiently impressed with the company to buy shares in it and arrange for his son Allen, then 22, to join it. Allen had been wounded and slightly shell-shocked in the war, and had not persisted in any of several jobs he had since taken on; introducing him to Heyne, his father had said "See what you can do with this big fella, try and make an engineer out of him". In the event, after turning his hand to every aspect of the business for a couple of years Allen Clark emerged as an excellent salesman and an effective, if autocratic, manager, ideally complementing Bill Heyne. In the early summer of 1922 B G Clark received inside information from a friend that Marconis were looking for firms to manufacture wireless sets under contract. The two of them, together with a mutual friend, thereupon formed the British Radiophone Company specifically to tender for radio orders, which they proposed to sub-contract to Plessey, and on 4 July they received from Marconis an order for 500 'Junior' crystal sets, 5,000 'A' crystal sets and 5,000 V2 receivers, worth a total of £30,625. British Radiophone's contract with Plessey totalled £5,000 less than this, and following complaints from Heyne to B G Clark, more equitable arrangements were negotiated for future contracts. The initial contract price for the V2 was £2 10s (£2.50); with valves, batteries and headphones added, it retailed at over £20.

The Marconi order made a move to larger premises necessary. Heyne and B G Clark saw a suitable freehold factory on offer at Ilford for £20,000 including a quantity of machinery. This was far beyond their means, but on B G Clark's recommendation Heyne made an offer of £7,500, which to his surprise was accepted, and Plessey moved into the factory early in 1923. It proved an excellent bargain, the property and its remaining machinery being valued at almost £13,000 even after they had raised over £3,000 from the sale of unwanted items.

In 1923 Marconis formed their Marconiphone department into a subsidiary company, and late in 1924 Marconiphone asked to participate in Plessey's shareholding. As their orders made up about 80% of Plessey's turnover, they were not to be refused. The Plessey Company (1925) Ltd was formed, and although Marconiphone took up only £1,550 of its nominal capital of £20,000 they nominated two directors, to whom Heyne and Allen Clark, completing the board as joint managing directors, submitted monthly reports.[36] In these, Marconiphone were comprehensively criticized. Their designs, it was asserted, were often unproven and were unsuitable for mass production, whereas a receiver in whose production design Plessey had been allowed to have a say had "a much neater and more workmanlike appearance than the one made up from the original Drawings and Specification." By placing numerous small orders for immediate execution instead of a few large ones well in advance, they forced Plessey to do the same to their own suppliers, with consequent breaks in the continuity of production. Thus all receiver-cases were made by a single firm of cabinet makers who, being under pressure, would send cabinets whose polish was not properly dry, made from wood not fully seasoned.

Heyne and Clark saw that their future lay in mass production, and were already initiating this on small items. They suggested buying two additional automatic lathes to meet the electrical trade's strong demand for screws, and they relentlessly urged Marconiphone to increase their orders for the Ideal low-frequency transformer, "bearing in mind that we are producing a better and cheaper article than anyone else." In under five months they increased weekly output from under 1,000 to 2,500, but even then deplored Marconiphone's failure to place orders for the 4,000 per week that they were geared up to produce. Plessey's work-force had now reached 250, and so firmly were they bound to Marconiphone that each week they telephoned the amount of the wage bill to Marconiphone's accounts department, who then sent a cheque to cover it.

Within a year this close relationship ended abruptly. After acquiring Sterling, Marconiphone sold back their Plessey shares (at par, but reaping a 50% dividend), their nominees left the board, and orders were run down. Several years elapsed before Plessey were able to find other outlets for complete receivers, and as a stopgap they designed and manufactured a kit for a five-valve portable known as the 'National', which was made up by local agents. However, their major response to the loss of Marconiphone orders was to build up the component side of the business. Heyne's engineering skill enabled them to fulfil orders quickly and cheaply, and allied to Clark's salesmanship established them as leading suppliers to setmakers.

Distribution and retailing
Manufacturers marketed their receivers in a variety of ways. GEC sold through general wholesalers, through its own 'Magnet House' wholesale/retail branches in major cities, and also through music and record shops, using the Columbia Graphophone Company as agents; Marconis opened branch offices in 9 provincial cities. At the other extreme, many of the smaller companies sold only in their own areas. In June 1923 Harold Elston & Co, The Modern Garage, Brecon demonstrated their range of Elstonphone receivers at the town's Palace Cinema, and showed the film *How We Wireless*; in order to familiarize the people in isolated areas with the meaning of wireless, they also offered to provide the equipment for locally organized demonstrations in surrounding villages.[37] Two nationwide wireless wholesalers, Lugtons and Brown Brothers, had begun in bicycles then branched out into gramophones and records. They mainly supplied the smaller retailers, many of whom had little technical expertise, and serviced sets for them in large well-equipped service departments,

The Wireless counter at
a branch, thought to be
Southampton, of the
wholesalers Brown Bros,
c. 1929

which also assessed new models submitted by manufacturers before it
was decided whether to stock them.

Specialist wireless shops, initially selling war-surplus equipment
and components to experimenters, sprang up in large cities soon after
1918. Lisle Street, just behind Leicester Square, became a focus for
them in London. It had been, as it later became again, a street given
over to commercial sex, but for almost half a century the words that
drew men compulsively to shabby stores, eyes a-sparkle with desire,
were successively 'Wireless', 'Radio' and 'Electronics'.

Though the number of shops devoted exclusively to wireless
increased with the advent of broadcasting, there were many more
where wireless was added to an existing business, occupying anything
from a counter in a suburban newsagent and tobacconist's to a large
area in a department store; Gamages, in Holborn, had an especially
noted wireless department. Bicycle shops were particularly likely to
diversify into the trade, their first contact with it often being as
battery-charging depots. Lead–acid accumulators were both heavy and
dangerous to carry, so people wanted charging facilities within easy
walking distance of home. In residential areas cycle stores, with their
workshops and their 'mechanically minded' proprietors, were the
shops most likely to take up this profitable sideline, which brought the
shopkeeper into frequent contact with those local households that
owned valve receivers. Selling valves, components and receivers was
thus a natural progression, the more so if the wholesaler supplying
the shop's cycles also carried wireless.

The enterprising proprietor of a North London cycle shop not only
installed a number of demonstration crystal sets and headphones, but
borrowed benches from the local church for the public to sit on while
they listened. He erected 20-foot poles in customers' gardens and
rigged aerials to them, though initially more fences were knocked
down than aerials put up. Armed with a circuit for a three-valve set,
which a friend who had been a ship's operator had sketched out for
him, he made a profitable foray into manufacturing. His teenage son
was given the task of drilling precisely located holes through sheets of
ebonite. Thinking to save himself work, the lad drilled through four

sheets clamped together; all were wrong, and his attempt at mass production earned him a hiding.[38]

Home-built Receivers

The BBC and the home constructor[39]

Broadcasting tempted many people to take up wireless as a hobby. Building a crystal set was cheap, easy, rewarding and addictive, leading on to valve receivers. The home constructor also enjoyed some economic advantages. Working in the garden shed or on the kitchen table he had neither overheads nor wages to pay, and initially the manufacturer was not sufficiently superior in either efficiency or scale to offset this. But for a time a loophole in the law gave home construction a further advantage that seriously undermined both the financing of the BBC and the profits of its member companies. To understand this episode we must go back to 1922.

It had been assumed by those setting up the BBC that except for a small number of experimenters all listeners would contribute to the cost of broadcasting both through the licence fee and through the tariff payable on BBC receivers. But by claiming to be an experimenter, anyone could legally operate a home-made set, on which no tariff was payable, on an 'experimenter's licence' costing the same as the BBC licence and similarly yielding the BBC 5s (25p). By January 1923 the BBC estimated that four-fifths of such licences were not going to bona fide experimenters but to people who simply wanted to 'listen in' without the expense of buying a BBC receiver. The 'pseudo experimenter', as P P Eckersley termed him, mostly bought either an easy-to-assemble kit from a non-BBC company (since BBC companies charged a tariff on kits) or the components to build a circuit from one of the numerous wireless magazines that had sprung up. Either way, the BBC lost its tariff. Moreover components, as distinct from ready-built receivers, enjoyed no protection against cheap imports from countries paying very low wages.

This problem had been foreseen in September 1922 by a Marconi representative on the negotiating committee; Marconis were doubly vulnerable, since they stood also to lose the patent-royalty payable to them on all BBC sets. The Post Office disregarded his warning but in January 1923, following representations by the BBC, they began holding back questionable applications for experimenters' licences, and by mid-April had built up a backlog of 33,000. This, of course, only made things worse, since it deprived the BBC even of its income from the licences themselves, and encouraged a general belief that it was all right to listen without any licence at all. The BBC had been set up on the assumption that 200,000 BBC licences would be issued during the first year of broadcasting. After three-and-a-half months there were 80,000 in force, but the BBC estimated that the number of listening families was four or five times that number. Though homes with wireless sets mostly had prominent aerials, the Post Office did nothing to identify let alone prosecute evaders, and were bitterly criticized by the BBC for failing to honour their side of an agreement that had established properly regulated broadcasting without expense to the state. The Post Office were prepared to introduce a 'constructor's' licence for home-assembled sets, but would not agree to its covering only components made by BBC members, nor to its costing more than a BBC licence to compensate the Company for the

MODERN WIRELESS

February.

THE LARGEST
BRITISH
WIRELESS
MAGAZINE

1/-

VOL. I. No. I.   Edited by JOHN SCOTT-TAGGART, F.Inst.P., Member I.R.E.   February, 1923.

No. 1

OF
THE **GREAT NEW MAGAZINE**
FOR ALL INTERESTED IN WIRELESS
INCLUDES PAGES FOR ABSOLUTE BEGINNERS, ARTICLES BY SIR OLIVER
LODGE AND OTHER EXPERTS.
Also articles on How to Receive Broadcasting; Choosing a Receiver;
How to make your Own Sets; How to obtain a Licence, etc., etc.   **BUY IT NOW!**

First issue of Modern Wireless

Peto-Scott specialized in making up receiver kits for designs published in constructors' magazines. The S.T.100, current in 1923, was the first of a popular series designed by John Scott-Taggart, who published and edited several such magazines

Scott-Taggart's Radio Press, in addition to magazines, issued a series of constructors' envelopes with more detailed instructions more opulently presented. This one dates from 1925

loss of its tariff. Why, it was argued, should the poor man building a crystal set pay a higher licence fee than the rich man buying a luxury receiver?

With broadcasting only six months old, the whole elaborate structure was in jeopardy, and a government committee under Major-General Sir Frederick Sykes was appointed on 24 April 1923 to assess the problems and advise on their solution.

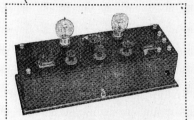

Reith fights his corner

John Reith had been appointed General Manager of the BBC in December 1922. He is justly famed for having dedicated the company from the outset to 'public service' broadcasting, but he never forgot for a moment that it was at bottom a commercial organization, and that it was paying his salary. As the BBC's representative on the Sykes Committee he proved to be a skilled negotiator wholeheartedly committed to both its broadcasting and its manufacturing interests, making a lone stand for continuing protection. The Company stood in great need of such an advocate. As an alleged monopolist in manufacture and an actual one in broadcasting it faced a hostile campaign from a section of the press allied to trade associations representing importers and non-BBC companies. However, it was solidly backed by its member companies, now organized into the industry's principal association: the National Association of Radio Manufacturers of Great Britain (NARM). The Association's spokesman to the Committee was Burndept's Frank Phillips, and he argued that, since the interests of manufacturers lay in the provision of good broadcasting, the BBC should be adequately financed and should continue even after its existing licence expired.

Summer was coming, which was always to be a slack period for receiver sales, and the public were aware that changes were on the way that might make sets cheaper. The Secretary of the BBC wrote of its member companies "Many report that they have not sold a single BBC set since the agitation commenced." The Sykes Committee's report, as presented to the Post Office on 23 August, recommended that the BBC should be funded entirely from licences, and that both the tariff on BBC receivers and their protection against imports, originally scheduled to continue until the end of 1924, should be abandoned forthwith.

These changes would have have done great harm to the industry in its enfeebled state, and Reith knew that his best hope of avoiding them lay in reaching a compromise agreement with the Government before the report was published. Fortunately, a new Postmaster-General sympathetic to the BBC had just been appointed, and he agreed to let the BBC's board consider the report at once, and even to delay publication a little. After intense bargaining, the Postmaster-General was able to announce an agreed compromise by the time the report was finally published on 1 October. Both protection and the tariff on BBC receivers would continue until the end of 1924 as originally planned, though the tariff was greatly reduced. The BBC's share of the BBC and experimenters' licences was increased by 50% to 7s 6d (37.5p), and a 'constructor's' licence was introduced at 15s (75p), of which the BBC received 12s 6d (62.5p); the principal parts of sets covered by this licence had to be British-made. By way of an amnesty, an 'interim' licence on the same terms was put on sale for a fortnight to cover existing home-constructed sets, with no questions asked. The BBC's licence to broadcast was extended by two years to the end of 1926, during which extension the Sykes Committee's recommendations would apply: no protection, no tariff, and a single 10s (50p) receiving licence.

Thus Reith had won back for the industry a period of just over a year in which to prepare itself for the full rigours of free trade. The new licences flushed out many evaders. When the agreement was published a total of 180,000 licences had been issued; within ten days they were augmented by no fewer than 200,000 'interim' licences as well as 27,000 of the new 'constructor's' licences. These figures show the prevalence of the home constructor, but do not fully reflect his commercial importance, which in August 1923 was expounded by a

magazine recommending a sister publication as an advertising medium:

> "*Wireless Weekly* is read by the very best types of Wireless enthusiast...He is not merely a passive user of a Broadcast Receiving Set — rather he is a constant buyer of components ...His Receiving Set is always being altered and improved upon and new ideas incorporated...In the present difficult times...the backbone of the industry is the experimenter, the man who is a prolific spender on his hobby."[40]

This insatiable consumer may have begun as one of Eckersley's 'pseudo experimenters' but was now firmly addicted, with a fair probability of failure heightening the satisfaction of success. Few constructors had either theoretical knowledge or the experience to get by without it, while components were far from reliable; *Wireless World* complained that a dozen grid-leak resistors from a reputable supplier contained four duds.[41] Thus there was a good chance that when the constructor had completed his set it would not work properly and he would not know why; a faulty receiver would seldom yield to observation and common sense the way a bicycle would. Desperation breeds gullibility, and many of the advertisements in constructors' magazines had a distinct aura of quack medicine: if you used this or component you could be assured of having a radiantly healthy receiver.

The components industry

As well as attracting cheap imports from Europe, home construction supported manufacture in Britain, much of it by companies catering specifically for this market. If setmakers such as Witt Burnham and Leslie McMichael are thought of as members of the industry's 'Gentlemen' team, two component manufacturers, Thomas Noah Cole (b.1891) and Edward Ezra Rosen (b.1898) typified its 'Players'; although quite unlike each other in character, both rose from modest origins to found considerable set-making empires.

Though T N Cole could be charming when he chose, those who knew him recall chiefly his air of furtiveness, and the profoundly mistrustful disposition it reflected. He was also rather short; a keen supporter of Cardiff football team, he would enter the ground carrying an orange box to stand on. Cole was born in a humble cottage in Llanllwni, near Lampeter, but was brought up in Cardiff, probably in quite comfortable circumstances since his father was a marine engineer, and it was there that he began his business career by selling bananas from a hand-cart.[42] The precise nature of his merchandise was of less concern to Cole than its potential for profit, and he was quick to spot that potential in wireless components, moving to London and trading as 'The Lissen Company' for some time before creating Lissen Limited in September 1923.[10] He operated in the Goldhawk Road area of Shepherd's Bush, and marketed a wide range of components, mostly made in his own factory, under the slogan "Well thought out, then well made".

He might justifiably have added "then well promoted", for his advertising was most cunningly judged. Each advertisement featured several components, described in terms that were relatively restrained and informative. The reader thus lowered his guard, leaving himself wide open to the advert's punch line: "Don't use mixed parts!" Only by using Lissen components throughout, it was explained, could the constructor ensure that the circuit's various parts would combine harmoniously. Though this was nonsense it was plausible nonsense, offering the constructor an explanation for past failures and a pointer to future success.

'Teddy' Rosen was one of the industry's most generally liked men, with warmth and kindness behind his ebullient personality, and a boyish enthusiasm for the business of making things. His parents, Rachel and Samuel, were Polish-Jewish immigrants to London's East End. Samuel earned his living by running a grocer's shop but his work as a lay teacher speaking five semitic languages made him a man of some standing in the community. A friend who was head of the Post Office's Wireless Department recommended young Edward to the General Manager of Marconis, and he was articled to the company as a thirteen-year-old pupil in 1911, amid gloomy predictions from Samuel's other friends that once a few ships had been fitted and land stations built there would be no further scope for wireless. During the war he served in the Royal Flying Corps, commissioning and repairing radio stations; he had lied about his age to get into the RFC, and as a result eventually received his old-age pension a year early.

At the end of the war Samuel Rosen was dying of dropsy, and

Edward desperately needed money to support the family. He returned to Marconis for a year, but on 1 January 1920, aged 21, set up in business as Edward E Rosen & Co, renting a share in a basement office in Devonshire Square, E.C.2 for £1 per week (including telephone). Rosen founded his business principally on headphones. He knew from his experience with Marconis that most existing

headphones were poorly suited to telephony, being tuned to respond
strongly to the narrow band of frequencies encountered in Morse
reception, so he designed an improved type and had them
manufactured under contract. These were sufficiently successful to
support a move in 1921 to larger premises in the City Road, where he
began to produce horn loudspeakers as well, and by the time

broadcasting began Rosen was well established, albeit on a very small scale. Since headphones and loudspeakers were usually bought separately from receivers he was in the happy position of not caring whether listeners made or bought their sets, and in June 1923, when the sale of BBC receivers was virtually at a standstill, he was able to move into a factory in Harrow Road with potential for expansion. Initially he employed only 20 people there, but soon he began to

Ultra horn loudspeakers, 1925

*In 1923 the whole concept
of broadcasting still needed
to be publicized*

manufacture components from raw materials rather than merely assemble them from bought-in parts.

Rosen gave his products the name 'Ultra', and in 1925 the company was re-formed as Ultra Electric Limited. At about this time he also changed the family's name to 'Rose'; now a married man raising children, he believed that it would be better for them not to have an obviously Jewish name. However, it was as Teddy Rosen that he had become known and trusted in the wireless business, and Rosen he himself remained for the rest of his life.[43, 44]

The Key Component

A receiver's valves were its most critical components, and most advances in receiver design were associated with improvements in valves. They were also the components whose development and production involved the highest technology, so that relatively few companies could muster sufficient expertise to stay in the game for long. After the war there were large surplus stocks of the 'R' valve already mentioned and only a few amateurs as potential buyers of valves, apart from the small market represented by the Marconi Company's 'professional' applications. Thus there was little commercial incentive for either development or manufacture, and the lampmakers who had made R valves returned to their main business. At the Osram works at Hammersmith the wooden building that had been hastily put up for valve manufacture was now occupied by GEC's new Research Department, which showed much less interest in valves than lamps even when, in 1919, Marconi and GEC pooled their valve interests and created the Marconi–Osram Valve Company (soon

abbreviated to 'M-O V')[45]; hitherto, Marconis' valves had been made for
them at Ediswan's Ponders End factory.

Demand rose sharply, of course, when broadcasting began.
Although the design of the R valve was by then seven years old, it was

From Wireless World, *1924, and opposite, an Ediswan advertisement from* Popular Wireless *in 1925 — equally informative but much more imaginative*

Pump tables at M-O Valve Works, 1920

Popular Wireless and Wireless Review, June 13th, 1925.   753

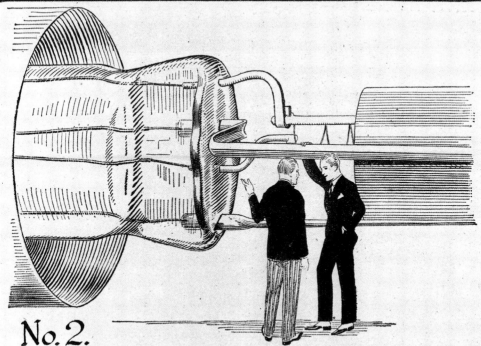

put back into production and continued to be made for several years in versions differing only in details of manufacture. Indeed, a year after broadcasting began an advertisement for M-O V's version boasted "Marconi valves made at the Osram lamp works are not a product of the Broadcasting era. They were being made long before wireless reached its present popularity — and they have lost none of the lead they thus obtained."[46] However, two companies, neither of them large, had already designed valves differing significantly from the R valve, and they were to be richly rewarded for their farsightedness.

A C Cossor Ltd, of Highbury, North London, descended from a firm founded in 1859 as makers of thermometers and barometers, was headed by a dynamic Australian, W R Bullimore. Since 1895 Cossor had built up a high reputation making specialized electrical glassware, from Crookes tubes through cathode-ray and X-ray tubes to low-vacuum thermionic valves, before playing their part in the production of R valves towards the end of the war. Anyone could see that the valve they launched in the autumn of 1922 was nothing like an R valve, its electrodes being of totally different shape. Moreover, each electrode was credibly claimed to have a specific advantage: the anode collected the current more effectively, the grid was more rigidly supported so that the valve was less microphonic, and the arched filament did not sag as the valve aged. It sold well, and established Cossor in the first division of contemporary valve-makers.[47]

The Mullard Radio Valve Company Ltd was just a year old when it launched its successor to the R valve in the autumn of 1921. This differed from the original much less radically than Cossor's, but for Stanley Robert Mullard, then almost thirty-eight, it marked the end of a long apprenticeship and the start of his rapid emergence as a major figure in the industry.

The market finds its man[48]

Stanley Mullard's early history was distinctly unpromising. Born on 1 November 1883, he was rejected by his mother and had an unhappy childhood. Soon after leaving Board school at 14 he went to work in a small, doomed electric-lamp company managed by his father, and spent ten years there until it failed. Early in 1910 he landed a good job at a large well-run lamp factory in France, but after being there only a few months he caught typhoid and had to return to England, where he joined Ediswan, at a wage of £3 10s (£3.50) a week. Ediswan no longer dominated Britain's lamp industry as they once had, and Mullard made his mark by tightening up lax procedures to reduce high reject rates. In 1913 he was put in charge of the company's small and under-resourced Lamp Laboratory, where he encountered the thermionic valves being made for Marconis. However, only low-vacuum triodes were then in production, and Mullard appears to have been involved only through making some specimens with his own hands — that is, primarily as craftsman rather than as technologist. As it turned out, he helped his career more by developing the Pointolite — a specialized lamp radiating intense light from a tiny ball of tungsten. It was through demonstrating this very successful device that he

Testing valves at Mullard's factory at Hammersmith, 1920

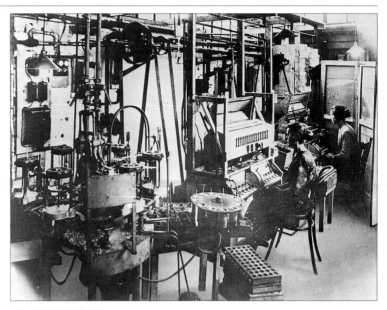

Pumping valves at Mullard's factory at Hammersmith, 1921

Exhibition at the Horticultural Hall, 1922

July 25, 1923   **Wireless Weekly**

EVENTS WE NEVER EXPECT TO WITNESS
No. 3.

Mr. Mullard buys a Marconi valve for his broadcast receiver.

Mullard vans of 1924. Note that the sidelight on the wing of the rear van is also in the shape of a valve

*Mullard's works at
Nightingale Lane, Balham,
c. 1924*

*Life-testing valves at
Mullard's Balham
works, c. 1924*

established an all-important contact with the Royal Naval Signal School at Portsmouth.

As already related, R valves were put into large-scale production in Britain in 1916. In charge of this operation, and needing someone to look after testing and development, was a naval officer who knew of Mullard through the Signal School. It must be assumed that Mullard's exceptional resourcefulness, toughness and 'drive' were already in evidence, for he was asked whether he would accept a commission in the RNVR and set up a large laboratory and valve-testing station in London. Personal qualities apart, he was incompletely equipped for such an important post, in that he had no specialist knowledge of thermionics, no managerial experience in a major company, and very little higher education; against this, he had great practical experience of lampmaking, and thus spoke the same language as the people he would be principally dealing with.

The proposal offered Mullard a major advance both in responsibility and in status, and he eagerly accepted. The new post gave him contact, on terms of equality, with academic scientists, and dealing with problems at the various factories making R valves enhanced his practical 'know-how'. One measure of his success in the post was the award of an MBE in the New Year's Honours of 1919. Another was that when he was demobilized the following month Ediswan offered him £1,000 a year to return to his old job. Although this was a very handsome salary, Mullard would still have been under the same Works Manager, whom he disliked. Instead, he took over the running of the ailing 'Z Electric Lamp Manufacturing Co Ltd', at Southfields, Wimbledon. The salary was smaller but he was to get a share of the (highly problematical) profits, and was allowed to carry on small-scale valve manufacture under his own name in a corner of the works. He succeeded in 'turning the company round', to the extent that it gave him a remuneration of £1,250 during his first year, with a further £500 from the valves he made, most of them R valves. However, the East India merchants who owned the Z company were not really interested in its long-term survival, and it was fortunate for Mullard that he had yet another string to his bow.

During his service career he had worked closely with officers from the Signal School, and had been a strong advocate for one particular proposal under discussion there: the use of fused silica instead of glass for the envelopes of high-power transmitter valves; it offered a higher melting point and lower expansion, but was extremely difficult to work. After returning to civilian life Mullard had continued to work on the idea with ex-colleagues still at the Signal School. By mid-1920, with his name on all of the relevant patents, he had made successful experimental specimens at the Z works, though he did not have good enough pumps to evacuate them, and had altogether played a leading role in establishing the silica valve as of great potential importance to the Royal Navy. A conference was held at the Admiralty, and Mullard was asked whether if he were given a substantial order he could raise the necessary money to set up a company and make the valves in quantity. Though he had no idea where he would get such money, he agreed to try.

The venture proved unexpectedly popular, and the Mullard Radio Valve Co Ltd was registered on 17 September 1920. Major shareholdings were taken up by the Radio Communication Company who, as competitors of Marconis in marine radio, were eager to break their monopoly in transmitting valves, and by an American engineer, C F Elwell, who was heavily committed to the obsolescent 'arc' mode of transmission and thus anxious to have a stake in any development likely to supersede it. Mullard maintained good relations with the Z company's owners. His impending departure finally decided them to put it into liquidation, and several of them became shareholders in his company. By paying the liquidators a small rental Mullard was able to continue valve-making at the Z works while his own company's premises were made ready, and to acquire useful plant from the works at bargain prices.

The Mullard Radio Valve Company's first premises, purchased for £3,300, were in Claybrook Road, Hammersmith and were variously described as a 'disused laundry' and as 'converted stables'. By spring 1921 they had been fitted out with the necessary services for valve manufacture, largely by Mullard's own staff of artisans taken over from the Z company, and production had been transferred there from Southfields. Although the nominal capital of the company was £30,000, less than half that amount had actually been subscribed at this time, and the factory was not lavishly equipped. In particular, it had no means of making liquid air, which was needed for the evacuation process. The Osram Lamp Works at Brook Green, a mile or so distant, was well provided with liquid air, but, as the place where Marconi-Osram valves were made, it was enemy territory. However, Stanley Mullard had long been a personal friend of Chris Wilson, Osram's Managing Director, so every morning a boy would trundle a five-gallon copper vacuum-flask on a sack-barrow from Claybrook Road to Brook Green and return with it full of liquid air — or rather 60% full, the rest having evaporated on the way back.

Sustained by the silica valve, Mullard now applied his unparalleled expertise in the manufacture of R valves to producing a variant of the basic design that would be better engineered yet cheaper. He made the electrode assembly more rigid by mounting it with its axis vertical instead of horizontal; this also allowed the envelope to be cylindrical instead of spherical, making the valve easier to pack and less liable to damage in transit. Equally important, he organized its manufacture into processes suitable for mass-production using relatively unskilled female labour. By the early autumn of 1921 the valve was ready to be launched, and a name had to be found that would commend it to amateur constructors. Mullard consulted Laurence Harley, a young graduate he had just recruited as his first technical assistant. Harley suggested that as the valve amplified, rectified and oscillated it might be called 'ARO'. Mullard liked the concept but rearranged the initials, and launched the valve as the 'ORA'.

It was a great success, with output of the order of 1,000 per week well before broadcasting began. An ORA performed no better than a good R valve, but Mullard was running a well-disciplined operation that achieved low reject rates and a consistent, reliable product that he could profitably sell at 15s (75p); this was just half what his competitors were charging for an R valve, and they were soon forced to come down to his price. The explosive growth that ensued would have made a classic Hollywood montage: plans labelled 'New Factory', deft fingers assembling valves, vans distributing them and trilby-hatted customers clamouring to buy them, interspersed with newspaper headlines proclaiming financial triumphs. Net profits for 1922 exceeded £33,000 (over ten times up on 1921), the total dividend for

Capping valves at Balham, 1926

Making the shaped glass 'foot' into which the electrode-bearing wires are set, at Balham, 1926

General view of assembly at Balham factory, c. 1926

Ageing racks at Balham,
1926

the year was 61% on the Ordinary shares, and shareholders received a one-for-one bonus issue; a year later profits and dividend were both up again. These results were achieved even after buying and equipping a new factory from current revenue. It was sited amidst good-class residential property in Nightingale Lane, Balham, and Mullard moved there in the summer of 1923 with only the first inklings of problems ahead.

The principal advance in receiving valves during the early-1920s was the change from the 'bright emitter' to the 'dull emitter'. The bright emitter's tungsten filament was very similar to that of a light bulb, and an advertisement for a receiver pointed out that "there is no glare from the valves as these are placed inside the cabinet." The dull emitter's filament needed to reach only a dull red heat to emit copious electrons, so it consumed only a quarter or an eighth as much power. To the listener, having to get filament-heating accumulators re-charged was both a nuisance and an expense, so manufacturers were under great commercial pressure to produce dull-emitter valves. Initially, their filaments were made from tungsten containing a small percentage of thorium oxide; later, these were superseded by still-more-efficient filaments coated with the oxides of various metallic elements.

Both types were more susceptible to 'poisoning' than bright-emitter filaments, necessitating a much better vacuum, and altogether the advent of dull emitters put a premium upon research resources; even then, mistakes could still be made, for as late as the end of 1925 scientists at the GEC Research Laboratories thought oxide-coated filaments too unpromising to be worth pursuing.[49]

Lacking such resources, Mullard entered the field of dull emitters by manufacturing under licence the Western Electric 'Wecovalve', importing plant from America for the purpose. This was not a good move, for although the filament power required by the Wecovalve was quite low the current of 0.25A was punishingly high for a dry cell, and the voltage of 1V wastefully low for an accumulator. Competing valves soon appeared that took 0.06A at 3V and ran happily off a pair of dry cells. It took many months for Mullard to catch up by producing comparable dull-emitter valves of their own design, and they were able to do so only because Chris Wilson of Osram, who had earlier supplied the company with liquid air, again put friendship before commercial rivalry, this time by letting Stanley Mullard into a trade secret: a little magnesium vaporized inside the valve formed a deposit on the glass that absorbed residual gases and prevented poisoning of the filament.

Between the autumn of 1922 and the spring of 1924 Mullard were involved in a celebrated patent action with the Marconi Company, who believed themselves to hold two master patents covering current designs of receiving valve, and chose Mullard as a suitably small company upon which to demonstrate that fact. Marconi's action for infringement was dismissed, whereupon they appealed against the judgement. Defeated again in the Court of Appeal, they proceeded with a further Appeal to the House of Lords, which in turn was dismissed. This was not, however, quite the classic 'David and Goliath' story it appeared; as a company founded to supply the Royal Navy with silica valves vital to its communications, Mullard had received an assurance of Admiralty support in their defence.

Technical support — at a price
Stanley Mullard's awareness that the silica valve brought security as well as profit no doubt added to his alarm on learning, late in 1923, that a new copper-to-glass sealing technique had been developed in America, giving promise of high-power transmitting valves that would displace it. In an attempt to find a way round this threat, he approached the Dutch electrical giant, Philips, asking for a licence to use another metal-to-glass sealing technique, on which they held patents. On 24 July 1924, accompanied by his Company Secretary, Mullard met over lunch Herman van Walsem, a legally trained economist from Philips, with a representative of their London Agent. The matter of the metal-to-glass seal was discussed, but the main business was something altogether more far-reaching. Van Walsem wrote a memorandum which, in translation, begins:

> "Mr Mullard stated that he not only wished to discuss a licence...but also eventual cooperation in England. He thought that the latter might be arranged by Philips acquiring a proportion of the shares, perhaps about 30%. Van Walsem immediately stated that if such a course should be entertained, Philips would in any case have to own 50% of the shares and to have a completely free hand in the technical control as well as being in charge of the Sales Department."

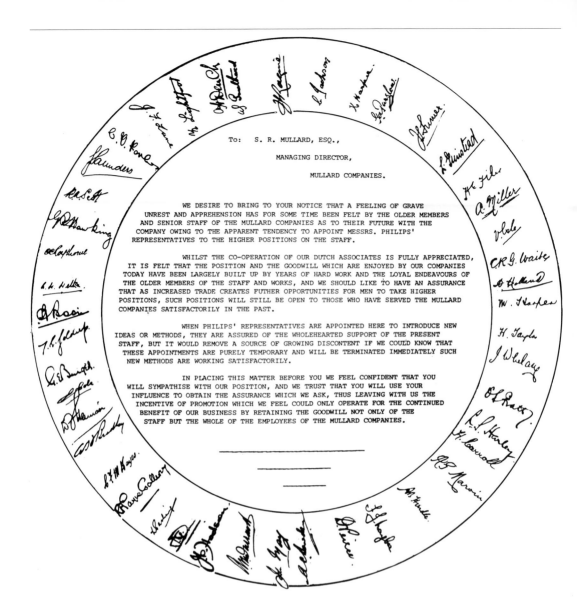

The following text appears within the circular document:

To: S. R. MULLARD, ESQ.,

MANAGING DIRECTOR,

MULLARD COMPANIES.

WE DESIRE TO BRING TO YOUR NOTICE THAT A FEELING OF GRAVE UNREST AND APPREHENSION HAS FOR SOME TIME BEEN FELT BY THE OLDER MEMBERS AND SENIOR STAFF OF THE MULLARD COMPANIES AS TO THEIR FUTURE WITH THE COMPANY OWING TO THE APPARENT TENDENCY TO APPOINT MESSRS. PHILIPS' REPRESENTATIVES TO THE HIGHER POSITIONS ON THE STAFF.

WHILST THE CO-OPERATION OF OUR DUTCH ASSOCIATES IS FULLY APPRECIATED, IT IS FELT THAT THE POSITION AND THE GOODWILL WHICH ARE ENJOYED BY OUR COMPANIES TODAY HAVE BEEN LARGELY BUILT UP BY YEARS OF HARD WORK AND THE LOYAL ENDEAVOURS OF THE OLDER MEMBERS OF THE STAFF AND WORKS, AND WE SHOULD LIKE TO HAVE AN ASSURANCE THAT AS INCREASED TRADE CREATES FUTHER OPPORTUNITIES FOR MEN TO TAKE HIGHER POSITIONS, SUCH POSITIONS WILL STILL BE OPEN TO THOSE WHO HAVE SERVED THE MULLARD COMPANIES SATISFACTORILY IN THE PAST.

WHEN PHILIPS' REPRESENTATIVES ARE APPOINTED HERE TO INTRODUCE NEW IDEAS OR METHODS, THEY ARE ASSURED OF THE WHOLEHEARTED SUPPORT OF THE PRESENT STAFF, BUT IT WOULD REMOVE A SOURCE OF GROWING DISCONTENT IF WE COULD KNOW THAT THESE APPOINTMENTS ARE PURELY TEMPORARY AND WILL BE TERMINATED IMMEDIATELY SUCH NEW METHODS ARE WORKING SATISFACTORILY.

IN PLACING THIS MATTER BEFORE YOU WE FEEL CONFIDENT THAT YOU WILL SYMPATHISE WITH OUR POSITION, AND WE TRUST THAT YOU WILL USE YOUR INFLUENCE TO OBTAIN THE ASSURANCE WHICH WE ASK, THUS LEAVING WITH US THE INCENTIVE OF PROMOTION WHICH WE FEEL COULD ONLY OPERATE FOR THE CONTINUED BENEFIT OF OUR BUSINESS BY RETAINING THE GOODWILL NOT ONLY OF THE STAFF BUT THE WHOLE OF THE EMPLOYEES OF THE MULLARD COMPANIES.

The preferment given to Dutch personnel at Mullard following the Philips purchase caused discontent, culminating in a 'round robin' signed by senior staff in about 1927

Although the memorandum credits Mullard with initiating this proposal, its tone suggests that van Walsem already had such a possibility well in mind; with Mullards as a bridgehead, Philips could gain access to Britain and the British Empire. There is no indication that Mullard bridled at the suggestion of selling half the company's 46,000 £1 shares, which he valued at £5 each; this does not seem excessive, given that a 75% dividend had been declared a month or two previously.

A further meeting was held in London in October 1924, at which Mullard and his Company Secretary were confronted by joint Managing Director Anton Philips, with van Walsem and one of Philips' young high-fliers in attendance. The Philips memorandum of the meeting states, again in translation, "Mr Mullard is prepared to hand over half the share capital of this company, i.e. £23,000, to Philips in exchange for a cash payment of £60,000. Philips would take over control of the technical management...". Mullard's statement is remarkable on two counts: first, he and his wife together held only about 20% of the shares, and there is no evidence that at this stage

the other shareholders even knew that negotiations were taking place; secondly, his valuation of the shares was now little more than half the already-modest figure he had proposed less than three months previously. To an extent this reflected the fact that Philips would be contributing much more technical assistance to Mullards than they could hope to receive in return, but Philips were nevertheless driving a hard bargain. Mullard evidently believed that he could still persuade

SALESMANSHIP and **INITIATIVE THE DRIVING FORCE BEHIND MULLARD PROGRESS**

1928 SALES
1927
1926

Home and Overseas Trade

Modern manufacture—Modern marketing—
Modern methods of salesmanship, have made
Mullard the universal modern radio valve.

Mullard
THE·MASTER·VALVE

his fellow-shareholders that they had done very well — as indeed they had. By virtue of the bonus issue, they stood to receive over £5 for each £1 they had invested four years previously. Moreover, the association with Philips was almost certain to enhance the value of their remaining shares. Mullard's expectation proved correct, and the deal went through in January 1925, though at £65,000 instead of £60,000.

Within a year Mullard told Philips that he wanted them to buy the rest of the shares, and after another year he set about persuading the other shareholders to sell. Joint ownership of the company had already undermined the total authority he had previously enjoyed, and selling out entirely could only worsen that situation, so he must have had some motive strong enough to outweigh this. The most likely explanation seems to be that he engineered the sale as the only way of cashing in his own holdings. He could hardly ask his fellow-shareholders to buy him out at a much higher price than they had recently received, and he was prohibited from selling to Philips without the other shareholders' agreement, which they obviously would not give.

Whatever Mullard's motive, by initiating the sale he showed little concern for the other shareholders' interests and by his way of negotiating it he showed none at all. The company was prospering, and by their accountants' reckoning the shares were already worth well over £7 by the end of 1925, yet in November 1926 Philips offered only £6, which Mullard unsuccessfully tried to get the other shareholders to accept; it is to be doubted whether he told them that Philips had offered him an extra £1 for his own shares. He then wrote to Anton Philips saying that if the offer were raised to £7 he was confident that by visiting shareholders individually he would be able to get a majority of them to accept that price, whereupon "the minority would then be left with the alternative to take up our interest or to agree to your proposal". He warned "that it would complicate the situation very considerably if delays occur and the good results we are now realising are allowed to materialise in the form of a financial statement…".

The second purchase took place in January 1927 for £161,000, and was kept secret, for at that period there would have been a great outcry had it become known that a major British manufacturer was being taken over by a foreign company. In 1925 it had been thought advisable for only half of the shares acquired (i.e. 25% of the total) to be registered in Philips' name, the other half being in the name of The Swiss Bank Corporation as nominees. In 1927 all the shares acquired were registered in Stanley Mullard's name. This fiction was maintained until 1938, though it almost came unstuck in 1929 when the Inland Revenue wanted to know why he was not declaring the dividends; fortunately they probed no further when assured that he was merely a nominee, and that the shares were not rendering any individual liable to declare a beneficial interest in them.

There were immediate and major consequences of this take-over, but by January 1927 the industry as a whole had undergone developments that demand our return to it.

A Separation and Some Associations

The British Broadcasting Company smoothly mutated into the British Broadcasting Corporation on 1 January 1927, keeping its initials but

Olympia 1926. Alphian Wireless Ltd soon failed, but was re-born as Adey Radio

Close-up of Alphian's 'Wireless Chair'

losing its link with the industry. In just over four years a body formed with no higher purpose than to promote the sale of wireless sets had become a national institution and was on the way to becoming an international byword for broadcasting free from either commercial or political domination. The industry deserves credit for continuing to support the Company even when John Reith adopted a programme policy that many thought too highbrow, and Peter Eckersley, by giving as many people as possible a signal strong enough for a crystal set, limited the more-profitable market for valve receivers. In fairness to these gentlemen it should be said that Reith also gave the public such immensely popular programmes as late-night dance music from the Savoy Hotel, and that Eckersley also urged them to buy professionally built receivers rather than dabble in home construction.

The number of licences stood at 2.2 million. This was twice as many as two years previously but only a quarter of the way to the near-saturation figure attained by 1939, and the public were still far from taking radio for granted. A travel writer of the period describes lodging in a remote Cornish cottage in 1926 and being invited up to the neighbouring farmhouse especially to listen to the wireless. It picked up London programmes, presumably from the Daventry long-wave transmitter, and the farmer was very proud of it, relating how it had kept them informed during the General Strike; an old lady pronounced Mr Baldwin a much better broadcaster than Mr Churchill. With pictures of Queen Victoria and General Gordon gazing down from the walls, the farmer handed the visitor a pair of headphones and himself put on another pair, lustily joining in as the Savoy band played 'Valencia'. They could hear not just the music but, between numbers, the chatter of the dancers.[50]

The setmakers combine
The passing of the British Broadcasting Company did not leave the industry unstructured. In 1923 member companies had formed the National Association of Radio Manufacturers of Great Britain (NARM), to fight price-cutting by retailers and to promote exhibitions; two other organizations were united by hostility to the BBC: the British Radio Manufacturers' and Traders' Association (BRMTA), and the Electrical Importers' and Traders' Association (EITA). The major exhibition of 1923, at White City, was organized only 'in conjunction with' NARM, and non-members were also represented, but in 1924 and 1925 NARM itself ran exhibitions at the Albert Hall, and these were for members only; at the opening of the 1924 show, with protection about to end, NARM's Chairman, Witt Burnham, exhorted everyone to "buy British goods and keep the old flag flying".[51] Opening membership to traders late in 1924 converted NARM to NARMAT, but in both these years there were separate exhibitions for non-members, a generally unpopular arrangement. Manufacturing members of NARMAT began to desert it for a newly formed Society of Radio Manufacturers.

No doubt this all seemed less tedious then than it does now, but there was nevertheless general relief when on 6 September 1926, at the first National Radio Exhibition, held at Olympia, a single body was established to represent all British manufacturers.[52] Known simply as the Radio Manufacturers' Association (RMA), it continued to run 'Radiolympia' until the war, performed valuable liaison work during the war, and in 1944 was re-constituted as the British Radio Equipment Manufacturers' Association (BREMA).

Between 1927 and 1929 the RMA won its spurs, albeit with less than total success, by organizing its members' opposition to the patent-royalty of 12s 6d (62.5p) per valve-holder levied by the Marconi Company;[53, 54] this was payable if a receiver used any of thirteen Marconi-controlled patents, and it was almost impossible to avoid using at least one of them. As sets had grown cheaper the royalty had become increasingly burdensome, and the RMA formed a Royalty Committee to negotiate a reduction. Marconis, however, refused to budge. In 1928 there was a test case in which the Marconi Company was challenged by the Brownie Wireless Co of Great Britain Ltd, who had formerly made crystal sets. Marconis had previously told Brownie that they were not liable for any royalty on a two-valve amplifier they were making, but when Brownie asked for a licence to use just two patents in a cheap two-valve receiver they were told they had to pay the full royalty; since the receiver was made to retail at 25s (£1.25), this doubled the price. Moreover, their amplifier could be used with the receiver, so it too would now have to pay the royalty. The Comptroller-General of Patents found that Marconis were abusing their monopoly rights and recommended a smaller royalty, whereupon the RMA held a mass meeting of manufacturers, at which it was unanimously agreed that they would thenceforward pay only a reduced royalty; the RMA would bear the expenses of any legal action in which a manufacturer (whether or not a member of the Association) might become involved through doing so.

Marconis had appealed against the Comptroller-General's recommendation, and in November 1928 their appeal was allowed, leaving the RMA in a vulnerable position. However, in 1929 a new agreement was drawn up, with a royalty of only 5s (25p) per valve-holder, and the RMA praised "the courteous and conciliatory attitude" adopted by Marconi's Managing Director. This magnanimity in victory becomes less surprising when the terms of the new agreement are considered. It was to run for five years, during which time most of the important patents would run out, and the royalty was payable even if no patented devices were used.

The valve-makers conspire

Valve-makers combined much more aggressively, as befitted their descent from the lamp industry, which had formed price-fixing rings before the first world war.[55] By the beginning of 1924 the post-war ring, the Electric Lamp Manufacturers' Association (ELMA) had a 'Valve Manufacturers' Committee' meeting under its auspices. In June 1924 this became the Valve Manufacturers' Association and in July 1926 the British Radio Valve Manufacturers' Association, usually abbreviated to 'BVA', but continued to operate at ELMA's offices until May 1927.[56] The Association's declared object was "To promote, encourage, foster, develop and protect the interest of the Public, the Trade and Manufacturers of British-made thermionic valves", but citing the public as its main beneficiary carried little conviction. No-one who handled BVA members' valves was allowed to handle anyone else's, and when Metro-Vick, who made 'Cosmos' valves, joined the Association in 1926 they had to raise their prices considerably to conform to its price list.[57] Mullard, who had begun their rise to prominence by underselling their competitors, were founder members. The prices that could be maintained for BVA valves were limited by competition from imports (despite a $33\frac{1}{3}\%$ 'key-industry' tariff), from

non-BVA British firms, and even, until about 1926, from firms that repaired burnt-out valves by replacing their filaments and re-evacuating them.

Price-fixing meant that competition was based mainly on performance, with various valve-makers securing an 'edge' through particular technological advances. In 1924, at Metro-Vick's prestigious research department at Trafford Park, Manchester, a team headed by E Yeoman Robinson produced the Cosmos 'Shortpath' valve. This was constructed to achieve much smaller clearances between electrodes than had hitherto been possible, with a corresponding improvement in performance. One of Mullard's first benefits from their association with Philips was an oxide-coated filament developed in Eindhoven. This 'PM' filament maintained its emission much better than previous types, and a batch of six valves submitted to the National Physical Laboratory for life-testing showed only slight loss of emission after 1,000 hours of use. On the whole, however, valves did not then last nearly as long as they did later, and the 'replacement' market was correspondingly more important. Since a valve was almost always replaced with an identical new one, the valve-maker was prepared to supply the setmaker at little more than cost price in order to ensure the replacement sales, at prices several times higher, from which he derived much of his profit.

Home Construction without Tears

For all but the truly expert, building a wireless set was a gamble. Even if you were fortunate enough to pick a good design from the daunting number on offer you had to judge for yourself the relative merits of competing components, while conflicting advice came at you from all sides. Thus a magazine asserted, concerning ebonite component-strips, "As usual, it is necessary to remove the surface skin of the ebonite with emery paper or cloth, or the set may be very noisy in use, due to imperfect insulation"; another magazine deplored this practice — by leaving a rough surface that would accumulate grime it actually encouraged leakage. As an advertisement for a leak-proof brand bluntly put it: "Even an expert cannot tell by looking at an ebonite panel whether it is leaky or not — what chance, therefore, have you?"

A Mullard 'Raleigh' receiver of 1927, built to a design from Radio for the Million

But while many were reluctant to enter the challenging world of the constructor, there was still a widespread feeling that it was extravagant and slightly effete simply to buy a set. The dilemma was resolved by the 'kit' set, of which the most celebrated was the Cossor 'Melody Maker', launched at Radiolympia in 1927.[47] Initially Cossor supplied only instructions and valves, but other major components were completely specified, including the brand, thereby removing a potential source of anxiety. The cost was £7 15s (£7.75) and building the set ("as simple as Meccano") was claimed to take only 90 minutes.[58] The Melody Maker was by no means the first kit set, but it was among the first to be marketed by a well-known manufacturer, and it sold particularly well. The following year the company went over to supplying complete boxed kits, and set up 'Melody Works' exclusively for this purpose in an old factory near their main premises at Highbury. A new model was introduced each year up to 1936, and the total number of kits sold exceeded 750,000.

For the valve-maker, the kit set shared with other home-built sets the attraction that its valves yielded him the high profit he otherwise obtained only from replacements, and in 1928 M-O V were to enter the field with the Osram 'Music Magnet', which also ran through many versions. Mullard, meanwhile, had embarked on a related scheme almost a year before Cossor. The firm's publicity was managed with great flair by Charles Orr Stanley, soon to become one of the industry's dominant figures but at this time running Arks Publicity, an advertising agency specializing in wireless. Late in 1926, concurrently with exploiting the NPL's report on PM valves, C O Stanley worked out a scheme for publishing a constructors' magazine featuring easy-to-build sets, to be sponsored by the manufacturers of the components specified and distributed largely through radio dealers, who would sell kits for the sets. The magazine's title would proclaim its aim: *Radio for the Million*.

With some misgivings, Stanley Mullard was persuaded to commit company money to sponsoring this frighteningly expensive venture, and the first issue was prepared. It contained circuits and blueprints for no fewer than four receivers designed around PM valves, the kit for the cheapest costing only £2 15s (£2.75), and although it had a cover price of a shilling (5p) dealers could give away copies to likely customers. To launch it C O Stanley spent £900 of Mullard's money on a full-page advertisement in the *Daily Mail*, inviting readers to send to Mullard House for a free copy (described as "This gift to the nation"). The advertisement appeared on a Saturday. Early on the following Monday morning Mullard, full of foreboding after a sleepless night, entered the office at Mullard House used by C O Stanley. In Stanley's words:

> "The first post arrived; it was small and contained not a single response to our great advertisement. Mullard was beside himself. He grew white and started to shout at me, standing up he cursed and swore at me, getting louder and shriller, and finally he wrenched the telephone from its moorings and threw it at me. At that moment, and just as it would have happened in a fairy tale, a Post-Office van drew up at the door. There had been so many replies to our advert that a special delivery had had to be arranged."[59]

Radio for the Million maintained its initial success, and continued (though latterly divorced from Mullard) throughout the remaining years of home construction's popularity.

The Product Evolves

As late as November 1928 *Wireless World* described the typical British wireless receiver as "an aggregate of highly finished units, any one of which could be boxed in an attractive carton and sold as a separate component."[60] The occasion for this tart comment was the appearance of a very-untypical receiver, GEC's 'Victor 3', engineered for mass production and costing only £6 17s 6d (£6 87.5p). Its components, mostly designed specifically for the set, had no unnecessary casings or terminals, rivets replaced screws, every detail was devised to be cost-effective and compact. *Wireless World* commented that its interior looked more like an alarm clock than a wireless set, but pronounced its performance quite equal to that of the best three-valve sets in a much larger cabinet. GEC advertised "Don't trouble to make your own set when you can buy this famous Gecophone for less",[61] while *Wireless World* suggested that the Victor 3 might do for wireless reception what the Morris Cowley had done for motoring, and its readers voted it the Radio Show's most outstanding "receiver or amplifier of four valves or less". Tactfully, *Wireless World* made no mention of the fact that the Victor 3 was identical in design and construction to a Telefunken receiver they had featured in their review of the Berlin show a full year earlier.[61]

The revolutionary character of the Victor 3 did not extend to its circuit, which was conventional and indeed old-fashioned. Many of those who bought it were acquiring their first radio of any kind, and for many others it was their first valve receiver; after six years of broadcasting the number of licences was still only a third of the 1939 figure, while crystal sets had only recently been outnumbered by valve receivers. But more ambitious receivers available in 1928 embodied two major developments in valve technology that would soon make most existing receivers obsolete.

The GEC Radio and Telephone Works, Coventry, in 1928. Note the plume of smoke spreading to obscure the top right-hand corner

From triode to tetrode to pentode

The sensitivity and selectivity of early receivers were limited by an inherent property of the triode valve: at radio frequencies the capacitance between its anode and grid coupled the output back to the input, drastically reducing the amplification the valve could achieve without oscillation. This situation was transformed by the introduction of an additional 'screen' grid, situated between grid and anode. When suitably connected, it virtually eliminated the capacitance between them, thus making possible much higher amplification. The newcomer was named, by extension, the 'tetrode', but was more usually known as the 'screen-grid' valve. The first type commercially available in Britain, designed by H J Round of the Marconi Company, was introduced by M-O V in 1926, and other manufacturers soon followed. However, it was not until 1928 that it was widely adopted by setmakers, prompting *Wireless World* to announce "Real H.F. amplification, formerly the privilege of the few, is now open to everyone."[62] The applications of the screen-grid valve were limited by an unfortunate 'kink' in its performance curve, and to suppress this Philips introduced a fifth electrode, between screen-grid and anode. The resulting 'pentode', eventually to become the most widely used of all receiving valves, found immediate application as the 'power' valve driving the loudspeaker, its high gain as welcome at that end of the receiver as the screen-grid valve's was at the other.

The high amplification of the screen-grid valve demanded a careful layout with metal screens, beyond the capabilities of many home constructors. This difficulty did not apply to kit sets, and though their price advantage was no longer very great they remained popular; making one's own set still imparted a certain kudos even when reduced to following easy instructions.

Music from the mains [18]

Another advance in valve technology liberated the increasing proportion of households with AC mains from the inconvenience and expense of powering their wireless sets from batteries. Mains-driven 'battery eliminators' could already replace high-tension batteries, but so long as a valve's electron-emitting cathode and its heating filament remained one and the same thing the low-tension heating supply still had to come from accumulators or dry cells; even nominally DC mains had too much ripple for satisfactory operation. However, a separate heating element electrically insulated from the cathode could be run off low-voltage AC from a transformer, making an 'all-mains' set practicable. Moreover, the entire cathode of such a valve operated at the same potential, which improved its performance.

A means of making such 'indirectly heated' valves was patented in America in 1923, whereby the heater was threaded through two holes in a ceramic cylinder inserted into a tubular cathode. However, it was the simpler technique patented in 1926 by E Yeoman Robinson of Metro-Vick that was eventually adopted worldwide. A thin 'hairpin' heater was insulated by baking onto it successive coatings of a suitable sludge. Because the heater remained flexible it could operate inside a cathode less than 1mm in diameter, as required for optimum performance, without distorting it. Moreover the heater's snug fit enabled it to be run relatively cool, which helped to give the valve a long life; in the mid-1930s one such valve began a life of 200,000 hours, remaining in uninterrupted use for a quarter of a century. A number of all-mains sets were shown at the 1928 Olympia show, including models by Metro-Vick, Pye, and GEC; the year's best-remembered example, however, was barred from Olympia by the RMA, being the Philips 2514, made in Holland.[63]

Tidying things up

The valves used in early receivers could deliver very little power to the loudspeaker, so they needed this above all to be sensitive, which is why the horn-type speaker was at first used almost exclusively. The horn coupled the diaphragm of an uprated telephone receiver to the surrounding space, achieving such high acoustic efficiency that it was probably no exaggeration when an early Burndept catalogue said of one of their receivers "...within fifty miles or so of a high-power broadcast station, music on the loudspeaker is so loud that it can be heard five hundred yards away." However, unless a horn is inconveniently large its acoustic efficiency falls off rapidly at low frequencies, producing nasal speech and tinny music. By 1927 the 'hornless' loudspeaker had largely taken over, with a 'moving-iron' mechanism driving a shallow paper cone though a rod fixed to its apex. Producing more low-frequency output than the typical horn, the cone loudspeaker could be fitted into a neat cabinet, and from 1929 was increasingly incorporated into the receiver cabinet, which also housed the batteries.

The 'moving-coil' loudspeaker, virtually universal to-day, was already available in 1927 from BTH and Marconiphone, who made the American 'Rice-Kellogg' design under licence. *Wireless World* considered that "for those who must have the best the choice of a Rice-Kellogg is a foregone conclusion",[64] and indeed the BBC would use a somewhat later 'RK' as its monitoring loudspeaker until about 1950. However, in 1927 the moving-coil speaker was still considered too exotic for any but the most dedicated perfectionist. It was expensive, it used an electromagnet drawing a heavy current, and it needed to be driven by a relatively powerful amplifier incorporating a high-quality output transformer.

The moving-iron cone loudspeaker was more suitable than the horn type for fitting into a portable receiver, and became popular just as portables were coming into vogue. An overworked joke in the 1920s was that the word 'wireless' was used to describe a device which, with its external batteries, separate loudspeaker, earth connection and aerial, festooned the living room and garden alike with wire. But while the concept of a self-contained, portable wireless set was an attractive one, realizing it was beset with problems. Bright-emitter valves used too much current, but early dull-emitters were 'microphonic' — the filament vibrated readily, tending to produce a 'ponging' sound and distortion when used in the same enclosure as the loudspeaker. An acid-filled accumulator, moreover, did not make an ideal travelling companion. By 1927 these problems had been overcome by valves with more robust filaments and by unspillable accumulators, and there were forty or fifty portables at Olympia. However, sensitivity was still poor, because portables used frame aerials, whose low efficiency was further reduced by their having to be switchable between the two wavebands. Also, their radio-frequency circuits tended to be rudimentary, because it was alleged that the public insisted on a portable having single-knob tuning. Pye sidestepped both these problems in one of their portables by pre-tuning it to receive only the

3 Valve Receiver

PHILIPS
for Radio

Van decked out as 2514 receiver, 1928

opposite: *An early Philips mains receiver, 1928*

Philips' first service depot, near London Bridge, 1929

long-wave signal from Daventry — often the only signal of useful strength available in the rural and seaside areas where portables were chiefly used, on holidays and picnics. Most portables of the late-1920s had five valves, and could more correctly have been termed transportable. However, that word was already in use to describe even heavier self-contained sets that could with some difficulty be lugged from one room to another. A number of small companies, some of them highly volatile, specialized in portables. Pell and Cahill, originally directors of Rees Mace, formed their own company in 1925[65] but were in liquidation by 1927.[66] Rees's partner, K S Spencer, was to leave Rees Mace in 1930 after a dispute, set up on his own, and in 1939 buy up the company.[67]

Vol. XXIX. No. 374

May 11, 1927

The
LADY'S
PICTORIAL
With which are incorporated
THE WOMAN'S SUPPLEMENT
THE GENTLEWOMAN and MODERN LIFE

For postage rates see Frontispiece

*From a 1929 catalogue
issued by Rees-Mace in
France, where they traded
as Rees Radio.
The illustrations are
photographic prints, not
half-tone reproductions,
suggesting that very few
catalogues were produced*

Arrivals and Departures
The right product at the right time

One of Britain's most successful setmaking companies was founded upon an accessory that saved the listener a lot of money and trouble: the 'battery eliminator'. In 1924 Eric Kirkham Cole was making 'Ekco' receivers as one facet of his small electrical business at Westcliffe-on-Sea, with an average weekly output of six and a workforce of two: Cole and his future wife.[68] The chance circumstance that was to transform his career was an encounter with one William S Verrells, a schoolmaster who had been gassed during the war and, still a semi-invalid, was earning his living as a freelance journalist at neighbouring Southend-on-Sea. As Verrells lay in bed one evening unable to listen to his radio because its LT battery had run down, he wondered whether a set could be made to run off the mains, and wrote a brief article on the subject for a local newspaper. This was brought to the attention of Cole, to whom the same thought had occurred and who was already working on the problem. Encouraged by the article, he was soon afterwards able to visit Verrells and demonstrate in his bedroom the arrangement he had devised to solve it.[69] To convert the 230-volt DC mains to a 6-volt LT supply he used electric lamps to drop the voltage and a large capacitor to smooth out the hum; the HT still had to come from a battery. Verrells was delighted and, when Cole subsequently developed his 'eliminator' to provide HT as well as LT, persuaded him

"EKCO" RECEIVING SETS.	**E. K. COLE** Sole Manufacturer. 505, LONDON ROAD, WESTCLIFF-ON-SEA.	"EKCO" HIGH-TENSION UNITS.

EKC/RD.   18. 5. 26.

Tel. No. SOUTHEND 1382.

Dear Sir, (or Madam),

               I have to inform you that after Saturday, May 22nd 1926, I an discontinuing the charging of accumulators and wireless repair work, and shall after that date only be open for business in connection with "EKCO" Receiving Sets, "EKCO" High Tension UNITS and Electrical Installations. No repair work of any description will be undertaken to receiving sets.

               Thanking you for past favours.

        Yours faithfully,

          p.p. E. K. COle.

P. S., Mr. W. Bolton, B.Sc. (Eng) of 473, Fairfax Drive, WESTCLIFF-ON-SEA, has taken over the accumulator charging and repair work and if you will extend your kind patronage to him I am sure he will give you the attention and excellent service I have always tried to give you myself. Accumulators will be collected and delivered.

Ferranti at the Manchester Radio Exhibition in 1926. They had not yet begun to produce receivers, but were establishing an excellent reputation with their intervalve transformers, one of which is featured on the stand

By 1929 Ferranti's stand at the Manchester show included all-mains receivers

to advertise it in the technical press. Sales were so encouraging that the two men went into partnership, with a capital of £50. Cole built the eliminators and Verrells sold them, calling at every house where an aerial pole denoted the possession of a radio. The device could only be used on DC supplies, which were already in the minority and fast-declining, so with the help of people better qualified technically than he was, Cole produced a model for AC mains; in this it was the HT battery that was eliminated, and accumulators were once again needed for the LT supply.[70]

In October 1926 a private company, E K Cole Ltd, was formed, with an authorized capital of £2,500. Verrells was chairman, Cole (then just 25) vice-chairman, and three local men who had put money into the company became directors: John A Maxwell, who ran a seafront amusement park, Henry J Manners, a builder and estate developer, and E R Pring, a milkman. In 1927 a factory was built at Leigh-on-Sea, employing about 50 people, and by 1929 annual profits were around £30,000. With the advent of indirectly heated valves it

A 1929 bull-nose Morris van, principally pubicizing the Daily Mirror but incidentally benefiting Ferranti

was clear that the future would increasingly lie with all-mains receivers, and Ekco's heavy dependence upon eliminators made it vital for them to enter this new field without delay; companies already making battery receivers could make the transition rather more gradually, since households with a mains supply were still in the minority. As we shall see, Ekco rose triumphantly to the challenge.

A reluctant recruit

When broadcasting began, the Gramophone Company (HMV) wanted no part of it. Their Chairman, Alfred Clark, was an American whose involvement in the phonograph business went back to 1889, and he shared the widespread perception of wireless as a threat to the gramophone industry. In 1925 electrical recording, using microphones, amplifiers and electromagnetic cutter-heads, quickly displaced the purely acoustic methods previously used, but HMV were still reluctant to embrace electrical reproduction, on both technical and commercial grounds. Early in 1926, Clark wrote to an associate in HMV's controlling company, the Victor Talking Machine Company of Camden, New Jersey. He thought there might be a small market for a gramophone whose tone arm bore both an acoustic sound-box and an electric pick-up. The pick-up would be used only when loudness was the prime requirement, as in providing music for dancing, but the sound-box would be preferred whenever good quality was required. He added "Eventually, it might be necessary to add a third part to this combination, which would be radio, but we would hold off on this as long as possible" and ended "...we are particularly anxious to keep our dealers away from wireless as far as possible."[71]

Late in 1927 HMV demonstrated to dealers an Electrical Reproducer, which was very well received, and early in 1928 wrote to them announcing that the first instruments were ready for delivery,

A Gramophone Company
van, 1929

though warning that "we are entering into this new sphere of Electrical Reproduction with the utmost caution…" and that "The electrical reproducers are such that the vast majority of dealers will be unable adequately to demonstrate them on their premises…".[72] However, by November of that year Clark was reconciled to the necessity of the company entering the field of wireless, and approached F G Kellaway, Managing Director of the Marconi Company, with a view to negotiating a licence to use their wireless patents.[73]

But Marconis, who were going through a period of retrenchment, were at this time trying to dispose of the Marconiphone Company, which was unprofitable, and Clark soon became involved instead as a potential purchaser. In the autumn of 1928 an attempt to combine the radio business of Marconiphone, AEI and GEC into a single entity failed, through GEC refusing at the last moment.[74] Philips, too, had discussed possible purchase, but had not been offered the Marconi name.[75] At the end of December, BTH obtained an option to buy the Marconiphone business for a million pounds, and only when this expired at the end of February 1929 did the company become available to HMV. By this time Victor, who controlled HMV, had been taken over by the Radio Corporation of America (RCA), and the head of RCA, David Sarnoff, saw the purchase of Marconiphone as a first move in his plans to strengthen HMV's position in both the radio and recording fields.[76] He personally took part in the negotiations, and on 8 March drafted an enthusiastic press release announcing their successful conclusion.[77] Payment was to be made in cash for tangible assets, expected to be valued at about £500,000, and in addition 20,000 fully paid £1 shares were to be issued and paid over for patent rights, for the use of the Marconi name, and for Marconi's interest in M-O V, the valve company owned jointly with GEC.[74] Marconis, moreover, would stay out of domestic radio for twenty years.[76]

The Eindhoven–Balham axis[78]

The Philips takeover brought about a profound transformation of Mullard, most obviously in its structure, most significantly in its managerial centre of gravity. In 1925, after the first transfer of shares, it was split into a selling company, the Mullard Wireless Service Company, and a manufacturing company, the Mullard Radio Valve

Company. Stanley Mullard was Managing Director of both, but he was quickly made aware that his authority was greatly diminished. When he suggested diversifying into the manufacture of receivers, Dr Anton Philips wrote a letter explaining why it was that although Philips were themselves contemplating just such a step in Holland he did not think it appropriate for Mullard to do so in Britain. Stanley Mullard pursued the idea at the next two board meetings, but to no avail; although they were eventually to make receivers, in the short term Mullard would get no closer to it than sponsoring *Radio for the Million.*

But for Stanley Mullard, whose factory embodied all his experience and endeavour, a worse humiliation was that Eindhoven lost no time in sending over a twenty-six-year-old engineer, Wim Julius, to modernize it; Dutch inspectors had reported that too much work was still being done by hand and that some of the machines were 'primitive'. Semi-automatic machines quite new to the British workers were brought over, and installed by a team of Dutch engineers and technicians. The Dutchmen had urns for coffee, which they brewed whenever they chose, whereas the British workers were liable to threats of dismissal if even caught with a teacup in their possession. From such petty beginnings on the shop floor, resentment began to spread to more senior levels as Dutch penetration of the company increased and the British staff felt their promotion prospects and even their jobs to be threatened; their unawareness that the company was by this time a wholly owned subsidiary of Philips made these changes less easy to understand and thus even more disquieting.

Conflict also developed on the commercial side. In January 1925 Philips had set up a British subsidiary, Philips Lamps Ltd, to be their selling company for all classes of product; Philips receiving valves were barred by the terms of the agreement with Mullard, but later that year it was agreed that Philips travellers should be allowed to sell Mullard valves on behalf of the Mullard selling company.[79] The clash of interests arose over radio components and accessories, which Mullard had made as a sideline for some years. Had the two companies' products remained distinct all would have been well, but under the natural tendency for Eindhoven's technology to take over from Balham's a situation developed whereby the two selling companies were competing in the sale of often-identical products. The scale of these non-valve activities increased when, in 1927, Mullard acquired an 11-acre site at Mitcham to relieve pressure on the Balham factory, and transferred the manufacture of components to existing buildings there. Neither side was willing to give way. Philips saw no reason why Philips Lamps Ltd should not sell the full range of their products like any other of their foreign subsidiaries. Stanley Mullard asserted that the status and sales record of the Mullard company established it as the more logical and effective outlet; in New Zealand, where Philips and Mullard valves were in competition, he had outsold Philips.[79] But both companies agreed that the current situation was untenable, so a compromise was worked out: essentially identical articles would continue to be marketed by both companies, but would be made to differ in external appearance.

It is not known whether components imported from Holland were always marked accordingly, as the law required. Electric lamps certainly were not, for in 1927 ELMA brought a successful action against Philips Lamps for selling unmarked imported lamps; their selling techniques reportedly included hawking the lamps from door to door in the poorer districts.[80] Nor were valves always marked, for Stanley Mullard later stated that large quantities were imported between 1924 and 1926 without exciting comment, their source being camouflaged by shipping through third and even fourth parties by different routes.[81] But whether they were made in Holland or Britain it was not thought wise to draw attention to valves even having been designed by Philips. When the 'PM' range first appeared they bore the legend 'Philips-Mullard', as had been laid down in the two companies' agreement of July 1925, but soon the word 'Philips' was rigorously excluded from all valves except rectifiers[82], and from everything to do with them; only the initials were used, and in a rather naive attempt to mislead the public over their significance the terms "Pure Music" and "Perfect Music" were freely used in advertisements. As a leading member of the BVA Stanley Mullard was in a delicate position, and in 1926 piously pointed out in a company memorandum that although they had hitherto been liberal in ordering raw materials and other parts from Holland, in future the Association's regulations would make it necessary for them to import raw materials only;[83] in fact, however, Mullard valves were predominantly assembled from imported parts until at least 1936.[84]

Notwithstanding their internal stresses, and Stanley Mullard's growing frustration, the Mullard companies prospered greatly under their new ownership, their combined annual profits increasing from £128,000 in 1926 to £381,000 in 1928. Stanley Mullard later claimed that in 1929 they had had 76% of the total business of setmakers who were not controlled by other valve-makers.[85]

C O Stanley branches out

By 1927 the radio-receiver side of W G Pye & Co occupied over 27,000 square feet, double its original area, and was the more profitable part of the firm. Two of the firm's partners welcomed this successful diversification. Tom Robinson, who had served his apprenticeship there and later returned as Works Manager, had wanted to spend

W G Pye in 1932

H J Pye in 1931

£2,000 on advertising receivers even in 1923;[86] W G Pye's son Harold had, as already related, produced the company's first successful models in 1924, and had unsuccessfully urged the creation of a plastic-moulding division to serve both sides of the company.[87] But W G Pye himself, now approaching 60 and steeped in the traditions of instrument-making, understandably felt ill-at-ease with the company's increasing dependence on a particularly volatile domestic product.

As Pye's advertising agent, C O Stanley could see that the company's reputation for quality and its links with the scientific community, given resonance by its location in Cambridge, endowed it with an 'edge' the current management were incapable of exploiting. Following the Mullard takeover, Philips had appointed Stanley as a merchandising adviser, and he now set out to negotiate the sale of Pye to Philips;[88] many years later Harold Pye recalled how, as a necessary preliminary, Stanley and Tom Robinson had "thoroughly brainwashed" his father at an RMA luncheon. Initially Stanley, H J Pye and Robinson agreed on a price of £85,000 for the entire business, but Harold was able to prevent the sale of the the instrument side, where he was to spend the rest of his career. Early in 1928 Stanley approached Philips with a proposal that they should purchase the radio side for £60,000 and pay him a commission of £5,000.

Philips were prepared to accept the price but jibbed at the commission, whereupon Stanley backed his judgement with great audacity and undertook to buy Pye's radio business himself for £60,000. It was agreed that he would pay a £5,000 deposit forthwith and the balance after a year, during which period he would take over the running of the company, in the expectation of acquiring profits to pay off much of the balance. However, since Stanley had only £800 in the bank there remained the problem of raising the deposit, and in later years he would relate how he won over a banker, initially reluctant to back what he termed a flash-in-the-pan business, by taking a Pye portable into his office and demonstrating it. Evidently unaware of recent advances in receivers, the banker had been inordinately impressed, exclaiming "It plays when you move it!".[89] All went according to plan, the annual rate of profit doubling during 1928, and in February 1929 Pye Radio Ltd was duly registered as a public limited company with an authorized capital of £180,000. A detailed report on the company made later in the year showed that £45,000 had been allotted, and that Branch Nominees Ltd were large shareholders, but made no mention of C O Stanley.[10]

T N Cole stays put

By the late-1920s T N Cole had built Lissen Ltd, of which his wife was the principal shareholder, into a company employing almost 3,000 people in three well-equipped factories, one of them devoted entirely to the production of batteries.[10] In 1928 the Ever Ready Company (Great Britain) Ltd, as part of a programme of expansion, bought Lissen Ltd for something over a million pounds, but retained T N Cole as Managing Director.[90] Part of the deal was that for ten years he would not "carry on either alone or in partnership with others…any companies competing with the present business of Lissen Ltd."[91] Like Stanley Mullard, T N Cole would come to resent being no longer his own master, but for the present the change of ownership went unnoticed by the general public.

STEADY VOLTAGE

CONVENIENT

SILENT

current from
the mains
better than
before !

The

LISSEN

H·T· ELIMINATORS

POPULAR MODELS "A" & "B"

Front cover of leaflet, 1929

The fall of Burndept

Throughout the mid-1920s Burndept maintained a high profile, its Chief Engineer as prominent in technical circles as Witt Burnham was in commercial ones. In 1925 it was re-formed as a public company, Burndept Wireless Ltd, and its issue of capital greatly over-subscribed.[92] Existing shareholders had been told that "there was every indication that the new Company which would arise out of the old would be thoroughly successful",[93] but it soon started to make heavy losses and was forced into receivership in June 1927, just as the head of its research department published an enthusiastic description of his well-equipped laboratory.[94] It seems likely that a strong but inevitably limited demand for luxury receivers had led a euphoric management into immoderate expansion, and that they were caught out when that demand declined just too soon for advances in technology to have created a replacement market. And there were certainly other weaknesses. Enthusiasm for making their own components led the management into a valve-making venture at Acton that produced appalling reject-rates.[95] Witt Burnham, busy as a Director of the BBC, was never seen by workers on the shop floor at Blackheath, where discipline was slack and pilfering rife. One model of receiver conveniently consisted of a shallow structure on a large board, so a worker walked out of the building after work with one stuck up his back under his clothes. Unfortunately the main gates were by this time shut except for a small wicket-gate, which he was quite unable to negotiate; he turned back, and was caught before being able to dispose of his burden. Smaller items were well wrapped then dropped out of a window onto soft earth on the common for later recovery.[96] (Unattributable rumour has it that many years later light-fingered workers at Mullard's Mitcham plant used a variant of this technique, depending on a stream flowing through the site, and the high buoyancy of valves.)

Instead of liquidating the company the receiver took over control, succeeded in restoring it to profitable working, and in August 1928 became Chairman of a new company, Burndept Wireless (1928) Ltd,

The Burnham family celebrates the Golden Jubilee of Burnham & Co, at the Cafe Royal in 1927 — the year when Burndept went into receivership. Witt Burnham is second from the left in the front row

which took over the assets of the old company and paid its major creditors 6% 10-year notes for 50% of the amounts owed. The new company, however, was never to approach the stature of the old. Witt Burnham severed all connection with the company, and soon re-emerged as Chairman of Ediswan.

The AEI merger

In the autumn of 1928 BTH, which had recently bought Ediswan, merged with Metro-Vick to form Associated Electrical Industries (AEI), although the two major companies largely maintained their separate identities and even their traditional rivalries.[97] With the electrical industry under economic pressure, the merger was made the occasion for the group to rationalize its radio and valve-making interests. Metro-Vick Supplies, the subsidiary that made and sold wireless receivers and other domestic products, had lost £100,000 in a year,[98] and production of 'Cosmos' receivers ceased. BTH receivers were briefly marketed by Ediswan alongside their own sets,[99] but both companies were soon to drop receivers altogether.

The valve interests fared better. 'Cosmos' valves were highly successful, and Metro-Vick had recently transferred their design and manufacture, still under E Y Robinson and his team of engineers, from Trafford Park, Manchester to the Cosmos Lamp Works at Brimsdown, Essex. Just a mile away from Ediswan's factory at Ponders End, Brimsdown was now to be AEI's sole centre for receiving valves. The 'Cosmos' tradition was maintained, though the name was dropped and the valves were thenceforth marketed by Ediswan under the same brand name as BTH lamps: 'Mazda'.

A Time for Expansion

The BBC's network of 'main' and 'relay' stations, all sited in cities and large towns, substantially achieved Eckersley's initial aim of giving the main centres of population a signal strong enough for crystal-set reception, but with the general use of valve receivers this became

When broadcasting began S G Brown was already established both as a manufacturer and as a prolific inventor, with a non-electronic amplifier and a gyro-compass to his credit. His company was a major manufacturer of headphones and loudspeakers, and later diversified

Publicity photograph of the S G Brown 'Disc' loudspeaker, 1928. Although British radio products were not notably successful in export markets, they were frequently photographed in exotic settings

One of a series of four advertisements for an S G Brown loudspeaker of 1929. Another was entitled "The drummer finds his sticks"

SALES COME FROM A

This Window Display

(specially designed and photographed for the "Brown Budget") shows what an—

DISPLAY LIKE THIS!

—imposing appearance the new "Brown" Display Material has when attractively used. Its vivid "colour splash" cannot, of course, be portrayed in a photograph

The Brown Budget   197

Assembling S G Brown equipment, 1929

From S G Brown's dealer magazine The Brown Budget, *1929–30*

Mr. Stanger knows how to do it!

An enterprising dealer relays the Cup Final, 1930

the PORTABLE !

The Brown Budget   181

S G Brown, 1930

Mr. White (of Colwyn Bay) again!

A prize-winning display van, 1930

irrelevant. Many people received a needlessly strong signal from their local transmitter, while coverage of rural areas remained inadequate, particularly outside the range of the long-wave transmitter at Daventry; indeed coverage actually deteriorated, as European transmitters grew ever more numerous and powerful. In 1925 the BBC, eager to avoid anarchy in the ether, had played a leading role in establishing the Union Internationale de Radiophonie (UIR), which had its headquarters in Geneva, and the following year UIR members agreed to adopt its 'Geneva Plan'. Although this allotted the BBC fewer wavelengths than they were currently occupying, its combination of 'exclusive' and 'common' wavelengths (the latter extending the broadcast waveband to wavelengths below 300 metres) enabled the existing network to be accomodated.[100] However, to meet the strong public demand for a choice of two programmes and for better coverage, the BBC would need to adopt a totally different approach.

Eckersley and his engineers had in fact already worked out the main features of a 'Regional Scheme', based on pairs of high-power transmitters; to minimize the number of receivers 'blanketed' by an excessive signal, these were to be at rural sites near major population-centres. One of each pair would radiate a 'Regional' programme, partly local in origin, and the other a 'National' programme common to the whole country, which Daventry would also carry. Coverage would be greatly improved, but listeners would need receivers capable of separating their two local stations, and the scheme was already influencing receiver design two years before the first transmitter opened. Reviewing the 1927 show at Olympia, *Wireless World* noted approvingly "...manufacturers have realised that when the Regional Scheme comes into operation a set which now gives satisfaction to the average 'local' listener (who seldom requires real selectivity) will become hopelessly out of date."[101] Sadly, the Regional Scheme was to be P P Eckersley's swan-song as a major figure in British broadcasting, for in the autumn of 1928 it became known that he was about to be named as the guilty party in a divorce action. Reith was

October, 1929

MEN *of the* MOMENT

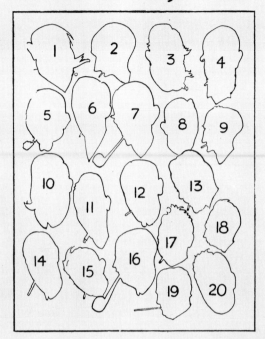

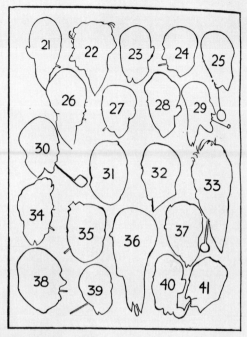

Page 108.

1.—*D. Grant Strachan, Secretary R.M.A.* 2.—*A. E. Bowyer Lowe, Bowyer Lowe, Co., Ltd.* 3.—*J. T. Mould, Igranic Co., Ltd., Chairman R.M.A.* 4.—*J. Joseph, Radio Instruments, Ltd.* 5.—*J. W. Barber, Brownie Wireless Co., Ltd.* 6.—*W. H. Goodman, Dubilier Co., Ltd.* 7.—*R. B. Weaver, General Electric Co., Ltd.* 8.—*G. Paton, J. L. Goldsman, Ltd.* 9.—*J. L. Goldsman, J. L. Goldsman, Ltd.* 10.—*P. R. Coursey, Dubilier, Co., Ltd.* 11.—*W. H. Lynas, Wireless Pictures, Ltd.* 12.—*J. M. Richard, Graham Amplion, Ltd.* 13.—*W. G. Davies, Graham Amplion, Ltd.* 14.—*C. A. Partridge, Partridge and Mee.* 15.—*L. Sharland, Bedford Electrical.* 16.—*F. W. Perks, Columbia Radio.* 17.—*W. B. Goodwin, Gambrell Radio, Ltd.* 18.—*A. E. Watkins, Watmel Wireless.* 19.—*R. I. Denham, M.P.A., Ltd.* 20.—*A. E. Moody, R.M.A., Exhibitions Organiser.*

Page 109.

21.—*T. A. W. Robinson, Pye Radio, Ltd.* 22.—*R. M. Ellis, Pye Radio, Ltd.* 23.—*H. C. Goodman, S. G. Brown, Ltd.* 24.—*C. F. Tripp, B.T.H., Co., Ltd.* 25.—*A. Wragg, Selfridges.* 26.—*W. S. Verrells, E. K. Cole, Ltd.* 27.—*E. K. Cole, E. K. Cole, Ltd.* 28.—*K. S. Spencer, Rees Mace, Ltd.* 29.—*H. C. Shaw, Cossor, Ltd.* 30.—*S. Wilding Cole, Kolster-Brandes, Ltd.* 31.—*L. McMichael, L. Mc-Michael, Ltd.* 32.—*R. Klein, L. McMichael, Ltd.* 33.—*R. F. Payne-Gallwey, Mullard Wireless Service, Ltd.* 34.—*C. W. Hayward, Universal and General Radio.* 35.—*G. H. Rees, Rees Mace, Ltd.* 36.—*S. R. Mullard, Mullard Wireless Service, Ltd.* 37.—*D. Hart-Collins, Hart-Collins, Ltd.* 38.—*A. J. A. Osbourne, Bedford Electrical.* 39.—*C. Lovely, Selectors, Ltd.* 40.—*S. Montague, Montague Radio Inventions.* 41.—*W. R. Lawson, Brown Bros., Ltd.*

Key for caricatures on pages overleaf

Here are some forty of the leading personalities of the Industry as seen by Frank Leah. As the sketches were secured before the opening of the Exhibition, we do not guarantee that these gentlemen will be exhibiting the same sprightly expressions at Olympia.

108

October, 1929   *The Broadcaster and Wireless Retailer (Supplement)*

The identity of the subjects is readily apparent, but, for the benefit of posterity, we publish key drawings on page 110. Mr. Leah is holding a one-man exhibition of portraits and caricatures of members of the Exhibitors' Club at Olympia during the Show period.

109

Caricatures, 1929

FOR 1929
STILL MORE FROM
MARCONIPHONE

In the world of wireless, Marconiphone leadership has always been
supreme. Year in, year out, the ever-active organisation devotes
the great resources at its disposal to a continual striving
after perfection. Patient and extensive research is always
producing something new, something better, and
for 1929 Marconiphone offer to wireless enthusiasts all the world over a range of
new receivers, each possessing
exceptional features, and
representing the ut-
most value.

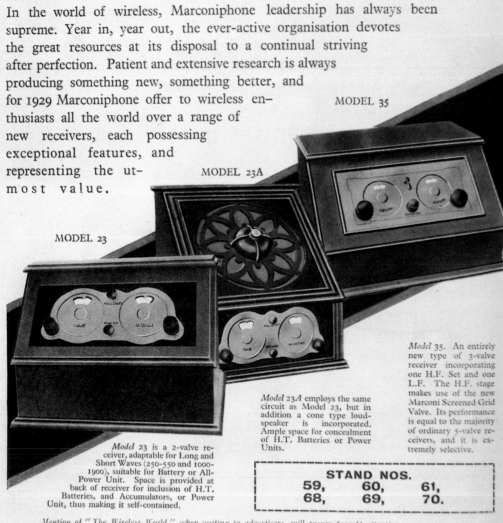

MODEL 35

MODEL 23A

MODEL 23

Model 23 is a 2-valve re-
ceiver, adaptable for Long and
Short Waves (250-550 and 1000-
1900), suitable for Battery or All-
Power Unit. Space is provided at
back of receiver for inclusion of H.T.
Batteries, and Accumulators, or Power
Unit, thus making it self-contained.

Model 23A employs the same
circuit as Model 23, but in
addition a cone type loudspeaker is incorporated.
Ample space for concealment
of H.T. Batteries or Power
Units.

Model 35. An entirely
new type of 3-valve
receiver incorporating
one H.F. Set and one
L.F. The H.F. stage
makes use of the new
Marconi Screened Grid
Valve. Its performance
is equal to the majority
of ordinary 5-valve re-
ceivers, and it is ex-
tremely selective.

STAND NOS.
59, 60, 61,
68, 69, 70.

Mention of " The Wireless World," when writing to advertisers, will ensure prompt attention.

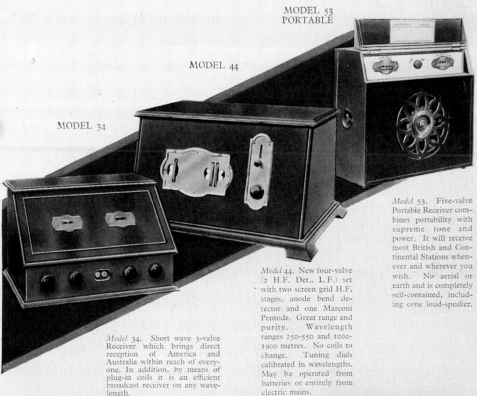

SEPTEMBER 26TH, 1928.   THE WIRELESS WORLD   ADVERTISEMENTS.

MODEL 53
PORTABLE

MODEL 44

MODEL 34

Model 53. Five-valve Portable Receiver combines portability with supreme tone and power. It will receive most British and Continental Stations whenever and wherever you wish. No aerial or earth and is completely self-contained, including cone loud-speaker.

Model 44. New four-valve (2 H.F. Det., L.F.) set with two screen grid H.F. stages, anode bend detector and one Marconi Pentode. Great range and purity. Wavelength ranges 250-550 and 1000-1900 metres. No coils to change. Tuning dials calibrated in wavelengths. May be operated from batteries or entirely from electric mains.

Model 34. Short wave 3-valve Receiver which brings direct reception of America and Australia within reach of everyone. In addition, by means of plug-in coils it is an efficient broadcast receiver on any wavelength.

MARCONIPHONE
MOVING COIL SPEAKERS AND UNITS

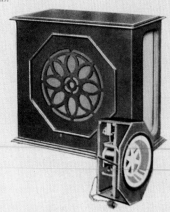

These new Marconiphone productions are radically different from anything that has gone before. For workmanship, design and reproduction *there are no better*. An entirely new system of double suspension is employed, which assures completely parallel movement of the coil at all times. Resonance is thus eliminated. Supplied completely assembled in Oak or Mahogany Cabinets from £10 10 0. Moving Coil Units for home construction are available in three models, for battery, A.C. or D.C. operation. Price £6 6 0 each.

Full particulars and prices of all Marconiphone new Season's models sent on request.
THE MARCONIPHONE COMPANY, LTD.,
Showrooms: 210-212, Tottenham Court Road, London, W.1. *and* Marconi House, Strand, W.C.2.

Advertisements for " The Wireless World" are only accepted from firms we believe to be thoroughly reliable.

As is described in the next chapter, Marconiphone was less healthy than this advertisement would suggest

not prepared to have such a transgressor in the BBC, and summarily dismissed him.[102]

Some of the specific technical advances in receivers at this period have already been mentioned. But the mere passage of time brought about a more general improvement through the accumulation of experience and the operation of natural selection, affecting both the engineering and commercial sides of the industry; and by this time many prospective buyers had heard a lot of wireless sets, so were less easily imposed upon. The contributor to the BBC's 1928 Handbook who looked back to the early days of broadcasting was no doubt exaggerating when he wrote "at least 50 per cent of the radio sets and parts purchased by the public were utterly and entirely useless".[103] So, perhaps, was *Wireless World*, reviewing the 1929 Olympia show: "Today it is almost impossible to sell 'junk' to the public...every stand impresses the visitor with confidence that the firm represented is a bona fide unit of the industry."[104] But it is undeniable that the industry had shed many of those we would now term 'cowboys', and that with recent improvements in technology, and the prospect of a better service from the BBC, it was poised for rapid expansion.

This mini drama of 1930 was not produced for prospective constructors, as its style would suggest, but distributed to dealers to persuade them to stock the kit

"Shall I?"

" This seems worth looking into. If I can build a Screened Grid Receiver with those parts in a few hours as it says here then I ought to save money on that Wireless Set Ethel wants me to get. And I've always wanted a 'Brown.' "

"Yes—I will!"

" There is probably a catch in it somewhere (there usually is in these things which seem too good to be true), but anyhow I will go and have a look and see what they have to say about it. I needn't buy it if it isn't as good as it seems."

"This is how it's done, sir."

" *Easy? It seems simple enough and I don't think I should have much difficulty in following those very clear diagrams. 'Kit of parts costs £9 10s, you say? And includes loud speaker?' 'Righto! I'll have it.'* "

"Now for home!"

" *By jove! Won't Ethel be surprised? She'll never dream that I'll be able to build this Set myself—but I'll show her. Let me see, it's now 5 o'clock. With a bit of luck we ought to have it ready by bedtime.*"

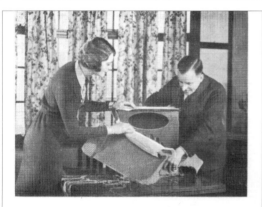

"Oh! How lovely."

" *What a beautiful cabinet! Did you say it was a 'Brown'? But are you really sure you can build the Set yourself? You know you have never done anything like that before.*" " *Just you wait and see, my dear —let's have tea and then I'll get busy.*"

"Now for it!"

I'll read carefully through the instructions and study the diagrams before I begin on the first stage, so that I can see just what I am doing. Pretty clever the way Brown's have worked out these diagrams so that a man like me can follow them."

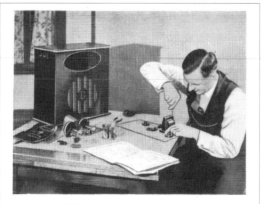

"First the Baseboard."

" *There is nothing I can go wrong with here. I see they have got the position of each component marked on the board itself and the diagrams show me the right way to mount the parts on it.*"

"Then the Panel."

" *This seems easy enough, too. There are only four components to be mounted here, and even a fool can see where they should go. By jove! This is interesting. No stopping now until it's finished.*"

"Now the next stage."

" Let's see—that wire goes there and this one here. Now it's beginning to look like a Set. Not much to do now. With a bit of luck I should have it finished in an hour and have it actually working, too. That'll surprise Ethel ! "

"Wiring as we go."

" Only a few more wires now, and then I will have ready to put in the cabinet. Let's see—how do we connect up the battery ? Easy. Now where are those valves ? Good! I'll soon have it working now."

"And now for Music!"

" Now let me see whether it's right or not. It's certainly not taken me long to build, but maybe I have not got it right. Ah ! By jove ! It works. That's Stainless Stephen. And—yes—I can tune him out and get chamber music from the Regional Station. And to think I'd hardly even handled a screw driver ! "

"Isn't that fine, Daddy ?"

" Yes, you wouldn't think it was a home-made Set, would you ? Without the 'Brown' Kit we'd never have had such a fine Receiver. I am going into the shop where I bought it and tell them I have got it working and heard 14 foreign stations. When this is over we'll have a shot at that German Station again."

References

1   Tim Wander, *2MT Writtle: The Birth of British Broadcasting* (Capella Publications, 1988) p. 2

2   Brian Munt, *A Short History of Ediswan, Mazda and Brimar* (Unpublished, 1989) p. 7

3   G R M Garratt, The Mullard Story (Unpublished) Part 2, p. 23: Mullard Archives

4   Asa Briggs, *The History of Broadcasting in the United Kingdom*, Vol I (London, Oxford University Press, 1961) p. 39

5   Asa Briggs, op. cit., p. 40

6   Asa Briggs, op. cit., p. 57

7   Asa Briggs, op. cit., p. 53

8   Tim Wander, op. cit., pp. 153–4

9   *Thermionic Valves 1904-1954* (IEE, 1955) p. 43

10   Reports on 150 British radio companies by Bradstreet's British Ltd, c.1929: Philips Archives

11   Brochure *The Diamond Jubilee of McMichael Ltd* 1919–1979: Gordon Bussey Collection

12   G R M Garratt, private conversation, 1989

13   Tim Wander, op. cit., pp. 13 & 149–50

14   Asa Briggs, op. cit., p. 85

15   S G Sturmey, *The Economic Development of Radio* (London, Gerald Duckworth & Co Ltd, 1958) p. 154

16   Asa Briggs, op. cit., p. 116

17   *Wireless World*, 16 August 1935, p. 195

18   J H Ludlow, *Who Invented the AC Mains Valve?* (Typescript article, June 1972, of which a shortened version subsequently appeared in Wireless World)

19   P P Eckersley, *The Power Behind the Microphone* (London, Jonathan Cape, 1941) p. 75

20   M J Lipman, *Memoirs of a Socialist Business Man* (London, Lipman Trust, n.d.) pp. 47–8

21   Charles G Wright, private correspondence, 1989

22   Agreement, 31 March 1922: Document in possession of Gordon Bussey

23   *Wireless World*, 26 March 1924, p. 796

24   Letter to Shareholders, 17 February 1923: Document in possession of Gordon Bussey

25   Directors' Reports, 1923, 1924: Documents in possession of Gordon Bussey

26   N Dundas Bryce, reminiscences in RTRA Dealer Journal, April 1946 p41, June 1964 pp. 25–9

27   *L McMichael Ltd*, British Vintage Wireless Society Bulletin, June 1978, pp. 9–10

28   Gordon Bussey, *The Story of Pye Wireless* (Pye Limited, 1986) p. 10

29   Typescript by E V Root, in possession of Gordon Bussey

30   *Wireless Weekly*, 14 November 1923, p. 612

31   P P Eckersley, op. cit., p. 46

32   Publicity hand-out, Sterling Telephone and Electrical Co Ltd (undated): Marconi Archives

33 Internal Memorandum, The Marconiphone Co Ltd, 4 April 1930: EMI Archives

34 *Wireless World*, 26 August 1925, p. 256

35 Keith Trace, A History of the Plessey Company (Unpublished, c.1971) passim: Plessey Archives

36 Reports to Board, 1925: Plessey Archives

37 Documents in the Telecommunications Collection of the Science Museum, London

38 Percy Adams, private conversation, 1988

39 Asa Briggs, op. cit., Chapter IV, passim

40 *Modern Wireless*, August 1923, p. XXXVIII

41 *Wireless World*, 7 April 1926, Editorial

42 Information gathered by Gordon Bussey from official documents and private conversations

43 Dr Alan Rose, private correspondence, 1989

44 Publicity Brochure, *The Romance of Ultra Radio*, 1935: Gordon Bussey Collection

45 Robert Clayton and Joan Algar, *The GEC Research Laboratories: 1919–1984* (London, Peter Peregrinus Ltd, 1989) p. 115

46 *Popular Wireless Weekly*, 17 November 1923, p. 433

47 A C Cossor Limited, *BVWS Bulletin*, September 1978, pp. 30–2

48 G R M Garratt, op. cit., passim

49 Robert Clayton and Joan Algar, op. cit., pp. 115–6

50 H V Morton, *In Search of England* (Methuen & Co Ltd, 7th edition,1929) pp. 68–69

51 *News of the World*, 28 September 1924

52 *BBC Handbook*, 1928 pp. 372–3

53 S G Sturmey, op. cit., pp. 216–20

54 *RMA Monthly Bulletins*, 1928–9: BREMA Archives

55 Robert Jones & Oliver Marriott, *Anatomy of a Merger* (London, Jonathan Cape, 1970) pp. 27–9

56 Michael Mason, *The BVA: A Personal Memoir* (Unpublished, 1986) p. 1

57 Monopolies Commission, *Report on the Supply of Electronic Valves and Cathode ray Tubes* (London, HMSO, 1956) Para. 99

58 Gordon Bussey, *Wireless: The Crucial Decade* (London, Peter Peregrinus Ltd, 1990) p. 110

59 G R M Garratt, op. cit., Pt 4 pp. 27–32

60 *Wireless World*, 21 November 1928, p. 706

61 Gordon Bussey, *Wireless: The Crucial Decade* (London, Peter Peregrinus Ltd, 1990) p. 68

62 *Wireless World*, 3 October 1928, p. 461

63 Information supplied by Gordon Bussey

64 *Wireless World*, 5 October 1927, p. 481

65 Reference 10, 'Rees-Mace' entry

66 Keith Geddes & Gordon Bussey, *The History of Roberts Radio* (Roberts Radio Ltd, 1987)

67 *A Brief History of K S S Spencer and the Three Associated Companies* (Unpublished typescript): Gordon Bussey Collection

68 E K Cole Silver Jubilee publication, 1951: Gordon Bussey Collection

69 Art and Industry, December 1937, p. 217

70   M J Lipman, op. cit., pp. 54–63

71   Letter, Alfred Clark to E R Fenimore Johnson, 15 February 1926: EMI Archives

72   Draft Letter, 1928: EMI Archives

73   Memorandum by Alfred Clark of interview with Mr Kellaway of the Marconi Company on 20 November 1928: EMI Archives

74   Report, Alfred Clark to Board of Directors, 5 March 1929: EMI Archives

75   Memorandum of Mr Mittell's meeting with Mr Mullard, 6 March 1929: EMI Archives

76   W J Baker, *A History of The Marconi Company* (London, Methuen & Co Ltd,1970) p. 200

77   Memorandum of Telephone Message received by Mr Mittell at 12.30 pm, 8 March 1929: EMI Archives

78   G R M Garratt, op. cit., Pt 4, passim

79   Memorandum from S R Mullard, Sale of Philips Accessories in Great Britain and its Dominions, 23 February 1928: EMI Archives

80   Robert Jones and Oliver Marriott, op. cit., p. 36

81   Letter, S R Mullard to A F Philips, 10 June 1932: Philips Archives

82   Geoffrey Dixon-Nuttall, private correspondence, 1990

83   Memorandum by S R Mullard, MWSC: *Proposed increased and improved Selling and Publicity Campaign for MWSC*, 19 May 1926: Philips Archives

84   Recollections of A J van Hoorn, 14 March 1967 & 2 April 1986: Mullard Archives

85   Letter, S R Mullard to H F van Walsem, 31 January 1933: Mullard Archives

86   Gordon Bussey, *The Story of Pye Wireless*, passim

87   H J Pye, private communication to Gordon Bussey, 1980

88   *New Scientist*, 20 July 1961, pp. 156–7

89   *The Observer*, 21 August 1960, p. 3

90   L W Orchard, private conversation, 1989

91   *Wireless & Gramophone Trader*, 1 June 1935, p. 154

92   *Wireless World*, 29 April 1925, p. 378

93   Report of Extraordinary General Meeting, 20 March 1925: Gordon Bussey Collection

94   *Experimental Wireless & Wireless Engineer*, July 1927, p. 422

95   Pat Burnham, private conversation, 1989

96   John Street, private conversation, 1989

97   Robert Jones and Oliver Marriott, op. cit., p. 148

98   Ibid., p. 101

99   Ediswan "Radio Receivers" catalogue, 1929 imprint

100   Asa Briggs, op. cit., pp. 315–8

101   *Wireless World*, 5 October 1927, p. 478

102   Tim Wander, op. cit., pp. 100–1

103   *BBC Handbook*, 1928, p. 370

104   *Wireless World*, 2 October 1929, p. 368

2 • *The Industry Matures*

The Thirties Scene

Between 1929 and 1931 the turnover of the radio industry doubled, from £15 million to £30 million,[1] and continued to grow strongly despite the depression. Although unemployment reached almost 3 million in 1932 and was still over 2 million in 1935, those in regular employment enjoyed a 15% increase in real income during the 1930s, mainly through a fall in the cost of living,[2] and had ready access to expensive items through hire-purchase, which in the late-1930s accounted for about 70% of total radio sales.[3] Radio manufacture typified the new industries that were arising as staples like coal-mining, shipbuilding and cotton declined, but was concentrated in the South East and thus contributed to the grossly uneven distribution of unemployment; in 1934, when around 60% of the insured workers in depressed areas were out of work, the figures for some towns in the South East were only about 5%.[4] The demand for receivers was highly seasonal, however, and the prospect of being laid off in the spring and summer lay heavily on the industry's male breadwinners; it was less serious for the armies of women on the assembly lines, some of them part-timers.

The development of the all-mains radio coincided with a rapid increase in the proportion of homes with mains electricity, which had been only one in seventeen in 1920, but rose from a third to two-thirds during the 1930s.[5] In many of them the radio was one of the first possessions to extend the benefits of electricity beyond lighting. Two further technical advances that took place in the early-1930s brought the receiver to another plateau of development, from which it would not greatly advance for another twenty years: the general adoption of the 'superhet' (short for 'superheterodyne') form of receiver, and the advent of the 'variable-mu' valve.

Selectivity and the superhet

As broadcasting stations became more numerous and more powerful, a receiver required more and better tuned circuits to separate them. Having to adjust several controls to change stations was tedious and uncertain, but if three or even four tuning capacitors were 'ganged' onto a single shaft to give single-knob tuning it was difficult to design circuits that stayed precisely in tune with each other right across the waveband. Moreover, the performance of the individual circuits inevitably varied across the waveband, whether or not they were ganged. These problems do not arise in a superhet. The signal from the aerial is combined with the wave from an oscillator contained in the receiver, and thereby transposed to a fixed 'intermediate' frequency to which the rest of the receiver is permanently tuned. Changing stations is achieved by altering the frequency of the oscillator, thereby bringing each station in turn to the intermediate frequency. In effect, the waveband is shifted across the receiver instead of vice versa. Because the circuits determining a superhet's selectivity operate at a fixed frequency and are pre-tuned at the factory, they can attain a higher performance than those of a 'straight' (i.e. non-superhet) receiver. However, the aerial circuit of a superhet still needs to be tuned, though not very critically, by a second capacitor on the tuning shaft; otherwise it suffers interference from any station whose frequency exceeds that of the wanted station by a particular (but happily quite large) amount.

AND NOW FOR

THIS is the " S.T.400."
The Editor has placed forty-five pages at my disposal in which to tell you about it.

I shall need every page.

Why ?

Because ten months' solid work lies behind the " S.T.400 "; because this receiver has been tested—actually and literally—from one end of Great Britain to the other; because the circuit introduces new and vital principles.

But chiefly because I am enthusiastic about the set.

" S.T.400."

A simple enough name. My initials. The figure 4 to indicate four valves.

A Special Significance

Rather a meaningless name. A man who heard the set on his own aerial, however, gave it a special significance.

" Four valves and a 100 per cent from each," was his suggestion.

That makes 400, but to me " S.T.400 " is just a label. It looks curiously unpretentious side by side with the names of other sets which seek your patronage, sets often with fancy names and fancier claims.

This is the great season when you and thousands of others will build a set. What is going to be the influencing factor in your choice ? The designer's reputation ? The look of the set or circuit ? The cost ? The performance?

Frankly, I don't know. I will wager you have had a good look over the set before beginning to read this description. Which feature of the " S.T.400 " has appealed most I cannot say.

But I certainly hope you will not build it merely because I have designed it. Hundreds of letters have reached

76

A Full Description—

me telling me to " buck up and let's have it," or asking for a strictly private hint of the circuit ! (Stamped, addressed envelope enclosed.)

Hard Facts

All these letters contain the expressed determination to build the set. That is confidence. In me. Naturally I'm pleased. Who wouldn't be ?

But though I want you to build this set, I want you to do so as a result of studying facts—cold, hard, uncompromising facts.

I intend to give you them. Forty-five pages of them !

I shall tell you the reasons for every line in the circuit, every wire in the set. You will hear my views on modern designs and perhaps disagree with them !

With every set I have invented I have courted controversy, acrimony and criticism. I rejoice in the first, regret the second, and respect the last.

But when my sets cease to arouse controversy, acrimony and criticism I shall have ceased to be a technical rebel. And ceased to count.

Reflex circuits. Multi-valve neutralised sets. One-knob receivers. The " S.T.300." All radical departures in their different ways. No one can accuse me of ever having taken the path of least resistance.

It is so easy to turn out a different-coloured jelly from the same old mould. And it is obvious that many constructors would swallow it.

How else can one explain the construction and reconstruction of the same old circuits ?

The appearance of a new Scott-Taggart receiver was preceded by a crescendo of publicity built up over many months. In December 1932 the launch of the ST400 was approaching its climax

December, 1932

THE WIRELESS CONSTRUCTOR

THE S.T. 400!

—by John Scott-Taggart, F.Inst.P., A.M.I.E.E.

When, on January 15th last, I announced my own policy, I declared that only at long intervals would I issue new designs. "Fewer and better sets" was to be the slogan.

If a designer changes his mind every month, how can the public be expected to form any opinion?

Well, you have seen my methods in practice for ten months. You have had one circuit—the "S.T.300." Even after nearly a year I would still advise you to build it. I have nothing new in mind for a three-valve set. It still represents my conception of a three-valver for national construction.

Remaining Up-to-Date

If you build one of my designs you are certain of this: that it will not commence to become obsolete from the day it is built. You will not suffer the mortification of seeing a new competitive design displacing the set you have barely finished wiring.

Readers are tired of designers hurling a handful of burrs at them in the hope that one will stick.

Mr. Ramsay MacDonald's views on daily newspapers are, I believe, the real views of the wireless constructor. He recently declared: "I like the paper which stands by its colours, which wields a heavy sword deftly, and does not find it necessary to blazon forth daily sensations drawn from the imagination of the office in order to gain a circulation one day and produce a contradictory sensation so that it may be maintained the next."

Forecast Months Ago

On January 15th I wrote: "I am left unconvinced by announcements of new miracles every week or every few weeks. It will be my intention to break away from this method and to produce only two or three sets a year, each of which will be the result of the most careful preliminary work.

"There will, of course, come up for consideration other types of sets, such as two-valve, four-valve, superhets. But the 'S.T.300' is my screen-grid three."

This undertaking has been more than fulfilled to the letter. And now you are reading about the "four-valve" set forecast nearly a year ago. I have received only one letter from an "S.T.300" user who feels aggrieved that I should design anything new.

Looking Ahead

And I know of not a single "S.T.300" builder who has changed over to another S.G.3 design. No better proof could be offered of the security I try to give you with my sets.

Only yesterday I received a letter from a reader who says: "I have had the 'S.T.300' going for 8 months. It is the first set I haven't scrapped within a month."

It is, of course, essential to design ahead of time; to envisage what the ether will be like not next week or next month, but next year and after.

In my new "S.T.400" you are provided with controls which can make the set progressively more selective as conditions get worse. And you will need them!

Difficulties Increase

Every week one reads of some station planning enormous power, some fiddling little Continental will suddenly develop into an overpowering giant. Unless you have progressively-adjusted controls you may find yourself in the position of a paralysed man watching the rising of a tide which will ultimately drown him.

Those of you with fixed or semi-fixed selectivity are in for trouble. Every piece of news about a foreign station will be bad news

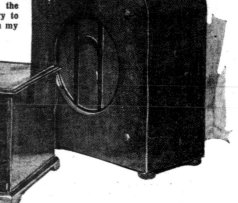

77

Front cover of the instruction book for a 1933 kit

The superhet had made a brief appearance in the early days of broadcasting, when its advantage had been that it could transpose the received signal down to a frequency low enough to be readily amplified by triode valves. The screen grid valve made this unnecessary, and the superhet virtually disappeared for several years. Now, the urgent need for better selectivity brought it back rapidly and permanently. Though none featured in *Wireless World's* review of the 1930 Radio Show, superhets made up 17% of the models mentioned in 1932 and 62% in 1934.[6] The ascendancy of the superhet contributed to the decline of home construction, since proper adjustment of its variously tuned circuits required the methodical use of calibrated instruments.

Strong and weak signals, loud and soft sounds
Until the early-1930s a variety of means were used for adjusting the amplification of a receiver to suit the signals of widely differing strengths delivered by the aerial; reaction was adjusted, in some early receivers whole stages were switched in and out of circuit, and even in 1928 it was common to dim the filaments of radio-frequency valves.[7] Moreover, simply adjusting the loudness could upset the operation of the radio-frequency stages, and screen-grid valves were particularly easy to over-drive, producing gross distortion. Such considerations forced compromises on designers and demanded skill from the user.

The situation was transformed by the introduction, around 1931, of valves whose amplification (symbolized by the Greek letter 'mu') could be varied over a wide range simply by changing the DC voltage on the control-grid, and which when set to low amplification could accept very large signals; this 'variable-mu' feature was achieved by winding the control-grid spiral at a pitch that varied along its length. By 1933 variable-mu valves were being widely used in circuits that derived the amplification-controlling voltage from the valve's own output signal, automatically reducing its amplification for stronger signals and delivering almost the same level to the audio section of the receiver for weak and strong signals alike. Thus tuning the receiver no longer produced shattering outbursts from local stations, and on distant ones the effect of fading was greatly reduced. The system was confusingly referred to as 'Automatic Volume Control' (AVC), implying that the receiver imposed a particular loudness upon the user. In fact, loudness was now controlled by a volume control that altered the input to the receiver's audio amplifier without affecting the operation of the earlier stages.

Some other selling points
With the introduction of AVC, the adoption of the superhet principle, and the demise of the oscillation-provoking 'reaction' control, the taming of the domestic receiver was complete by the early-1930s; concurrently, quality of reproduction improved as the moving-coil loudspeaker ceased to be exclusively for fidelity enthusiasts and came into general use. The remainder of the decade brought further technological developments, some of which became obligatory on all but the cheapest sets, but these did not comparably affect the listener's relationship with his radio.

Various forms of visual tuning indicators appeared in the mid-thirties, most memorably the 'magic eye' — a special cathode ray tube whose one-inch screen appeared, in the device's most popular version, as a green 'cake with a slice missing'; the set was on tune when the slice was at its smallest. This was something of a 'gimmick', in that anyone unable to identify correct tuning aurally (as what sounded least 'toppy') presumably didn't care whether or not they achieved it. Most makers showed at least one model with a short-wave band in the 1936 Radio Show and such 'all-wave' sets became general in 1937, although short-wave performance in competitively priced sets was unlikely to gain the band much use once the novelty had worn off. Push-button tuning was a convenience that was to drop out of fashion during the post-war decades, only to undergo a revival half a century after its widespread introduction in 1938. A valuable feature that proved lacking in sales appeal was variable selectivity. When receiving a strong signal free from interference, the listener could switch the intermediate-frequency circuits to reproduce a wide audio spectrum; under less favourable conditions he switched them to reject interference at the cost of fidelity. However, although variable selectivity looked like becoming a popular feature in the middle of the

Olympia Personalities Caught by our Artist.—1. C. A. Partridge, Partridge & Mee. 2. Guy R. Fountain, Tannoy Products. 3. C. French, Celestion. 4. H. Green, Telsen & Red Star. 5. "Bill" Miller, Garnett Whiteley. 6. E. K. Cole himself. 7. E. M. Lee, Belling & Lee. 8. W. J. Taylor, T.C.C. 9. Leslie McMichael. 10. R. Lillico, C.A.V. 11. J. Dempster, Burndept Wireless. 12. A. H. Whiteley, Whiteley Boneham.

decade, in 1938 *Wireless World* noted a considerable decrease in its use. A tone control offered a similar though usually much inferior facility more cheaply.

The radiogram keeps the tills ringing
Putting a radio, a pick-up and a turntable into a single cabinet was a simple matter technically, but commercially and socially significant. Although table models were made, it was primarily the console radiogram that displaced the wind-up gramophone from the nation's

SEPTEMBER 24TH, 1930.　　THE WIRELESS WORLD.　　ADVERTISEMENTS. vii.

Modernise that old Gramophone

Why pay big prices for electric gramophones when you can modernise your old gramophone for a few pounds? With B.T.H. Electric Gramophone equipment you can make your gramophone as modern-to-the-minute and the equal of factory built machines costing three times the price.

The NEW B.T.H. Electric Gramophone Motor costs only £3 3 0. It plays 200 12ꞌꞌ records on one unit of electricity. It cannot go wrong— there's nothing to wear out. Just snap on the switch and forget tedious winding.

The B.T.H. Tone Arm and Pick-up discovers all the hidden charm in your records. You do not realize your records are so full of interest until you hear them played with the B.T.H. Tone Arm and Pick-up.

with *Bring that old gramophone up-to-date with this easy-to-fit Electric Gramophone Equipment*

(B·T·H) ELECTRIC GRAMOPHONE EQUIPMENT

B.T.H. Pick-up and Tone Arm Price 45/- complete.
B.T.H. Electric Gramophone Motor £3 3 0 complete, also a Super Motor at £6 6 0 complete.

THE EDISON SWAN ELECTRIC CO. LTD.,
Radio Division
1a, Newman Street, Oxford Street, London, W.1
Branches in all Principal Towns.

OLYMPIA STAND Nº 67　EDISWAN

Advertisements for " The Wireless World " are only accepted from firms we believe to be thoroughly reliable.

TRUPHONIC
PEDESTAL TYPE RADIO-GRAM

A Handsome Burr Walnut Cabinet gives this instrument an immediate place amongst your most treasured possessions, being both neat and attractive, its modern design will lend itself to almost any furnishing scheme. Concealed behind its solid exterior lies a powerful radio chassis, offering you a varied choice of programmes with perfect quality and gramophone reproduction that will give your record library a new lease of life. At the back will be found a drawer for records, which can be conveniently used as a record carrier. Tuning is effected by a single dial marked in wave-lengths, and selectivity controls are provided when searching for elusive stations; changing to gramophone is effected by the combined wave change switch. There is no necessity for Aerial or Earth for your local stations, as a special Aerial device is incorporated which makes this instrument self contained.

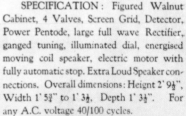

22 GUINEAS

SPECIFICATION: Figured Walnut Cabinet, 4 Valves, Screen Grid, Detector, Power Pentode, large full wave Rectifier, ganged tuning, illuminated dial, energised moving coil speaker, electric motor with fully automatic stop. Extra Loud Speaker connections. Overall dimensions: Height 2' 9½", Width 1' 5¾" to 1' 3½, Depth 1' 3½". For any A.C. voltage 40/100 cycles.

BACK VIEW

living rooms and became one of the great status symbols of the 1930s. The automatic record-changer appeared in 1931, and as it became increasingly popular took the shine off possessing a mere 'manual' model. Fully loaded with eight 10-inch records it played for 25 minutes unattended, while 12-inch classical recordings occupying three or more discs could be ordered in 'automatic couplings', which had the sequence of sides rearranged to allow the whole work to be

Decca's 'Portrola' radiogram of 1934 shows the influence of the company's beginnings, as makers of portable gramophones

Pye radiograms in the finishing department, 1936

played with a single turning-over operation; in 1932 *Wireless World* had reviewed a record-changer that played both sides of each record, with 18-second intervals, and expressed the opinion that all changers would have to work on that principle before they became really popular.[8] The radiogram's record-playing unit and its cabinet, often fitted with a larger loudspeaker, took the price up to around twice that of the same receiver in its table-model form. The advent of this essentially new product provided a timely stimulus to the industry as the market in receivers approached saturation. For those unable to afford a radiogram, almost all receivers made after about 1930 had provision for plugging in a pick-up,[9] and pick-up heads were available for mounting on the tone arm of a gramophone. In the late-1930s EMI marketed a pick-up and turntable unit for under £2 and a de-luxe version with a lid for under £3. These finally left only the 'portable' market to the acoustic gramophone.

The Big Names in Radio

The arrivals and departures noted in the last chapter were part of a general volatility that extended into the 1930s. Of the 52 firms exhibiting at the 1926 Radio Show only 15 exhibited in 1931, and of the 57 who exhibited that year only 17 did so three years later.[10] Radio manufacture also followed the general tendency of industry at this period to become concentrated into fewer, larger units,[11] and there emerged a few major companies who took setmaking into mass production, though many processes remained manual. Their names became truly 'household words' as they led the industry towards putting a radio into every home.

Three major manufacturers not dealt with here in detail must nevertheless be mentioned: GEC, Ferranti and Cossor. GEC receivers were made at the company's Telephone Works at Coventry, and it is not clear in what proportions that huge plant's 5,000 work-force and 750,000 sq ft floor area[12] were divided between radios and telephone equipment, though by 1938 it was re-titled 'GEC Radio Works'.[13] The design of receivers was one of the responsibilities of the Radio Group in the company's prestigious Research Laboratories at Wembley. However, GEC did not occupy the dominant place in the receiver industry that these facts would lead one to expect. Analysing the industry's pecking order as of 1934, the Financial Secretary of Murphy Radio did not put them in the first three (see later), while Murphy's then Chief Engineer has remarked of GEC's domestic-receiver business 'They never seemed to be very serious about it.'[14] They were probably hampered by both their diversity and their size. In *GEC Journal's* annual reviews of progress, domestic receivers were sandwiched in among electric cleaners, street lighting and industrial cooking appliances, suggesting that they occupied rather a small angle in top management's field of view, while the division of control between

The special train commissioned by Ferranti to take wholesalers and dealers to their new radio works in May 1935

*The Telegraph Condenser
Company Ltd, founded by
S G Brown in 1906,
made only capacitors*

Coventry, Wembley and the company's Kingsway Head Office[15] must have impaired the capacity for rapid and decisive action in a fast-moving game.

Ferranti were also long-established electrical all-rounders. In 1929 they began making all-mains receivers at their headquarters at Hollinwood, near Oldham, and also became known for their moving-coil loudspeakers. A 1934 superhet, the 'Lancastria', was praised by *Wireless World* for its exceptional selectivity but was remembered by a wholesaler, well over half a century later, for the high proportion of those delivered to him that didn't work, some being found to lack valves or even a loudspeaker.[16] However, Vincent de Ferranti, Chairman of the company, took a special interest in radio, and in 1935 he opened a 270,000 sq ft factory built exclusively for radio production, at Moston, Manchester. *Wireless World* considered it worthy of mention that the factory's machine tools were driven by individual electric motors rather than through belts from overhead shafting. Virtually all the components, including valves, were made on the premises from raw materials,[17] and this extreme degree of self-sufficiency may well have been uneconomic. And at a time when receivers aimed at the upper end of the market were increasingly being sold through franchised dealers it may have been unwise for Ferranti to distribute exclusively through wholesalers.[18] But for whatever reason, Ferranti never secured a major share of the market, and their radio venture consistently lost money, though it fulfilled one of Vincent de Ferranti's objectives by gaining them entry to the world of electronics.[19]

Cossor began to make complete receivers in 1930,[20] exploiting both the success of their 'Melody Maker' kits and the component-making capacity gained from them. They were a much smaller company than either GEC or Ferranti, and taken overall their other interests were more relevant to setmaking. They were beginning to make electronic instruments, marketing their first oscilloscope in 1932,[21] and were important valve-makers; in 1931 an informed guess by a competitor gave them almost a fifth of BVA sales in England — well behind Mullard but level with M-OV and ahead of Mazda.[22] Altogether Cossor had considerable expertise and resources concentrated in their two sites in Highbury, and their receiver operation took off rapidly, with ten models available by 1932.[23] Two years later a new five-storey factory had filled up all available space at Highbury, and the continuing demand for expansion was met by transferring cabinet manufacture to a site at Leyton.

Ekco set the pace [24]

When Cole and Verrells decided to concentrate on mains receivers rather than eliminators they realized that their company lacked the necessary expertise, and strengthened their technical staffing. Youth continued to be the keynote; their new Chief Engineer, John Wyborn, was 26 — a year younger than Cole — when he joined them from the design staff at Marconiphone in December 1928, just before the HMV purchase. In 1930 E K Cole Ltd became a public company,[25] and built a new factory. Over the previous five years the operation had occupied, and outgrown, rooms over Eric Cole's shop, a factory at Leigh-on-Sea, the 'Gliderdrome' skating rink and a sea-front amusement arcade. This time they were taking no chances, and chose a site with room for further expansion, at Prittlewell, on the outskirts of Southend-on-Sea;

it was literally a green-field site, having previously grown cabbages. This was the first large factory in Britain to be purpose-built for receiver manufacture. Even at the outset it covered 80,000 square feet and employed around a thousand people,[26] and by 1937 a succession of expansions would take it to 300,000 sq ft, with a work-force of 4,500.[27]

In the spring of 1930, while the factory was still being built, a chance encounter took place that was to affect the company profoundly. Michael Lipman, a London representative of the German electrical giant AEG, decided he would like a day at the seaside and visited E K Cole Ltd — a firm he had never heard of — in response to an enquiry for some special insulation. He finished his business with the buyer, who then asked if he had anything that might be of interest for the mass production of radio sets. As it happened, Lipman had in the back of his car a bakelite radio cabinet that AEG had made for Telefunken. This was the largest item yet produced in the material, and Lipman had unsuccessfully tried to interest several British radio manufacturers in it. The manager of HMV's cabinet department had been predictably unenthusiastic over a product so totally alien to the company's tradition of high-quality wooden cabinets, which its dealers and customers expected, and on which his own position depended. Other manufacturers had been put off by AEG's minimum production order of 10,000; each design of bakelite cabinet involved a heavy investment in dies and moulds. But when E K Cole's buyer saw the sample, his response was dramatic. He at once introduced Lipman to John Wyborn, who in turn took him to Cole and Verrells. Within an hour, they had expressed interest in having two types of cabinet made, with a total order of 30,000. Could a designer come over from Berlin at once? The sets were wanted for the Radio Show, which was only five months away. A telephone call to Berlin had AEG's chief draughtsman despatched by that night's boat, and an order was quickly placed.

Within a month Ekco had recruited Lipman, who was a trained electrical and mechanical engineer, as Production Engineer for the new factory; this was still an empty shell, and he was able to equip it as he wished. By 1931 there were ten conveyor-belt assembly lines and an overhead conveyor system two thousand feet long, designed with the help of a friend of Lipman's from the Ford plant at Dagenham. A feature of the factory was that the ratio in which the various models were produced could quickly be adapted to suit changing demand. The bakelite cabinets had proved a great success at the 1930 Radio Show and their use was extended in 1931, with a range of colours available. But in the autumn of that year, the National Government imposed an 'anti-dumping' import duty of 50%[28] on a wide range of goods, including the AEG bakelite cabinets. It therefore became essential for these to be produced in the UK, and a deal was negotiated with AEG whereby, in return for an annual fee and a royalty, the necessary plant would be erected by Ekco under AEG control in a new building adjoining the main factory.

Meanwhile, three key executives on the manufacturing side of the company were actively planning to leave and set up on their own. Michael Lipman, John Wyborn and Laury Jones, the Production Manager, felt that they were being given neither the authority necessary to discharge their responsibilities, nor their due share of credit for the firm's success. They got quite a long way towards raising the £30,000 that they needed, but eventually had to admit defeat. *continues on page 131*

The new Ekco factory, 1930

Moving into the new factory

The Countess of Iveagh, Conservative MP for Southend, campaigning at the Ekco factory in 1931

Ekco's motor-cycle service fleet, c. 1931

Chassis of Ekco Model RS2, 1931

117

Coil-winding at Ekco, 1932

*Receivers awaiting
dispatch, 1932*

*Loading receivers for
dispatch to the Continent,
c. 1933*

The main assembly bay at Ekco in 1932. About 2,000 people worked in this pillarless and mainly glass-roofed area of 100,000 sq ft

Research Department after the fire of February 1932

One of the giant presses for moulding bakelite cabinets being installed at Ekco, August 1932

A hinged mould was necessary to allow withdrawal of cabinets having impressed decoration or re-entrant design motifs. Because of the intricacy and expense of such moulds, these features were later avoided

Receivers being loaded onto a ship at the end of Southend pier in 1932, for dispatch to Newcastle

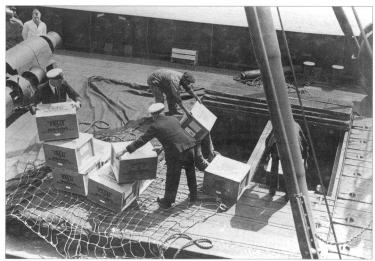

Public-address vans were a popular form of publicity in the thirties

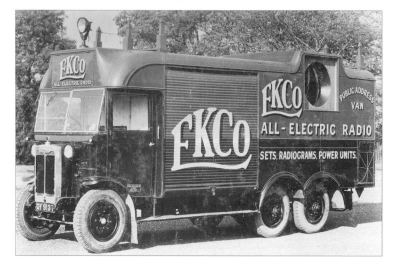

Finishing the assembly of Ekco radiograms, c.1932

The overhead conveyor at Ekco, c. 1932

Menu from a dinner given by Ekco's management on 27 February 1932, presumably in appreciation of the work done in the three weeks following the fire. Two caricatures are shown enlarged: John Wyborn was Chief Engineer and Norman Robertson, at that time in charge of testing, became Deputy Managing Director after the war

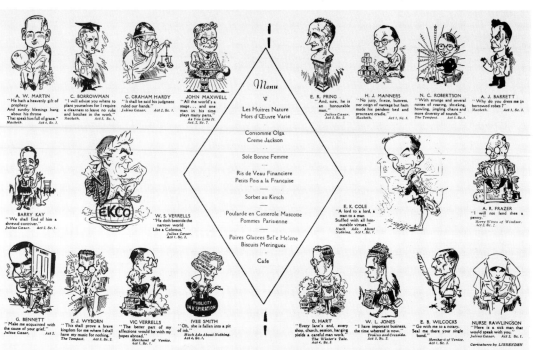

E. J. WYBORN
"This shall prove a brave kingdom for me where I shall have my music for nothing."
The Tempest. Act 3, Sc. 2.

N. C. ROBERTSON
"With strange and several noises of roaring, shrieking, howling, jingling chains and more diversity of sounds."
The Tempest. Act 5, Sc. 1.

Part of the company's fleet of vans, c. 1933

Spare capacity in Ekco's bakelite plant was used to make mouldings for other companies. This stand was at the British Industries Fair in 1935

Going-home time, c. 1934

A leaflet of 1935

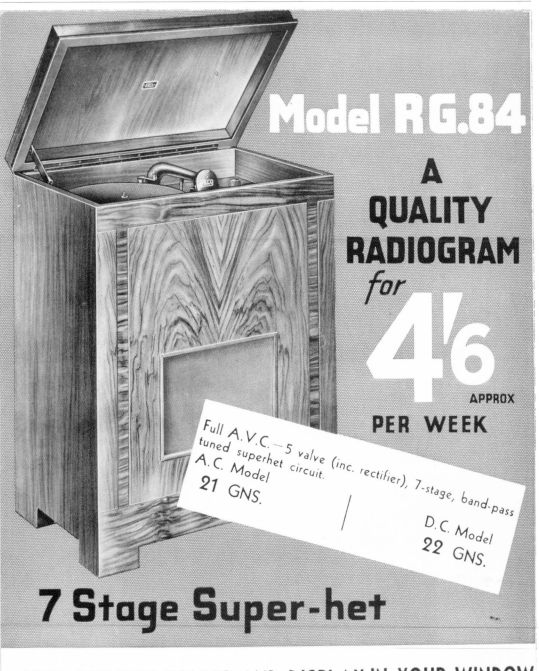

An Ekco leaflet of 1935. Note that the weekly hire-purchase payment is shown more prominently than the cash price

EKCO RADIO

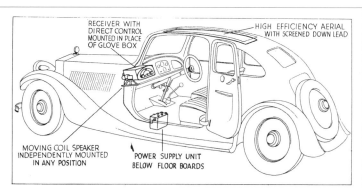

— Outstanding Features : —

7-stage Superhet Circuit, OPERATING ON MEDIUM AND LONG WAVELENGTHS.
Direct Control—no backlash.
Noise Suppressor — COMPLETE SILENCE WHILE TUNING.
Compensated A.V.C., giving steady volume under all normal conditions.
4 Watts Output — ample for all road speeds and conditions.
Light-beam and Shadow Tuning.

Non-dazzle Tuning Scale, with station-names and wavelengths.
Tone Control.
Unaffected by Change of Direction.

PRICE

Complete with Speaker, Power Supply Unit, and Comprehensive Suppression Equipment. Installation extra.

20 GNS.

above: *An Ekco leaflet of 1935. Tables were available to match specific models*

left: *Car radio, already well-established in America, was pioneered in this country by Ekco, who exhibited this model at Olympia in 1934. The receiver was sufficiently compact to be mounted on the fascia, whereas other makers often had only a control unit there, mechanically linked to the receiver itself. However, accommodating the power supply remained a problem*

opposite: *A leaflet of 1935*

HENRY HALL was in your car last night — and you didn't know it! So was the Chief Announcer — he read the News Bulletin in your car—and you didn't hear it!

All you heard was the swish of wheels on the road, the patter of rain on the roof and the incessant clickety-clack of the windscreen wiper.

The atmosphere around you was filled with music—throughout Europe, a thousand broadcasters were playing, singing and talking. Every word and note was in your car.

With Ekco car radio you could have brought this silent throng to life. You could have filled your car with mirth and melody; in short, you could have MOTORED TO MUSIC.

Instal Ekco Car Radio and drive with the pick of the radio programmes at your finger-tips.

Keep awake and alert on the longest journeys and realise to the full the unbounded joy of MOTORING TO MUSIC.

The Ekco car receiver installed, 1934

Ekco at Brussels in 1936. The sets were British models locally assembled, and contained locally sourced parts to minimize import duty, which was levied by weight

Ekco's Head of Service with his department under surveillance, 1936

Ekco receivers of 1938, with motorized push-button tuning, undergoing initial wrapping before being boxed

Ekco's drawing offices were unusually spacious and well-lit for the period. Wells Coates, who had designed some of the company's bakelite receiver cabinets, also designed the office shown with skylights. These were double sheets of glass, filled with glass wool to diffuse the light

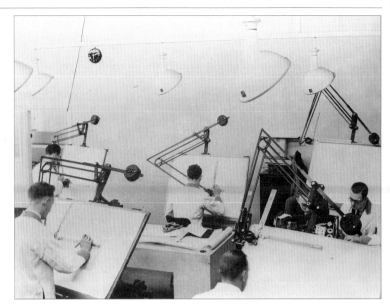

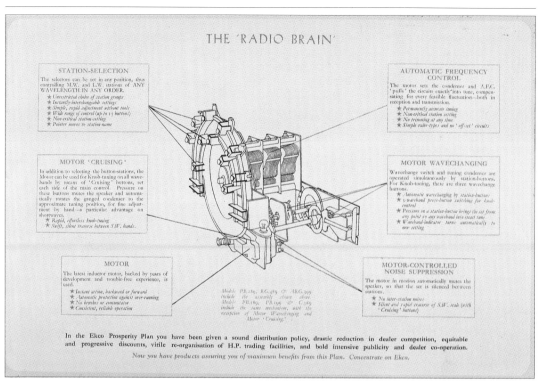

THE 'RADIO BRAIN'

STATION-SELECTION
The selectors can be set in any position, thus controlling M.W. and L.W. stations of ANY WAVELENGTH IN ANY ORDER.
★ *Unrestricted choice of station groups*
★ *Instantly-interchangeable settings*
★ *Simple, rapid adjustment without tools*
★ *Wide range of control (up to 15 buttons)*
★ *Non-critical station-setting*
★ *Pointer moves to station-name*

AUTOMATIC FREQUENCY CONTROL
The motor sets the condenser and A.F.C. 'pulls' the circuits exactly into tune, compensating for every feasible fluctuation—both in reception and transmission.
★ *Permanently accurate tuning*
★ *Non-critical station setting*
★ *No trimming at any time*
★ *Simple valve-types and no 'off-set' circuits*

MOTOR 'CRUISING'
In addition to selecting the button-stations, the Motor can be used for Knob-tuning on all wavebands by means of 'Cruising' buttons, set each side of the main control. Pressure on these buttons mutes the speaker and automatically rotates the ganged condenser to the approximate tuning position, for fine adjustment by hand—a particular advantage on shortwaves.
★ *Rapid, effortless knob-tuning*
★ *Swift, silent traverse between S.W. bands.*

MOTOR WAVECHANGING
Wavechange switch and tuning condenser are operated simultaneously by station-buttons. For Knob-tuning, there are three wavechange buttons.
★ *Automatic wavechanging by station-button*
★ *3-waveband press-button switching for knob-control*
★ *Pressure on a station-button brings the set from any point on any waveband into exact tune*
★ *Waveband-indicator turns automatically to new setting*

MOTOR
The latest inductor motor, backed by years of development and trouble-free experience, is used.
★ *Instant action, backward or forward*
★ *Automatic protection against over-running*
★ *No brushes or commutator*
★ *Consistent, reliable operation*

Models PB.289, RG.489 & ARG.399 include the assembly shown above. Models PB.189, FB.199 & C.389 include the same mechanism, with the exception of Motor Wavechanging and Motor 'Cruising'.

MOTOR-CONTROLLED NOISE SUPPRESSION
The motor in motion automatically mutes the speaker, so that the set is silenced between stations.
★ *No inter-station noise*
★ *Silent and rapid traverse of S.W. scale (with 'Cruising' button)*

In the Ecko Prosperity Plan you have been given a sound distribution policy, drastic reduction in dealer competition, equitable and progressive discounts, virile re-organisation of H.P. trading facilities, and bold intensive publicity and dealer co-operation.
Now you have products assuring you of maximum benefits from this Plan. Concentrate on Ekco.

Push-button tuning, currently enjoying a comeback, was very popular just before the war. The more ambitious models used elaborate motorized tuning, with electronic automatic frequency control to remove residual errors

Ekco, 1939

Had they succeeded, the strength of the company could have been seriously reduced, particularly if other key staff had joined them. That strength was soon put to the test. Early in 1932, a fire destroyed the design and research laboratories, and with them the design data for the 1933 models. As a result the season's two principal models had to be housed in the previous year's cabinets. No matter that the circuitry was new[29] and the cabinets themselves now made in the company's own plastics plant instead of imported from Germany.[26] Public and dealers alike expected manufacturers to present a completely new range at each year's Radio Show, and Ekco's sales slumped. In January 1933, with large stocks of unsold receivers, the company suffered a financial crisis. Two of the three 'financial' directors, Maxwell and Manners, pulled out, while Cole and Verrells mortgaged their houses and insurance policies to back the overdraft needed to keep the firm afloat.

By the end of 1933 Ekco had bounced back to prosperity with an up-to-date range of models, most of them superhets. Bakelite cabinets, initially introduced because they were cheaper than wooden ones, were now seen to be capable of actually enhancing a receiver's appeal, and top architectural designers were commissioned to create cabinets that fully exploited the potential of the new medium. It made sense to spare no expense at this stage, given the enormous tooling cost that followed; moulds and dies weighed upwards of 15 tons each, and were cut from solid blocks of chromium nickel steel. For the 1933 show, Serge Chermayeff designed a cabinet of pleasing proportions that could just as easily have been made from wood; a year later Wells Coates produced a circular cabinet that certainly could not have been. It was the first of a succession that Ekco produced in this shape, which lent itself to large tuning dials marked with station names; these receivers have subsequently been widely used to evoke Britain in the 1930s. In order to give the designer every freedom, it was initially the practice to adapt the chassis to the cabinet, although by the late-1930s some plastic cabinets were made to conventional designs that allowed a common chassis to be marketed in both wooden and plastic versions.

Ekco's impeccable reputation for reliability can be credited largely to Tony Martin, Deputy Chief Engineer,[26] and to R K Spencer, Head of Material and Components Research Section, who was an ex-colleague recruited from Marconiphone by John Wyborn. A quiet, even-tempered man, Spencer nevertheless maintained an iron grip on quality control, through the operation of a well-equipped laboratory. Such was the respect he had earned from the management that no-one challenged his decisions on what was fit to come into or go out of the factory, even if this meant keeping hundreds of people idle while a problem was ironed out.

Sunrise at Pye

Following C O Stanley's buy-out, Pye Radio Ltd took over the whole of the original factory site, thereby roughly doubling the area devoted to radio, and the instrument company moved to new premises. Between 1929 and 1937 the factory expanded further, from 57,000 to 138,000 sq ft, and annual production rose from less than 30,000 sets to around 200,000.[30,31] After completing purchase of the company, Stanley handed back the reins to Tom Robinson, and continued to run his advertising business, which he later told Harold Pye had in one year netted him £90,000. However, in the early-1930s Pye Radio's trading account was anything but healthy, and Stanley felt that his responsibility to the shareholders required him to involve himself more closely in managing the company.[32] Accordingly, he became a director. The announcement of this fact in *The Wireless Trader* of 29 July 1933 states that in 1929 Stanley's name had appeared on the prospectus of Pye Radio as having sold a block of shares to the public, but otherwise shows that the extent of his involvement with the company had gone largely unnoticed within the industry:

> "For years he has been an unknown quantity —
> associated with everything and tied down to nothing —

and now he has come into the open and associated himself as a director with one of our great national names in radio — Pye Radio Ltd."

In the early-thirties Pye's wooden cabinets were as distinctive as Ekco's bakelite ones. Back in the mid-twenties when fretwork loudspeaker-grilles were fashionable one of the staff had devised a 'rising sun' grille based on a design he had seen on a colleague's cigarette case. The management liked it, and late in 1927 used it for a portable receiver that proved particularly successful, achieving sales of almost a thousand in three months. Thereafter, Pye used the design intensively for several years on their table models, and by the time fretwork grilles went out of fashion in the mid-thirties it had acquired a fame that enabled it to continue effective service as a logo.[33] However, an attempt to re-introduce it soon after the war revealed that a 'rising sun' motif aroused strong anti-Japanese feeling. Pye recalled from its dealers 800 of the 1,000 personal portables that had been made with the offending design as their loudspeaker fret, and burned them.

Notwithstanding the many publicity pictures showing sets in exotic but unlikely locales, the export performance of the British receiver industry in the 1930s was poor, never exceeding 80,000 units a year, or a half of one per cent of the annual world absorption of receivers.[34] Pye Radio, however, made determined efforts to tackle some of the weaknesses hampering exports. Departments were organized for life-testing components, transport tests carried out to reduce the risk of damage in transit, and the effects of humidity and extremes of temperature assessed to enable receivers to be effectively tropicalized.

At Pye Radio Ltd, Cambridge, 1929
Staining and filling shop

Cabinet department and test cubicles

Coil-winding department

Plating room

Production and drilling shop

Machine shop

Central stores

NOVEMBER 12TH, 1930.　　THE WIRELESS WORLD　　ADVERTISEMENTS. 13

TRIUMPHANT AT OLYMPIA

IRRESISTIBLE PREDOMINANT

First in the Wireless World Ballot . . . First in public estimation! . . . There has never been anything in Radio to compare with the Pye TWINTRIPLE Portables. New in technique, new in presentation, new in performance. Completely portable and completely self-contained (Battery model or All-Electric models) . . . altering and widening the whole outlook of radio reception, the Pye TWINTRIPLE Portables have created the greatest public demand in the history of radio.

PYE TWINTRIPLE PORTABLES

Pye Radio Ltd., Sales Organisation, Paris House, Oxford Circus, W.1.

A13　Advertisements for "The Wireless World" are only accepted from firms we believe to be thoroughly reliable.

Pye Radio factory,1932

Counting screws by weight

A corner of the drawing office

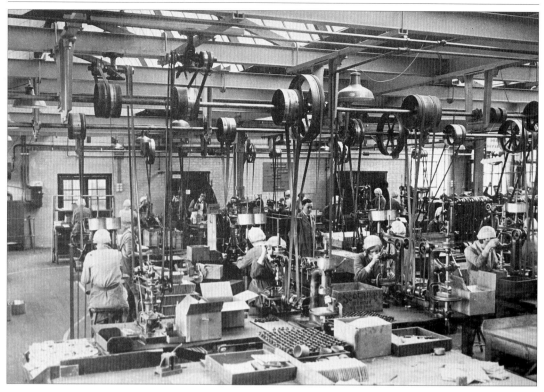

Drilling, tapping and milling machines. Caps are worn to prevent hair from being caught in the belting

Hazardous working conditions in the nickel, copper and cadmium plating department

Coil winding

Winding frame aerials

Cartoned receivers being taken up by the elevator...

...and down the chute onto the lorry

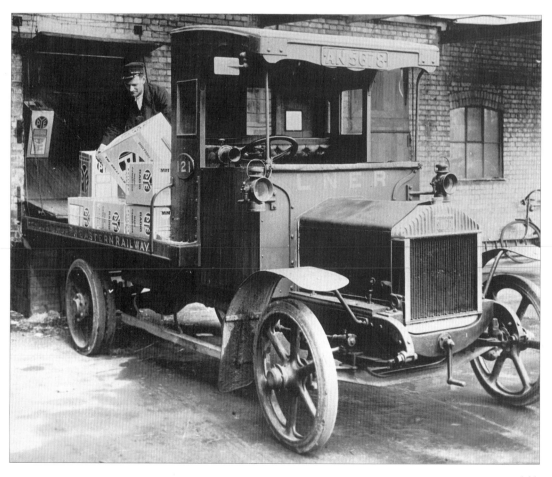

Assembly line with feeder benches

At the end of the day

Pye works outing to Southend-on-Sea, 1932

HMV weigh up their bargain

Disillusion set in at Hayes soon after the purchase of Marconiphone in March 1929. It became clear that the agreement on patents had not been adequately defined, and a dispute ensued over HMV's rights to patents acquired by Marconi from other companies under agreements in force at the time of the purchase.[35] Not until May 1931 did Marconi concede that these rights applied not just to those patents already acquired, but to any acquired subsequently.[36]

HMV's assessment of the Marconiphone company itself was far from reassuring. Even before the purchase it was reported, of the sales headquarters in Tottenham Court Road, "Their premises...do not look very businesslike, and are very untidy and dirty."[37] In fact Clark had been advised to keep the Sterling factory at Dagenham, where Marconiphone receivers were made, "as a separate manufacturing unit for the production of those lines where standards can be lower than that ruling at Hayes".[38] On 6 March 1929 an HMV executive visited the Works and reported that development of new models for the 1929/30 programme of production had barely begun. The manager, recently put in by Marconi to improve the plant's efficiency, said that although the aim was to produce cheap sets, output was too small for these to be competitive with such mass-production models as GEC's highly successful 'Victor 3', and that Marconiphone had "been forced to reduce their cost of production by the use of shoddy methods and finishes".[39] Some months later a senior HMV executive, B E G Mittell, gained the impression from a meeting with Marconi's Head of Research that Marconi's Managing Director "thought he was 'selling us a pup'."[40]

Immediately after the purchase Mittell lunched with Stanley Mullard, and sounded him out about taking over the management of Marconiphone. Chafing under increasing control from Eindhoven, Mullard expressed interest but deferred any decision until after his next Board Meeting, and no more was heard of the proposal. There is no evidence that Mittell even approached the other 'outstanding name' he was considering for the position, but it seems unlikely that, at a time when the BBC was just bursting into full bloom, Sir John Reith would have taken kindly to a suggestion that he should give up being its Director General to become head of an ailing manufacturing company.[41]

By the autumn of 1929, HMV were discovering that they had taken on further problems in acquiring Marconi's share of M-O V. Naturally, Marconiphone receivers were designed around M-O valves, but at a meeting held at Hayes in September between all parties (including representatives of GEC and Marconi) HMV alleged that "no confidence whatever could be placed in the Valve Works". The Works were finding it impossible to maintain quality standards, and had lowered the characteristics of one established type; they were informed that Marconiphone would only accept valves that met the original specification. In response to M-O V complaining that sets had been designed around valves not yet out of the development stage, it was asserted that these sets were already 30% behind those of competitors and would have been still further behind if designed only around valves successfully in production. The company produced 180 types of valve, many more than their competitors, "but admitted that they had never caught up the lead on some types which had been lost 3 years ago when Phillips [sic] came out with his metal-coated filament."[42]

Six weeks later, an HMV internal minute reported the situation as being desperate. Marconiphone had met M-O V's deadline for specifying the valves they required for the 1930 season, but the Works had only just received the information, so had withdrawn all previously made promises of delivery. It had emerged that both the Research Department and the Works had been instructed to go slow on work for Marconiphone, seemingly as a gesture of protest against an impression that the HMV takeover threatened M-O V's future. The memorandum spelled out the implications for Marconiphone receivers: "If we design them round valves we know we can get, it means designing round this year's valves which, from M.O., will be at least two years behind the times next summer...we are forced now to disclaim responsibility for a successful Marconiphone programme for next season."[43]

The possibility must be considered that the denigration of M-O V in these HMV papers was part of some political manoeuvre. However, two pieces of evidence suggest otherwise. In January 1930, Harrods wrote to HMV[44] expressing keen disappointment in their new radio gramophone, and after criticizing various aspects of the instrument the writer states: "I think it is general knowledge that the Marconi valve is not very successful, and this fact is proved by the selection of the Mullard valve for your electric reproducer which is really splendid and worthy of HMV."

And in September 1930, when a special meeting was held at Hammersmith to consider the quality of M-O V valves relative to those of its competitors, it was the GEC representatives who led the detailed and quite devastating criticism, saying that with the existing range they were finding it practically impossible to obtain orders from setmakers. At this period one important measure of a valve's performance — the change in current achieved by a one-volt change in grid voltage — was referred to simply as its 'goodness'. After Mr Fletcher of GEC had advanced the low goodness of M-O V valves relative to the competition as a major reason for their poor sales, an exchange took place between him and Mr Wade of M-O V:

"Mr Wade stated that in his opinion high goodness was very inadvisable, and could only be obtained at the cost of excessive breakage and rejections during manufacture. He suggested that the B.V.M.A. should arrange for its members to call a halt to the race for better goodness. Mr Fletcher said he did not believe for one minute that either Mullard or Mazda were producing valves involving the enormous scrappage losses mentioned by Mr Wade. He also remarked that the idea of getting the B.V.M.A. to call a halt in the race for increased goodness was a ridiculous one if the request for the arrangement came from a firm who was notoriously losing the race."

For each of many M-O V valve types, the report on the meeting details specific failings, and names the particular competing valve that outclasses it. Mullard valves are summarized as being of fairly conventional construction but more sensibly and more ruggedly designed than M-O V valves, while Cossor score over Mullard on originality. Mazda valves are stated to utilize methods of construction entirely dissimilar to their competitors, and to have "established a lead which it will be excessively difficult for anybody else to make up".[45]

Queuing for work at EMI in 1932

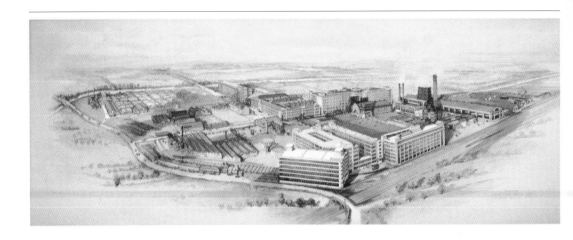

The Hayes complex shortly before the formation of EMI

Adversity the midwife at the birth of EMI

In April 1929, almost immediately after the Marconiphone takeover, HMV's Chairman, Alfred Clark, embarked on negotiations to merge the company with its principal competitor in records and gramophones, the Columbia Graphophone Company, as a further step towards Sarnoff's objective of a 'Radio Corporation of Europe'.[46] This time, however, Sarnoff was to leave things much more in Clark's hands.[47] Columbia was a British company (though more than half its total capital was held in America) with several overseas manufacturing subsidiaries and the world's widest distribution organization. A major attraction was that it offered access to territories from which HMV was excluded under an agreement with the Victor Company. However, Columbia's profits and assets were considerably less than those of HMV, and negotiations soon broke down over the terms of the proposed merger.[48]

The record industry was far worse hit by the depression than the radio industry, and a year later Clark wrote "...this is a very dangerous time in our history to make such a merger unless it can be made on extremely advantageous terms."[49] By January 1931 Sarnoff was confessing "I haven't much stomach now for buying other phonograph and record businesses."[50] However, at this point Columbia approached Clark in a much more conciliatory vein than before.[51] There was a general consensus that the whole record business might become subordinate to radio, and although Columbia had made a successful entry into the radio industry in 1929, with receivers made for them by Plessey, they badly needed access to radio patents. HMV's own patent position was in fact an unhappy one, and Clark was negotiating with various companies to improve it. But he felt that these companies, having seen Victor fall victim to RCA, regarded HMV as a similarly doomed gramophone-based company whose bargaining position could only weaken, and so were unwilling to come to terms. He confessed to Sarnoff "I feel particularly helpless when carrying on these negotiations".[52]

Thus it was two chastened companies that now re-opened discussions. Louis Sterling, Columbia's Managing Director, argued the need for an immediate merger so that the savings resulting from re-organization could be achieved as soon as possible; these were estimated at £100,000 a year, which had become much more important as profits had declined.[53] HMV made a show of demanding full information on Columbia's finances, but Sarnoff gave his blessing to taking some things on trust,[54] and the merger was quickly accomplished, with Clark and Sterling respectively appointed Chairman and Managing Director. The name chosen for the new company, Electric and Musical Industries Ltd, though itself unmemorable, had the merit of pronounceable initials, which over the years were to be incorporated into the names of many products, most notably the Emitron television camera.

By 1931 HMV had hardly begun the transition from gramophones to radiograms; the previous year they had produced only 5,000 radiograms and other electrical reproducers, as against 142,000 acoustic gramophones.[55] They did a large export business in gramophones, with Hayes supplying all territories from the same range of models. Clark did not think this would be possible for radio, where local requirements differed widely. Even success was bringing problems, as he explained to Sarnoff:

> "...there is evidence that the higher-priced Electrical Gramophone being so much better than the higher-priced Mechanical Gramophone, the public show hesitation in investing in lower-priced Mechanical Gramophones, in the belief that they may eventually be able to buy lower-priced Electrical Gramophones and, unfortunately, it has not yet been possible to design good low-priced Electrical Gramophones."[52]

Despite such doubts, and the weaknesses of Marconiphone and M-O V at the time of their acquisition, EMI rapidly moved into a leading position in the radio industry. A major asset acquired from Columbia was Isaac Shoenberg, who had joined that company's research staff from Marconi in 1929 and was now appointed EMI's Head of Research. He built up a formidable team of young scientists, and although their most spectacular work was to be in the field of television, sound reproduction and radio were not neglected. A D Blumlein's 1933 patent on stereophonic gramophone records led to successful experimental recordings, and embraced the technique adopted worldwide over twenty years later. Also in 1933, two members of the Department, C S Bull and S Rodder, were given the task of circumventing Philips' patent on the pentode valve.

John Street (left), radio buyer for Whiteleys of Bayswater, with an EMI representative at the Radio Show in 1937, holding a tray of models of their current range

valve. Within two days they had conceived the notion of the beam tetrode, in which the electron stream was brought to a focus between screen-grid and anode, and was thereby made to perform the function of the 'suppressor grid' that Philips had added to the tetrode to create the pentode. The idea was patented, and around 100 experimental valves were made in Research Department, but when manufacture was proposed to M-O V they declared that it could not be mass-produced. The patent was subsequently shown to RCA, who used it to produce the highly successful 6L6 valve, whereupon M-O V relented and belatedly developed its famous British counterpart, the KT66.[56]

The low status assigned to Marconiphone receivers at the time of the takeover continued, to the extent that they were distributed through wholesalers while the sale of HMV products was restricted to registered dealers, many of them piano retailers who had diversified into gramophones and records. However, by the late-1930s a Marconiphone radiogram or television set differed from its HMV counterpart only in details of cabinetwork.

Philips build up their British base

From their introduction in 1928, Philips all-mains receivers made a considerable impact on the British market, and a dealer's handbook of about 1930 lists eight different models;[57] initially all the sets had been imported, but by 1930 some were being made at Mitcham, on the site that Mullard had purchased in 1927. At first the public were nervous about using mains receivers, and with some justification. British

Throughout the summer of 1930 a Philips Radio Van, built on a double-deck bus chassis, toured England giving free concerts. It was equipped to relay radio programmes or play gramophone records, and had a 600W amplifier. An illuminated window displayed Philips receivers and loudspeakers

Lunch-time at Hercules cycle works, Birmingham

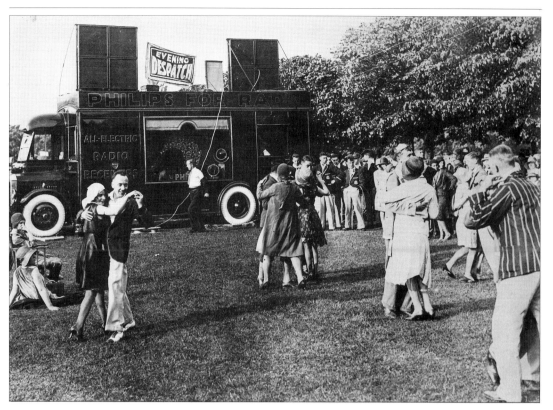

The two-shilling enclosure at Evesham Regatta, to which 10,000 people were admitted during the day

Gramophone recital at South Park, Darlington. Note the empty bandstand nearby

*Copies of this circular were
distributed to 300
Eastbourne boarding
houses and hotels*

TELEGRAPHIC ADDRESS:
"PHILLAMPS" WESTCENT, LONDON.
CABLES:
PHILLAMPS, LONDON

TELEPHONE Nº
REGENT Nº 7731 (PRIVATE EXCHANGE)
CODES:
BENTLEY'S, A.B.C. 5TH EDITION.
MASTER AND PRIVATE.

PHILIPS LAMPS LIMITED.

PHILIPS HOUSE
145, CHARING CROSS ROAD
LONDON·ᴡ·2

OUR REF.   SW/KG

YOUR REF.

DIRECTORS:
DR. A.F. PHILIPS (DUTCH)
L.G. SLOAN, J.P. (BRITISH)
SIR W. HORWOOD, G.B.E., K.C.B., D.S.O. (BRITISH)
C.J. POWELL (BRITISH)
MANAGING DIRECTORS:
D.C.F. VAN EENDENBURG, (DUTCH)
A. DE JONG. (DUTCH)

MANUFACTURERS OF ELECTRIC LAMPS,
WIRELESS APPARATUS, NEON SIGNS METALIX X-RAY TUBES
CARDBOARD, GLASSWARE, FITTINGS ETC.

BRANCHES AT:
GLASGOW, MANCHESTER, NEWCASTLE, BIRMINGHAM, BRISTOL, LEEDS, NOTTINGHAM, CARDIFF,
LIVERPOOL, BELFAST.

12th July, 1930.

RADIO DEPARTMENT

Dear Sir or Madam,

On Friday evening 6 - 9.30 p.m., and Saturday afternoon 2 -
5.30 p.m., July 25th and 26th, Philips Radio are sending
their wonder radio van to Beachy Head where, in collaboration
with the management of the Beachy Head Hotel, some wonderful
concerts will be given. These concerts will be featured in
THE DAILY MIRROR, who are also collaborating.

Arrangements have been made with Chapman's Coaches, Victoria
Place, Eastbourne, to run coaches at special fares to Beachy
Head on these two days. We take this opportunity of extending
an invitation to yourself and guests to see and hear the most
wonderful radio van on the road to-day. Please place the
enclosed poster in your hall.

Entertainment is one of the greatest factors in making your
business a success. Philips Radio will give entertainment
for one - ten thousand people. Music in one room, two rooms,
all your rooms - the lounge, dance-hall - anywhere at any
time. It's cheaper than a dance band - its modern - its
trouble free because it's all-electric.

Why not ask your radio dealer for a trial? He will willingly
give you a demonstration without any obligation on your part.

Yours faithfully,
PHILIPS LAMPS LIMITED:

Radio General Sales Manager.
All quotations and orders are subject to our confirmation, and all orders and agreements
are contingent on strikes, fires or any other causes beyond our control.

FORM NO. R142/50

Standard Specification No. 415, published in 1931, detailed the safety
precautions to be observed in the construction of a mains radio,
stipulating that no live parts should be accessible, but all that could
be specified concerning accessible metal parts, which sometimes
included the whole outer casing, was that they should be connected to
the receiver's 'Earth' terminal. It had to be assumed that the user
would provide this with an adequate earth connection, typically to a
water pipe or a buried rod, for earthed power points were still a rarity
and the set was commonly plugged in to a lamp socket through a two-
way adaptor. But the mains receiver's low running cost and its ability
to run for long periods without attention were powerful attractions,
and opened up new possibilities. Thus in 1930 *The Philips Announcer*,
a monthly magazine for dealers, carried an item on "Selling the '2515'
Radio-player":

> "It is perfectly safe and perfectly simple, so that any
> youth could manage it without fear of injury...Suggest
> that one be installed in the kitchen for the use of the
> servants in their leisure hours. Point out how much
> easier it would be to obtain and keep servants if they
> had this amusement provided for them."

PHILIPS ALL-ELECTRIC RADIO

Whether your mains are A.C. or D.C., or even if you have no electric light, there is a Philips Receiver that will exactly meet your needs. In the Philips range of receivers, the biggest range of any one radio manufacturer, you will find a set for every purpose and to fit every purse.

Philips 3-Valve All-Electric Receiver Type 2514 works entirely from A.C. Electric Mains (40/100 cycles).   Complete with valves and leads.
                                          Price £21 0 0
Philips 3-Valve All-Electric Receiver Type 2524, as Type 2514, but works completely from D.C. Electric Mains. Complete with valves and leads.
                                          Price £21 0 0
Type 2502, similar to Type 2514, but operates from batteries or a supply unit.   Price £12 10 0

Philips 4-Valve All-Electric Receiver Type 2511 is a de luxe receiver, all current being taken from A.C. mains. Complete with valves and leads.   Price £35 0 0

PHILIPS

Philips Lamps Ltd., Philips House, 145, Charing Cross Road, London, W.C.2.

Advertisements for "The Wireless World" are only accepted from firms we believe to be thoroughly reliable.

Philips promoted their sets with great flair, running lively advertisements and carrying out a number of publicity 'stunts' typical of the period. One was their 'Radio Van', which toured the country; another involved the Great Western Railway. On 2 March 1931 the technical press were invited to travel in a special coach attached to the 11.15 Paddington–Bristol express, to listen to a Model 2511 receiver driving up to 60 pairs of headphones. An inverted-L aerial had been fitted along the roof of the coach, and in the course of six trial runs all sources of interference had been eliminated. Excellent reception was maintained throughout the outward and return journeys except when the train passed through tunnels, when gramophone music was substituted. Although *The Trader* declared it very probable that Philips would equip certain GWR trains with radio in the near future, no permanent installation followed — probably no-one had seriously expected that it would.[58]

As the depression bit deeper, the pressure to 'Buy British' increased. The imposition of the 'anti-dumping' import duty in November 1931 prompted Eindhoven to issue a press statement saying that "As regards wireless, our British factories are already supplying the greater part of our sales in that country, and will shortly be able to satisfy the entire demand."[28] Philips Lamps Ltd thereupon sent a letter complaining that this put them in an embarrassing predicament, by arousing curiosity as to the whereabouts of these British factories. The Mitcham operation was run as 'Mitcham Works Ltd', and hitherto Philips had succeeded in preventing their connection with it from becoming widely known. Though Eindhoven's action had now compelled them to acknowledge that Mitcham was manufacturing for them on a large scale, they were still reluctant to admit that it was actually part of Philips, since to do so would prejudice the possibility of its manufacturing for other firms. Moreover, since Mitcham was generally known to manufacture for Mullard, the connection between Mullard and Philips would become more evident.[59]

Philips were slow to go over to superhets, introducing between 1932 and 1934, a series of 'straight' sets known as 'superinductance' models, which performed as well as good superhets of the period. However, an engineer who has restored one to working order concludes that the design was not cost effective.[60] Thus the large tuning coils justifying the name 'superinductance' were wound with expensive 15-strand 'litz' wire on low-loss glass formers, yet were liberally coated with lossy wax. To keep the set's four tuned circuits in step while retaining single-knob tuning required numerous variable capacitors to be pre-set at the factory, while to equalize performance across the waveband the bias on the valves was varied by a potentiometer driven from the tuning shaft through a phosphor-bronze belt. But the sets exhibited a high standard of workmanship, and surviving examples are treasured not merely for their cabinets, many in the company's domed 'cathedral' style. The following passage is taken almost verbatim from a collector's loving description.

"Their interiors were as handsome as their cabinets. Above the rather high, grey metal chassis there shone the large, bright copper-coloured coil-screens and the smooth roundness of the copper-sprayed Mullard valves (some sporting large, hooded, copper top-cap connectors), while there were occasional glimpses of the unique Philips pre-set capacitors, made of brightly burnished brass and sealed at the correct value by a dash of red paint. Components, in the main, were of Philips manufacture, most being quite unlike those used by other makers.[61]

However, the sets were expensive to produce, and in 1934 Philips introduced their last superinductance model and their first superhet.

Throughout the decade Philips receivers were designed in Eindhoven, and retained a 'continental' aura, initially with their use of unusual cabinet materials such as the tortoiseshell-like 'Phillite', later with their side-contact valves and such slightly flamboyant features as the 'mono-knob' — a single assembly into which all the receiver's control functions were concentrated. A comment in *Wireless World's* review of a 1935 model reflects their high standard of engineering: "...it is refreshing to find a set in which no effort has been spared to make it excel in all departments."[62]

Ultra catch up[63]

Between 1925 and 1929 Edward E Rosen's Ultra Electric Limited had produced at their premises in Harrow Road a varied but unremarkable range of products, centred on loudspeakers but also including pickups, battery eliminators and a portable receiver. After ceasing production of horn loudspeakers in 1928 they had produced the 'Air Column Exponential Speaker' for one year only, then progressed to the 'Airchrome' — a moving-iron model using a double diaphragm of doped and tensioned linen instead of a paper cone. Although their name is not to be found among the reports on 150 British radio companies, some of them very minor, drawn up in 1929 by a firm of commercial investigators, they were evidently prospering; between 1924 and 1930 the Harrow Road premises were extended from their original 6,500 sq ft to 24,000 sq ft, divided between two separate factories, and the work-force increased from 20 to 250. In 1930 Ultra produced their first mains receiver and shortly afterwards moved to a factory at Chalk Farm, where Rosen was able to increase what we now know as 'vertical integration' to the point where 95% of the components used were produced on the premises. Within three years Chalk Farm was in its turn outgrown, and in 1935 Rosen opened a resplendent new 150,000 sq ft factory on Western Avenue.

This phase of Ultra's growth was founded upon a range of 'straight' receivers produced between about 1930 and 1933, with such colourful names as 'Twin Cub', 'Blue Fox', 'Tiger', 'Panther' and 'Lynx'. Like Cole and Verrells at Ekco, Rosen had recruited a Chief Engineer from the Marconiphone stable around the time of the HMV take-over in 1929, and seems to have been equally fortunate in his choice, for E H Munnion designed receivers that were well matched to the middle of the market. They laid no claim to innovation, but were competitively priced, soundly engineered and, it was asserted, easy to service. A page of Service Hints in *Radio's Richest Voice*, the magazine circulated to authorized Ultra dealers, conceded that "For the more complex faults you will have to use a voltmeter", but concluded with the statement "When making a service call, a spare set of valves, a grub screw-driver and a large screw-driver are usually all you require to analyse any trouble". At the factory, resources were initially fairly basic; it was only in 1932 that a proper drawing office was instituted. Rosen kept development costs down by not attempting to produce a

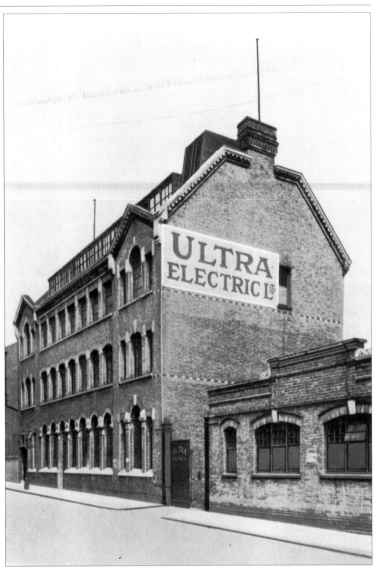

Two Ultra sites of the 1930s:
Chalk Farm and below,
Western Avenue

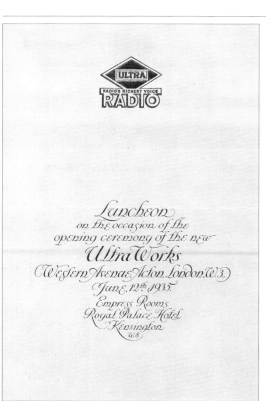

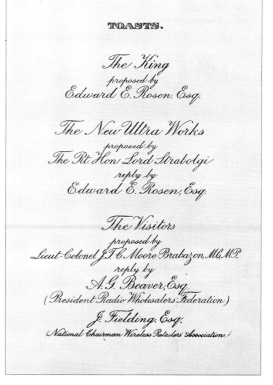

ULTRA
RADIO'S RICHEST VOICE
RADIO

Luncheon
on the occasion of the
opening ceremony of the new
Ultra Works
Western Avenue, Acton, London, W.3.
June 12th 1935.
Empress Rooms
Royal Palace Hotel
Kensington
W.8.

TOASTS.

The King
proposed by
Edward E. Rosen, Esq.

The New Ultra Works
proposed by
The Rt. Hon. Lord Strabolgi
reply by
Edward E. Rosen, Esq.

The Visitors
proposed by
Lieut-Colonel J.T.C. Moore-Brabazon, M.C., M.P.
reply by
A.G. Beaver, Esq.
(President Radio Wholesalers' Federation)
J. Fielding, Esq.
(National Chairman Wireless Retailers' Association)

Luncheon Menu from
opening ceremony of
Western Avenue factory,
June 1935

E E Rosen with
C A Charlesworth, factory
manager, at Chalk Farm in
1933. In the background is
Rosen's American car

Front cover of a dealer magazine

completely new range each year, though a model retained for a second year might well be given a new cabinet, and would introduce a new, low-priced model in the spring as a means of boosting trade during the slack months before the Radio Show. He was not over-interested in cabinets and tended to accept, sometimes with minor modifications, the patterns periodically offered to him by the East-End firm who supplied them. He did employ a cabinet designer for a short time, until the unfortunate man produced a design requiring modifications to the receiver's chassis.[64] Rosen was a staunch advocate of price maintenance, proudly announcing that in 1925 he had been the first person in the radio industry to take legal action in its defence, and using *Radio's Richest Voice* to publicize current injunctions obtained against offenders. Even when he reduced the price of a discontinued model to clear unsold stocks, the reduction was strictly controlled.[65]

At the opening of the Western Avenue factory, Rosen said that radio was the brightest spot in the industry of the whole country, and paid tribute to "the most loyal staff ever any fellow had the good fortune to have".[66] In their turn, those who worked for him found him tough but fair, flamboyant but totally without 'side', and with a strong vein of kindness. As a favour to a widowed acquaintance he took on her sixteen-year-old son, prematurely withdrawn from a public school. "You can't even hit a nail in straight!" he told the lad, then added "But don't worry — I'll teach you."[67] Very much the family man, Rosen built himself a roomy, well-appointed but by no means grandiose house in Mill Hill, where he and his wife Flora, who was French, brought up their three children. In the early years of their marriage Flora had helped him to run the business, and she continued to involve herself in its social activities.

The new factory was capable of an output of 1,000 sets per day, with a workforce of 1,500, as against 600 at Chalk Farm, and it soon became company policy not to introduce a new model unless sales of at least 100,000 were forecast for the basic table-model version. Himself a keen amateur cinematographer, Rosen had the building of the factory professionally filmed. Viewed to-day the scene has an almost Edwardian air, as moustached workmen wearing flat caps or bowler hats scurry about with wheelbarrows and hods, almost totally without mechanical aids. The finished structure, by contrast, was the essence of thirties' modernity, floodlit at night in red and blue[68] and outlined in red neon-tubing, with the name emblazoned several times across the sky-line.

The rise and fall of Frank Murphy[69]

Of the companies set up in the late-1920s specifically to manufacture radio receivers, Murphy Radio stand out as the most innovative, in their business philosophy, their circuit engineering and their cabinet design, which was already anticipating post-war trends in the mid-1930s. Frank Murphy, born in 1889, was the son of a London headmaster. He had some higher education in Mathematics and Electrical Engineering, but by 1914, with a wife and child to support, he had settled for a routine technical job with the Post Office, to which he returned in 1920 after a successful services career that had included setting up an Officers' Wireless Training School at Farnborough. However, the war had broadened his horizons, and he determined to start his own business, armed with a demobilization gratuity of £450.

Murphy Radio's first model, launched in 1930, undergoing field-testing the previous year. The lady was a friend of the Murphy family

Murphy was introduced to another discontented ex-officer, Rupert Casson, and together they sank their gratuities, with additional money subscribed by friends and relatives, into launching a publicity service targeted at engineering firms. C O Stanley worked for them for a time, but left after a row that occurred when he insisted on smoking, in the office, a cigar that a client had given him.[70] By 1928 Murphy was earning around £2,000 a year, but he resented the advertising agent's inherent subservience to the client, and was frustrated not to be using his engineering skills. The wireless industry appeared to him to offer a promising means of escape, for he considered that many contemporary receivers performed poorly and were unreliable, and that all but the most basic had more controls than the unskilled user could successfully manage. Murphy believed that he would be able to break into the market by producing reliable, competitively priced sets that performed well and were, above all, simple to operate.

Most of his friends understandably dismissed this as arrogance, for he had little relevant experience, but he was able to impart his enthusiasm to E J ('Ted') Power, a young radio engineer whom he knew because their wives were related. In 1910, inspired by radio's role in the capture of Dr Crippen, the ten-year-old Power had resolved to make it his career, and at 16 he had entered the Merchant Navy as an operator, so that he could transfer straight into the Royal Navy when he reached call-up age. He started manufacturing receivers before the beginning of broadcasting, selling mainly to Gamages, where he knew the manager of the wireless department, Ernie Kent.[71] By 1929, Power was a seasoned veteran of the wireless business, lively and resourceful yet with both feet on the ground, a practical engineer with experience of running a factory. Frank Murphy judged that the two of them would make a good combination, and persuaded Power to become his partner in Murphy Radio Limited, with the title of Chief Engineer.

WHO'S MURPHY?

THE MURPHY RADIO PORTABLE.

"THE disposition of the controls, for instance, with a projecting ledge upon which to rest the hands when tuning is at once evidence of *careful attention to detail on the part of the designers.*"

"In the space of half-an-hour after dark, twenty-four stations at programme strength were tuned in on the 200-600 metre band. This is a conservative estimate as several strong carrier waves were passed over which did not happen to be modulated at the time." *(Extract from "Wireless World" article, August 6th.)*

The above tells you something about Murphy Radio.

Frank Murphy

B.Sc., A.M.I.E.E.,
A.I. Rad. E.,
Chartered Elect. Engineer.

THE NEW MURPHY
RADIO PORTABLE.

MURPHY RADIO·LTD.

WELWYN GARDEN CITY, HERTS

MAKING WIRELESS SIMPLE M

4-VALVE SCREENED GRID RECEIVER

SINGLE TUNING CONTROL.—
Completely Ganged Circuits CALIBRATED IN WAVELENGTHS.
Fitted in beautiful Walnut Cabinet ; weight 32 lbs.
No aerial or earth required.
B.R.V.M.A. Valves.
2-volt 23 A.H. unspillable Accumulator, mounted on acid-proof rack.
108-volt H.T. Battery 12m/a *rating.*
Average H.T. consumption 8-9m/a.
Gramophone Jack.
External Loudspeaker Jack.
External aerial and earth sockets.
Excellent loudspeaker reproduction, giving very enjoyable music and particularly clear speech.
Range and selectivity equal to, if not better than, any other portable set on the market.

PRICE 17 GUINEAS

including valves, batteries, turntable and Royalties.

M.C. 121.

C 3

As a new manufacturer, Frank Murphy had to establish himself with dealers.

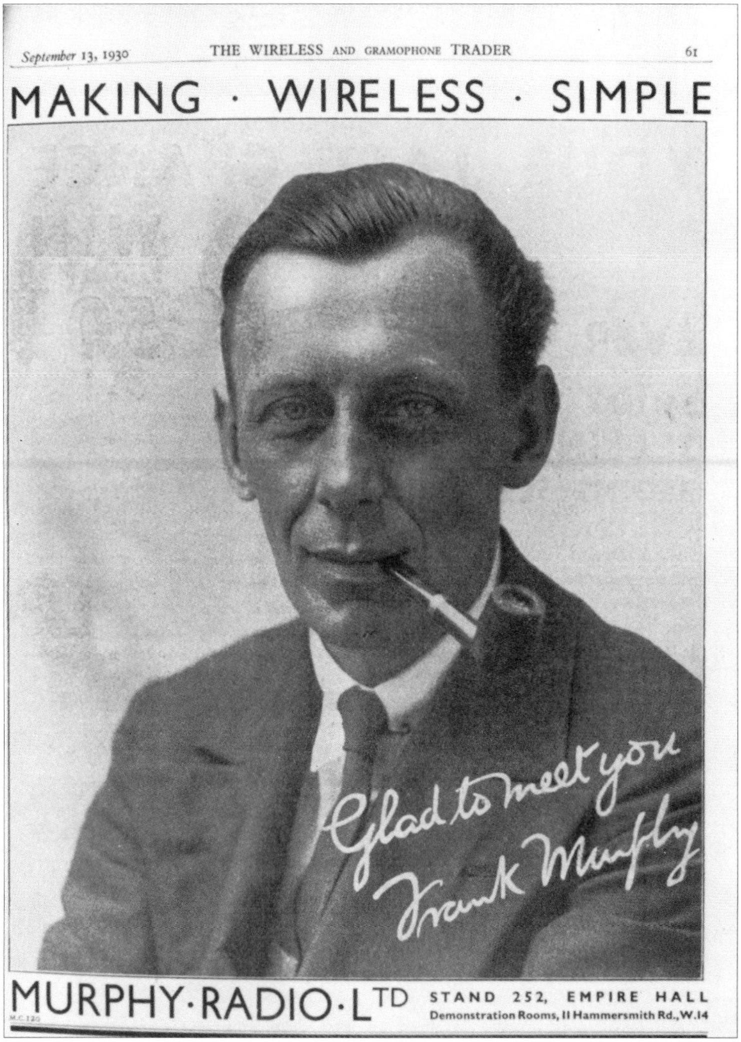
September 13, 1930
THE WIRELESS AND GRAMOPHONE TRADER
61
MAKING · WIRELESS · SIMPLE
Glad to meet you
Frank Murphy
MURPHY·RADIO·LTD
STAND 252, EMPIRE HALL
Demonstration Rooms, 11 Hammersmith Rd., W.14

An early appearance of 'the man with the pipe'

Murphy Radio's first assembly line, 1930

WOMEN

Dealer's window and demonstration room, showing table and console versions of the A24 receiver, 1934

The dealer's message, echoing Frank Murphy's eagerness to reduce seasonal unemployment in the radio industry, suggests that this 1934 photograph is of a shop in or near Welwyn Garden City, where Murphy were located

They rented a 10,000 sq. ft. factory unit at Welwyn Garden City — which offered a pleasant environment for employees — and embarked on designing their first model, a four-valve portable. They undertook this task jointly,[72] Power temporarily waiving his insistence on having total control of the engineering side of the business.[71] Concurrently, they revived Power's earlier connection with Gamages, and made low-priced sets for the store, to support themselves and to give their production arrangements a trial run; soon Ernie Kent joined the company, and subsequently joined Murphy and Power on its board. When they finally launched their own set, in the summer of 1930, *Wireless World* headlined its unreservedly favourable review "Outstanding Range and Selectivity with a Single H.F. Stage."[73] Priced at 17 guineas, the receiver comfortably undersold its rivals.

At Power's suggestion,[71] they sold their sets only through appointed dealers, thereby cutting out the wholesaler's mark-up and making it more likely that owners would get a square deal when the sets needed servicing. Murphy and his first representative, Arthur Herod, embarked on an exhausting programme of visiting and assessing wireless shops throughout the country, and by their diligence managed to establish a substantial network quickly without betraying the slogan "Murphy Dealers are People you can Trust." An advertisement of November 1930 announced that there were already nearly two hundred Murphy Dealers.

There remained the problem of mounting an effective advertising campaign on a small budget. Murphy consulted his old partner, Rupert Casson, who decided to base the advertisements on the personality of Frank Murphy and on his philosophy of "making radio simple". Casson also advocated using advertisements that were big enough to make the company appear important, even though this meant fewer insertions in less costly publications. *Radio Times* still charged relatively low rates, and the advertising budget was channeled into a full-page advertisement every fortnight. A picture of a pipe-smoking Frank Murphy introduced him to the trade in the summer of 1930, and in April 1931 'the man with the pipe' became the focus of the *Radio Times* advertisements. He quickly became a national figure: a symbol of competence and integrity, straightforwardly expressing his no-nonsense views on every aspect of the receiver business. Murphy advertisements of this period are still persuasive to-day; they were even more so at a time when the prevailing style in radio advertising was pompous boastfulness.

The Company's receivers lived up to the the advertisements; they did sound good, they were competitively priced, their reliability was above average. In recruiting his key staff, Murphy was quite prepared to be outshone by them, reasoning that he would share the benefits of their high ability.[72] To head his research team he engaged an outstanding young graduate, R C G Williams, at a salary higher than Power's, and under his leadership Murphy's engineering design came to occupy a leading position in the industry. Murphy was also determined to raise the standard of cabinet design, and enlisted the help of Gordon Russell, who produced craftsman-built furniture of high repute; subsequently, Russell's brother Dick joined Murphy Radio as their cabinet designer. Murphy cabinets sometimes outraged dealers, and it is arguable how many people bought the radios because of the cabinets and how many in spite of them, but they certainly reinforced the company's radical image, and the best of them have acquired the status of classics.

In 1933, Frank Murphy launched *Murphy News*, a fortnightly magazine for staff and dealers, which he also used as a forum for serious discussion of topics ranging from pacificism to business ethics. There is no doubt that he engendered a great *esprit de corps* amongst his dealers, who were encouraged to air their opinions, both in the columns of *Murphy News* and at the meetings he held up and down the country. To be a Murphy dealer was to belong to an exclusive club, but it was not an unmixed blessing. In November 1932, when the depression was near its trough, Frank Murphy had cut dealers' discount from $33^1/_3$% to $27^1/_2$%, and although the other manufacturers soon followed his example the move was resented. Murphy only appointed one dealer in each area, but was liable to sack anyone who failed to achieve the expected turnover, or declined to follow an instruction to move his shop to a better site. And when the company cut the retail price of a model without warning, they paid dealers no compensation on the sets that they had in stock, but pointed out that they could expect to sell more at the lower price.[74] Worst of all, during 1935 Murphy unwisely revealed that he was giving thought to establishing a chain of shops that would sell Murphy sets direct to the public, becoming in effect branches of the company. Although he soon dropped the idea, dealers' confidence was permanently scarred.

From the autumn of 1935 onwards, a succession of warnings was issued by those responsible for the financial side of Murphy Radio: C H Seaton, of their chartered accountants, P K O'Brien, the company's economist, and F J Osborn (later Sir Frederick Osborn), who early in 1936 became Financial Secretary.[75] Their gist was that the company was under-capitalized for its current turnover, let alone for the increased turnover planned for 1936. Analysis of the results for 1934 showed Murphy effectively standing still while the industry as a whole, led by EMI, Ekco and Ultra, moved ahead. And in May 1936 Osborn estimated that even if all went as planned the company would be £107,000 short at the most unfavourable period of the year and, without additional share capital, would be forced to adopt undesirable methods of financing that would undermine its good standing.

In fact, all did *not* go as planned that summer. On humanitarian grounds Frank Murphy hated laying off workers, so he brought out new models early in the year and issued advertisements exhorting the public to buy during the summer. However, there was an element of wishful thinking in this policy, and in May and June 1935 it had produced only half the sales estimated. In 1936 there were additional adverse factors at work: Murphy radio had brought out only one new model that year; all Murphy sets continued to have small tuning dials marked in metres, whereas many competitors were by then following the lead set by Ekco in 1931 and providing much larger dials marked with station names; and Murphy was one of the few manufacturers still without an all-wave model. There were good, rational reasons for all three of these perceived shortcomings. Their receivers were technically advanced, and there was no point in change for change's sake; Power had looked into the question of providing a dial marked with station names and concluded that it would put 10s (50p) onto the list price of a set but would have an uncertainty of one station in its calibration; and Frank Murphy had decided that short-wave listening did not offer the British listener enough entertainment to justify the extra cost of a properly engineered all-wave receiver. Nevertheless, to dealers and to the buying public Murphy sets suddenly seemed old-fashioned, and in May 1936 sales slumped badly, precipitating a financial crisis and a temporary 10% pay cut.[72]

Meanwhile, Frank Murphy's behaviour was giving rise to increasing concern in the company's higher ranks. He was progressively detaching himself from the current financial problems, and addressing abstract questions such as the role of directors in a company. Moreover, his views tended unmistakably towards the concentration of authority in his own hands, as Chairman, which office was variously likened to a Prime Minister (free to choose his own cabinet) and the captain of a ship (who chooses his officers and crew). In July 1936 Murphy sacked Kent (without discussing the matter with Power, the third director) and took over his post of Distribution Manager. This action sent a wave of dismay through senior staff, who had with Murphy's encouragement come to regard themselves more as apostles of a new religion than as mere salaried employees. Kent was a well-respected and longstanding member of the Company and, incidentally, Power's brother-in-law. A month later came a further shock, when *Murphy News* announced that "Mr Frank Murphy has decided to free himself from the executive work of Murphy Radio in order to devote more time to other activities which he has in hand." Power was to become Managing Director, though Murphy remained Chairman of the Board. Both Casson and Seaton wrote him warm personal letters expressing their great admiration for his outstanding merits, tactfully pointing out where he had gone wrong, and advising him how to get back onto the rails. Murphy responded by outlining his plans for initiating a weekly magazine, price 2d, which would be directed towards the masses, initially in this country but eventually worldwide, with the purpose of making its readers better men and women; it would be a cross between *The Saturday Evening Post, The Listener* and *Murphy News*.

In mid-September 1936 Murphy departed for the United States, taking his chauffeur and his Bentley. He returned early in November, Murphy News announcing that he had "...met and talked [you bet!] to close on seventy leading Americans in business and the universities...". But any hopes that the trip had mellowed his outlook were dashed at a Board meeting in January 1937. Murphy dumbfounded his fellow Directors by telling them, quite unequivocally, that thenceforward he would himself make all major decisions, their role being relegated to one of formal endorsement. When the Board protested, as Murphy must surely have known they would, he immediately resigned and left the meeting. That evening, with the Board's approval, Power went to Murphy's house to see whether he was prepared to reconsider the situation, but was not surprised to find that his mind was quite made up.[71]

The rest of Frank Murphy's life (he died, aged 65, in January 1955) has no bearing on the present story, and the interested reader is referred to his daughter's biography.[69] Power took over as Chairman, with Williams as Chief Engineeer, and together they restored Murphy Radio to prosperity while retaining its uniquely innovative character. Their A52 table model of 1938 was perhaps the industry's most advanced medium-priced receiver of the pre-war era. On the short-wave band it used the 'double superhet' technique that is normally found only in 'communications' receivers; the signal is successively converted to two different intermediate frequencies, each chosen to optimize a particular aspect of performance. The extra valve this refinement entailed was switched to provide automatic frequency control for the motorized push-button tuning on long and medium waves.

Bush: the radio company founded on television

Murphy's problems with his dealers in the mid-1930s were aggravated by the rapid growth of Bush Radio, which also made receivers of above-average quality and also sold only through appointed dealers. Many Murphy dealers took out Bush dealerships (which offered a higher discount) as a safeguard against becoming too dependent upon Murphy, and in consequence sold fewer Murphy sets.[74]

Bush Radio rose from the ashes of Graham Amplion, famous for their horn loudspeakers in the 1920s but liquidated during the depression. Their Managing Director, Gilbert Darnley Smith, approached the Ostrer brothers, who controlled the Gaumont British Picture Corporation and had also recently acquired control of Baird Television Ltd, and persuaded them that since the future of the cinema would probably involve television, Gaumont British ought to acquire expertise and experience in the field of electronics. This could be done at trifling expense by establishing a small radio company, which he would manage. The new company was formed in 1932, with a capital of £2,500, and began assembling receivers on the first floor of a small factory in Woodger Road, Shepherd's Bush, with a total workforce of about a dozen; the factory's primary occupant was British Acoustic Films Ltd, another Gaumont British subsidiary. The locale suggested the name 'Bush', and a shrub in a pot was adopted as the company's logo. A simple 3-valve AC table model was put into production with a list price of £11, and four thousand were sold.[76]

Distribution of radios was under the control of the Radio Wholesalers' Federation who, under an arrangement euphemistically described as a 'Fair Trading Agreement', only handled the products of members of the RMA. And under the depressed conditions of 1932 the RMA was not taking on any new members. Bush therefore adopted distribution through appointed dealers from necessity rather than choice.[16] Their link with Gaumont British was a valuable advertising asset, for at that time great kudos attached to the name, associated

Bush Radio's first works outing, in 1933

BUSH

BATTERY RECEIVER

opposite: *From a leaflet of 1933*

left: *From the leaflet promoting the Bush SAC5 superhet of 1934. As the text pointed out, the sets were so reliable that their chassis were seldom seen*

Below: *From a leaflet of 1937*

R·G 41

If they will be honest about it, and admit it, most keen Radio listeners will tell you that their aim and ambition is a good Radiogram ; for there is something so intensely satisfying about owning a Radiogram . . . Radiograms however are big instruments, hold a lot of mechanism, and usually cost a lot of money. Here is a splendid All-wave Radiogram built with all the care characteristic of Bush Radio, at a price which will do much to break down the money barrier. As a point of technical interest, an L.S. valve is used in front of the output valve, which is essential if really good quality is to be expected or even hoped for either on radio or records.

ALL WAVE RADIOGRAM

5 valve (inc. rec.), 7 stage superhet with 6 tuned circuits, for A.C. Mains Waveranges : Short 16.5-51 m. Medium 189-550 m. Long 850-2,000 m. Full A.V.C. Attractive scale station calibrated. Each band individually illuminated. Continuously variable tone control. Large, sensitive M.C. speaker. Provision for external speaker. Very lovely walnut cabinet. Size 3′ 2½″ high, 23″ wide, 15½″ deep.

FOR GUINEAS

12

For dealers intending to reproduce the Bush logo for themselves the company issued this leaflet in about 1938 to ensure that they did it properly

Stereos in both these forms of the trade mark can be supplied in a variety of sizes.

When reproducing in full colour these are correct shades of green and scarlet.

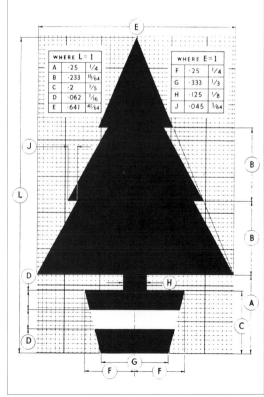

WHERE L = 1		
A	·25	1/4
B	·233	15/64
C	·2	1/5
D	·062	1/16
E	·641	41/64

WHERE E = 1		
F	·25	1/4
G	·333	1/3
H	·125	1/8
J	·045	3/64

BUSH IN PROPORTION

The Bush factory at Power Road, Chiswick, in about 1938, showing the small scale of production

Bush BP5 of 1937. The strap over the top qualified this receiver as a portable

My very best wishes for your success with Bush in the new season

Christopher Stone

BUSH
RADIO
1 9 3 7 — 8

with a major cinema circuit having its own studios and newsreel. Bush radios were promoted as "A Gaumont British Product", and displayed in foyers. The connection was fully exploited when the Silver Jubilee of King George V and Queen Mary was celebrated in May 1935. On the evening when the King broadcast his Jubilee speech, every Gaumont British cinema coupled a Bush radio to its sound system and relayed the speech to audiences estimated to total nearly a million; announcements told them the names of the agents who had supplied the receivers.[77] Meanwhile, all dealers participating in the RMA's Jubilee window-dressing competition were displaying the slogan "For Royal Broadcasts at their best, in a modern set you must invest. Get it here!"[78]

Bush expanded rapidly, though because they started late and were initially very small their absolute size remained modest. A new factory built on the opposite side of Woodger Road allowed the workforce to be increased to about 150, and in 1936 the company moved into a newly built factory in Power Road, Chiswick, which was doubled in size in 1938; at the outbreak of war, the work-force numbered 600–700.[79] Like Murphy, Bush centred their advertising on a pipe-smoking man approaching middle-age. But Christopher Stone, a well-known broadcaster who presented middle-brow record programmes, projected a blander personality than Frank Murphy, and this reflected a difference in the two companies' receivers, Bush sets being much more conservatively housed. Stone laid great emphasis on their reliability,[80] which was indeed high. A pre-war visitor to the factory commented upon this, and was shown a girl testing every component in an incoming consignment.[81]

K-B: from coupons to Cunarder[82]

Kolster-Brandes Ltd (K-B) was descended from a Canadian company, Brandes, established in Toronto in 1908 and acquired by the American Telephone and Telegraph company (AT&T) in 1922. In 1924 it established a British subsidiary, Brandes Ltd, in Slough, initially to produce headphones. The company soon diversified into loudspeakers with papier mâché horns, then cone loudspeakers and a simple receiver in kit form, all distributed through cycle shops. In 1928, having outgrown its original factory, Brandes Ltd leased part of a site at Footscray, Kent, formerly a silk mill, and the following year took over the remainder of the site. The American parent company had by this time been renamed Kolster Radio Corporation of America, and the British company was re-formed as Kolster Brandes, the whole being under the control of the American International Telephone and Telegraph Corporation (ITT).

The work-force was approaching 2,000, but although the product range now included complete receivers, these were not such as to take the firm into the league of major manufacturers. Indeed, their bakelite-cased two-valve 'Masterpiece' receiver of 1930 was distributed exclusively as a 'free gift'. The tobacco company Godfrey Phillips Ltd commissioned a total of 40,000 receivers to promote the sale of their BDV (Best Dark Virginia) cigarettes, and to obtain one it was necessary to spend £12 10s (£12.50) on 500 packets of ten. Cheap imported valves were supplied by Godfrey Phillips, since K-B were barred from fitting them by their agreement with the BVA.[83] Another two-valve K-B, launched in 1931, admirably met the demand for a simple, compact set that needed to do no more than receive 'National'

A K-B stockist, 1932

Radiolympia, 1932

*Final testing of
K-B Model 279, 1931.
Untypically for a radio
factory of the period, men
and women are working on
the same task*

*Visitors to the factory watch
a K-B 'Kobra' receiver being
tested, 1932*

*A publicity stunt of 1932.
K-B receivers were
delivered to Cardiff by air to
meet an urgent demand*

K-B van, with Marconiphone and Pye vans in the background, 1932

The K-B factory, 1932

K-B publicity picture, 1934

Publicity card individualized for a K-B stockist, with blotting paper on the reverse

Rolls-Royce adapted as a publicity vehicle, c. 1936

and 'Regional' from the local BBC transmitters. It was marketed under the inspired name of the 'Pup', and in its two versions — battery and AC — sold a total of 250,000, production at one period reaching 2,000 per day.[84]

On occasions, the company's American approach was counter-productive, as when a disciple of efficiency was sent over here in about 1930 to oversee the lab, and had each stage of a receiver designed by a different engineer as a separate project; testing the completed radio-frequency amplifier stage, he connected it into circuit with leads all of nine inches long, thereby unwittingly guaranteeing that it would oscillate, then proceeded to complain when it did.[85] But on balance the American link was of benefit, and is likely to have been the reason for K-B's early entry into short-wave receivers; they showed a six-valve all-wave superhet at Olympia in 1931, and in 1934 marketed a separate short-wave converter to work in conjunction with their two-waveband 1934/5 models. By the mid-1930s K-B were producing refined receivers quite at variance with their 'cigarette-coupon' image, and their standing received a considerable boost when they won a contract for the internal communications equipment on the liner *Queen Mary*. This was probably secured because the ship's radio equipment was installed by the International Marine Radio Company which, as a subsidiary of ST&C, was also controlled by ITT. In 1938 the link became even closer, when K-B was re-formed under ST&C's ownership.

Plessey re-entered setmaking in 1929, three years after losing their Marconiphone work, when the Columbia Graphophone Company, not yet merged with HMV, decided to diversify into receivers. Allen Clark won the contract to manufacture them, and Bill Heyne got Columbia's laboratory models drawn up, tooled and into production in six weeks. When the sets were shown at Olympia, *Wireless World* commented that they bore all the marks of the thoroughbred and could definitely be placed among the best half-dozen makes currently on the market. A typical Heyne touch was that on one of the models components were interconnected not by wires but by riveted strip connectors, thereby simplifying the assembly process. In 1930 the Plessey-designed 'National' portable, slightly modified, was resurrected in two different guises; one was supplied to a small company for normal marketing, the other to the tobacco firm Carreras, who gave it away in exchange for coupons from 'Black Cat' cigarettes. The following year they made sets for Alba — like Columbia a gramophone company hurriedly moving into radio. All these early sets apart from the 'National' were designed by their customers, but in 1933 they accepted an order from Alba to design a receiver as well as manufacture it, and engaged their first radio design engineer.

This was a most timely move, for later that year it enabled Allen Clark to land the first order from an organization that was for many years to be his principal outlet for complete receivers: the Co-operative Wholesale Society (CWS). The RMA were refusing to sell sets to the CWS on the grounds that the 'dividend' paid to customers was a form of price-cutting, and by undertaking to design and manufacture sets for them Clark was risking his own good standing with the RMA, whose members were his main customers for components. In fact, no action was taken against either Plessey or Ediswan, who supplied them with Mazda valves against the policy of the BVA, and the CWS thumbed their noses at the two associations by marketing the sets under the brand name 'Defiant'.

Components remained more important to Plessey than setmaking throughout the 1930s. Rather than attempt to develop scientific expertise over a wide area they bought in much of the necessary technology by taking out licences from specialist manufacturers: Jensen for loudspeakers, Mallory for electrolytic capacitors, Yaxley for wafer switches; like the first two of these, many of the licensors were American. The company's success owed much to Heyne's commitment to what would now be called 'value engineering' — constant re-assessment of the materials and processes used in making a product, so as to tailor it to its use without unnecessary expense. As their 1932 brochure put it, they offered "the accurate product at the right price from a firm which does not compete with you in your own market." Brochures, however, along with salesmen and advertising agents, played little part in Plessey's commercial strategy. In 1930 the company employed only one salesman, and in no year before the war did advertising and publicity together cost more than £870. Clark himself was the sales force, aiming to secure large-scale orders from the relatively small number of companies in a position to place them. Tall and well-built, he wore a Stetson hat at a jaunty angle, an upwardly inclined cigar between his teeth; as one colleague remarked "You only had to see him to know he was important." He always dealt with prospective customers at Managing-Director level, getting onto personal terms through lavish entertaining and the exercise of an outgoing personality.

Selling on a 'contract shop' basis was much more exacting than selling from a catalogue. The larger setmakers made many of their own components, tailored to the demands of their circuit designers, and expected to enjoy the same freedom when they bought components from an outside supplier. In order to clinch a deal, Clark would quote a price on the spot, relying on his experience and instincts. Thus on returning from a trip he would seek out Heyne and produce, say, a sample capacitor from his pocket. "Here you are, Bill. What can you make that for?" Heyne would examine it quickly, and reply "1s 9d", whereupon Clark might remark "Good. I've just taken an order for five thousand at 1s 3d." Usually Heyne's resourcefulness would enable such a gap to be bridged successfully. Sometimes, however, the gap would be too wide or the promised delivery time too short, or else Heyne would fail to make some decision quickly enough for Clark's liking, and the two would have a blazing row. Joint Managing Directors though they were, they still shared an office and a secretary. She would be sent out, and for half an hour the building would reverberate to shouting and desk-thumping. Between rows they worked together amicably enough, with Allen Clark's father, who was on Plessey's board, acting as peacemaker and confidant.

In the social and economic climate of the 1930s, bosses could and did sack people on the spot. It is said that Guy Fountain, of Tannoy, walked into his 'Goods Inward' area one day and found a youth who was obviously idling, and indeed admitted as much. Fountain simply asked him what his weekly wage was, produced it from his wallet, handed it to the youth, and told him he was fired; he then walked out again, very pleased with himself and quite unaware that the lad worked for a well-known haulage firm.[87] But even by such standards Plessey was notorious as a 'hire and fire' company. This was partly due to its particularly competitive environment, but also reflected Clark's combative personality and his autocratic attitude, typified by his consistent refusal to have any dealings with union representatives. No doubt he was only kidding the day he walked through one of the shops in a foul temper shouting "Sack everybody from A to K", but among 'progress chasers' sackings were so routine, at around one a month, as to arouse the suspicion that their purpose was simply to encourage the others; the men would organize a sweepstake on which of them would be next to go, the winner customarily giving his winnings to the victim.[88] Clark set great store by good timekeeping, and one day demanded to see all those who were more than five minutes late for work. Among them was one of the company's most skilled toolmakers, who seemed to Clark to be insufficiently penitent, so was told to collect his tools and go. This he did, pausing on the way out to unscrew every detachable handle and knob on Clark's Rolls Royce, in full view of the gatekeeper, who assumed he was doing a repair job.[89]

Sackings were also frequent at more senior levels. Clark was apt to appoint or promote people over-enthusiastically, because he liked them or believed in them, then sack them when they didn't measure up. However, the man who candidly admitted his shortcomings would often be given a second chance, and it would be quite wrong to portray Clark as heartless. Those who survived came to regard him with great admiration and even affection, and in the post-war era if he sacked

Plessey's factory at Ilford,
1935

Wafer-switch assembly,
c. 1938

Receiver assembly, c. 1938.

Company vans, c. 1935

someone who had nevertheless given good service he would privately instruct a senior executive to "look after him", perhaps by giving him one or two years' salary, but to keep quiet about it.[90] Clark and Heyne were familiar figures on the shop floor, and if a new machine had to be in production on a Monday they would be there in their shirt sleeves on Saturday afternoon helping to install it.

Versatile and competitive though they were, Plessey were not only up against specialized competitors — such as Dubilier for capacitors, Erie for resistors or Rola for loudspeakers — but frequently against the setmakers' ability to make the components themselves. Compared with valve-makers, in fact, the rest of the components industry was in a weak bargaining position. With no cartel equivalent to the BVA, it could neither fix prices nor force setmakers towards using a standard range of components, which would have made possible greater economies of scale. Such considerations encouraged Plessey to diversify during the 1930s, into telephone instruments for the Post Office, into car components and, increasingly, into armaments. In 1937 Plessey became a public company, and its issued capital was increased to £500,000.

Matters of Import
Philco join the fold
During the early days of broadcasting the industry had been threatened by cheap imports from Europe, but in the 1930s the principal threat came from America, where over-production and high productivity led to receiver prices well below those prevailing in Britain. It mainly involved two categories of receiver: those offering technological advances not yet common in British sets and, later, midget mains-receivers.

Early warning of the first category came in 1930, when in its review of the Manchester Radio Show, *Wireless World* included an eight-valve receiver sold under the brand-name 'Majestic', and mentioned it as being of American manufacture. The RMA had not organized this exhibition, so were unable to exclude foreign sets; they did not make the same mistake the following year. In March 1931, *Wireless World* reviewed the receiver at length, remarking that it "probably represents a forerunner of both the superheterodyne and the compact totally self-contained types", but unaccountably no reference was now made to its American origin, obvious though this was from its whole design, and from the absence of a long waveband. Anglicization, in fact, was confined to fitting the receiver with a mains-dropping resistor and re-tuning a hum-rejecting circuit for a 50Hz supply.[91] Soon a much larger American manufacturer, Philco, began exporting sets to Britain. By September 1931 Selfridges were sending out Philco brochures with a covering letter: "Our experience over the last few days of the performance of this model makes us more than ever pleased to be the first to be able to offer it to the public...PS: This set is an American one." The Sales Manager of Ferranti wrote to protest against this unpatriotic action, which he found especially galling "in view of the frequent publicity of your head, Mr Gordon Selfridge, who seems to advocate a policy of encouraging the sale of British goods."[92]

The importing of American sets created an immediate conflict of interests between setmakers and valve-makers, represented respectively by the RMA and the BVA. The sets used valves quite different from British ones, and by the end of 1930 the BVA were considering making the relevant American types. On learning of this the RMA objected vehemently, pointing out that it would encourage the import of American receivers by enabling replacements to be bought from BVA retailers, who were barred from selling foreign-made valves.[93] The BVA backed down, and by the end of the year all its members except Mullard had signed an agreement not to make valves specially suitable for imported receivers, or for receivers assembled here from foreign components;[94] this stayed in force until 1936.[95] The BVA had also been able to prevent members of the Radio Wholesalers' Federation from selling American sets complete with valves, whereupon some sold them without valves.[96] Early in 1933 an EMI internal memorandum stated "...concerted measures against Majestic and Philco have restricted their trading effectively so far", but the omens were not good. In response to the anti-dumping import duty Philco's British subsidiary had considered having sets made by Philips at Mitcham,[97] and were in fact having some made in this country by ST&C. Philco and ST&C were seeking to change an agreement to cease using American types of valve in them, and Stanley Mullard had declared that once a demand for such valves was established the Mullard company would supply them.[94]

By the end of the year, however, the whole situation had been transformed by a patent-pool deal. Such pools, operated by the holders of relevant patents, licensed manufacturers to use all the patents in the pool in return for a royalty shared out among its members; to be viable, a pool had to be comprehensive enough to enable a manufacturer to make good receivers using only circuit arrangements covered by its patents. Since 1930 Britain had operated a single pool, administered by Marconi's, but in 1933 a potential rival appeared when the Hazeltine Corporation of America, which held a powerful array of patents including that for automatic volume control, joined Philco and Majestic in forming a British company, Hazelpat, to exploit their combined patent resources. Several of the key patents in the British pool ran out around this period, and the British industry decided to admit Hazelpat to the pool rather than engage in a trial of strength. By doing so they legitimized Majestic and Philco but gained protection against other American manufacturers.[98]

Majestic only exploited their position to a very limited extent, but Philco rapidly built up their British subsidiary. Sales during the latter part of 1934 were 78% up on those for the same period in 1933,[99] and

To the British public of 1931 the American origin of these imported Philco receivers was obvious from their styling

THE PHILCO "FIVE"

Compact in size, yet a giant in performance

14 GNS.

Complete with 5 valves and moving coil speaker.

No longer need you pay high prices for perfect radio performance, for here at last is a set that outperforms and outclasses sets selling at considerably higher prices. Never have you heard such exquisite tone.

SINGLE DIAL TUNING

Never such power and selectivity. Never such simplicity of operation; for, at the turn of a *single dial*, you swing from the gay music of a Copenhagen restaurant to the mighty chorus of the Milan Opera House. Get Radio Paris, get Rome, get Madrid, Oslo, Stockholm — get all the important stations in Europe as well as all the home stations — for here is Europe at your fingertips. With the turn of a single switch you can get stations with equal clarity from 200 to 550 and 1,000 to 2,000 metres.

NON-REACTIVE; NO SQUEALS, NO HOWLS

Suffer no longer the blurred tone, dull selectivity and nerve-racking squeals of ordinary reactive wireless sets when you can save money and yet triple your radio enjoyment with this sensational set. The Philco Five is non-reactive; no howls as you tune.

The chassis is encased in a beautiful mahogany cabinet with rich Adam Brown Walnut finish.

The Philco Five is fully licensed in Great Britain under the Hazeltine British Patents.

Before you buy ANY Radio —
CHECK ALL THESE FEATURES!

FIVE VALVES	THREE TUNED CIRCUITS
MOVING COIL SPEAKER	
SINGLE DIAL TUNING	TRIPLE SCREEN GRID
ABSOLUTELY NON-REACTIVE	FINGER-TIP VOLUME CONTROL
MEDIUM AND LONG WAVE	HANDSOME MAHOGANY CABINET
2.5 WATTS PENTODE POWER OUTPUT	A.C. MAINS OPERATION
	SIZE 15" x 14" x 7½"

LUXURY RADIO PRICED WITHIN THE REACH OF ALL
In every respect designed and built to meet British broadcasting requirements.

THE "LOWBOY"

Another new Philco model — the beautiful "Lowboy" . . . same chassis specification as the Philco "Five," housed in this handsome walnut cabinet, complete with five valves and oversize moving coil speaker . . . at the amazingly low price of **19 GNS.**

PHILCO RADIO & TELEVISION CORPORATION
OF GREAT BRITAIN, LTD.
10, SMITH SQUARE, LONDON, S.W.1.

PHILCO
"FIVE" WIRELESS

an amazingly powerful 5-valve, dual wave length, non-reactive set with moving coil speaker complete, ready to operate on A.C. mains.

IT TAKES A BALANCED-UNIT PHILCO TO MEET MODERN BROADCASTING CONDITIONS

in 1935 the company opened a large factory at Perivale, Middlesex; that summer, sales achieved by their nationwide network of dealers qualified 800 of them for a week-end cruise to Holland and Belgium.[100] Philco continued to use American valve types until 1938, and were not admitted to the Olympia exhibition until 1939, but their Managing Director, Carleton L Dyer, cultivated a British image. One 1935 model was allegedly designed to celebrate King George V's Silver Jubilee, that year's all-wave set was marketed as the 'Empire', and Dyer criticized the patent pool for not taking effective action against the invasion of the British market by cheap American midget sets.[101] Introduced in America as a novelty to combat the slump in sales caused by the depression, these had become very popular. Initially they had been too expensive for the British market, but by 1935 were on sale for around 3 guineas. A British manufacturer of extension loudspeakers ruefully remarked, on returning from an American holiday, that there were no extension loudspeakers in New York; if they wanted wireless in another room they just bought another set.[102]

In Britain, however, there were still homes without even one radio, and in 1936 the Ullswater Committee, incidentally to extending the BBC's charter, criticized the industry for failing to provide a cheap receiver, and suggested that in collaboration with the BBC they should produce a standardized set.[103] Although this did not happen, Philips and Philco independently produced 6-guinea superhets that year. Both were remarkable value for money, but whereas Philips kept the production cost down to £2 10s (£2.50), by dispensing with a chassis and mounting the components directly onto the bakelite case, Philco used a conventional construction but saved by using three American valves, supplemented by a British one specially modified for them. Nevertheless, the cost of the Philco set was high enough to need large sales to make it profitable, and it was vigorously promoted as 'The People's Set'. A contemporary witness alleges that some Philco dealers took advantage of this title to encourage the belief that buying the receiver helped to support the International Brigade in Spain and the Labour Party in Britain.[104]

BVA's feather bed and Mullard's back door

Since 1927, receivers made by RMA members had to contain only valves made by BVA members,[105] but in the lucrative replacement-market foreign valves continued to be a serious threat to BVA valves. When the anti-dumping duty of 50% was imposed in November 1931, the BVA suggested to the Board of Trade that, since under the previous 'Key Industry' duty of $33\frac{1}{3}$% imports had increased by 89% in a single year, valves should enjoy the protection of a 100% duty;[106] in the event, the anti-dumping duty was removed from valves altogether five months after being imposed, and the rate reverted to $33\frac{1}{3}$%. The M-O V Company had thought the BVA's argument not only weak but dangerous, in that it might provoke unwelcome investigation of its members' manufacturing costs relative to their retail prices. Even after adding only $33\frac{1}{3}$% duty to its 'declared value' the average imported valve came out at 2s (10p), which was slightly more than the factory cost of an equivalent British valve. Yet the imported valve retailed at 5s 6d ($27\frac{1}{2}$p) and the British one at 8s 6d ($42\frac{1}{2}$p).[107] For the rest of the decade the BVA fought a rearguard action by reducing retail prices and by increasing discounts to retailers and wholesalers, sometimes linking these to agreements to handle BVA valves exclusively, but failed to arrest the decline in their market share.[108]

A FURTHER IMPORTANT NOTICE

BY THE MULLARD WIRELESS SERVICE CO., LTD., AND THE MULLARD RADIO VALVE COMPANY, LTD.,

AS a result of the Legal Proceedings taken by The Mullard Radio Valve Company, Limited, against certain dealers for importing and/or selling Tungsram and Dario Radio Valves a

PERPETUAL INJUNCTION

has been granted by The High Court of Justice against the London Radio Co. (Leeds) Limited of Leeds and Branches, under Letters Patent Nos. 209730, 229622, 245146, 245147, 283941, 287958* of the Mullard Radio Valve Company, Limited.

An order was also made for payment of

DAMAGES AND COSTS

Warning

Anyone infringing the above-mentioned Letters Patent will render themselves liable to be proceeded against.

The Mullard Radio Valve Company, Ltd.,
Mullard House,
Charing Cross Road,
London, W.C.2.

Sabre-rattling by Mullard, 1930

INDEMNITY BY IMPEX ELECTRICAL LIMITED

IMPORTANT NOTICE

Messrs. The Mullard Radio Valve Co., Ltd., have recently published notices in the trade press intimating that they intend to take legal proceedings against retailers and others who may infringe certain Letters Patent owned by them, amongst which are Letters Patent No. 283,941.

We are satisfied that the construction of our well-known Dario Valves is not such as to constitute an infringement of Letters Patent No. 283,941 and we desire to give notice to our trade friends that we undertake hereby to indemnify any person who may be sued for infringement of Letters Patent No. 283,941 by the sale of our Dario Valves in respect of any costs and damages which may be awarded against him provided that our Solicitors, Messrs. Philip Conway, Thomas and Co., of 80 Rochester Row, Westminster, London, S.W.1, shall have the conduct of any action brought to recover such damages.

For the purpose of enabling any retailer conveniently to avail himself of the benefit of this indemnity we are depositing with our Bankers in England in the joint names of ourselves and our Solicitors a large sum of money to be utilised for the purpose of making this indemnity effective.

In future, should any claim be made against any customer of ours for infringement of Letters Patent No. 283,941 by the sale of our Dario Valves, the document containing the claim should be sent immediately unanswered to our Solicitors at the above address in order to obtain the benefit of this indemnity and relief from the trouble of conducting legal proceedings.

IMPEX ELECTRICAL LTD., 538, High Road, Leytonstone. E.11
Telephone: Wanstead 2722

Reassurance in the following week's issue
to dealers who sold Dario imported valves

Mullard's stand at Radiolympia, 1933

Against this background it might have been expected at least that all BVA valves would be British-made. However, in 1931 valve imports from Holland were 346% higher than in 1930,[109] and in June 1932 Mullard were solemnly asked by the RMA for their assurance that they had not handled or marketed any of the 170,000 unmarked valves that the Customs returns showed to have been imported from Holland over a recent three-month period.[110] As we shall see later, Stanley Mullard was no longer in executive command of the Mullard companies, but he was evidently still a considerable asset in his capacity of General Adviser to Philips, for a few days later he was able to report, in a letter to Anton Philips, that having already managed to "smooth matters over" with the BVA he was hopeful of doing the same with the RMA. However, these heavy imports had been against his strong advice, and if they continued they could only lead to the company's expulsion from both associations. Indeed, he thought that harm had been done already, since competitors would undoubtedly suggest to setmakers that valves they bought from Mullard might not be British-made, and thus might land them in legal difficulties.[111]

Medium and Small Companies

The consolidation of the industry during the 1930s stopped well short of leaving it dominated by a handful of giants, some medium-sized companies like McMichael being almost as well-known as the leaders. Of the many small companies that did well, some staked out their own distinct areas of the market, others simply demonstrated that it didn't take research engineers to design serviceable circuits around valve-makers' data, and that assembling receivers was still labour-intensive rather than capital-intensive.

McMichael

McMichael became a public company in 1932, and continued to aim squarely at the upper section of the market. They were firm believers in selling only through accredited dealers, considering it "unfair to goods enjoying the McMichael reputation to see these displayed side by side with products whose only claim for public support is cheapness of the worst sort."[112] Their dealer-magazine, *McMichael Messenger*, dispensed service instructions and tips on how to boost sales. The summer slump could be reduced by offering a prospect safe-keeping for his existing receiver during the spring cleaning then, on returning it, hinting that it let down the re-furbished living room.[113] A lady coming into the shop for a new HT battery would be favourably impressed if the salesman dusted it, whether or not it was actually dusty.[114]

In 1934-35 McMichael went through a crisis. After a £50,000 trading loss Ben Hesketh, their engineering chief and co-founder, left first the board and then the company. The 1935-36 models were designed under new direction, and quickly restored profitability,[115] the transformation probably turning primarily on styling and on price. For the 1934-35 season the company had introduced a model with two loudspeakers, claimed to complement each other and give better sound quality, but had housed them behind a single grille, and had provided only a tiny tuning dial, which was coming to look old-fashioned; Murphy, it will be recalled, also discovered this to their cost. The receiver, in fact, lacked 'eye appeal', though at 18 guineas it lived up to the first part of the company's slogan (shortly afterwards dropped) "Costs a little more - so much the better". Its successor had the two loudspeakers behind separate grilles slightly splayed, while the controls, grouped around an enormous dial, lay under a lid. Highly distinctive and discreetly expensive-looking, it cost 15 guineas. A dealer reported that a lady came into his shop as he was unpacking one that had just come in. She so liked the look of it that she immediately asked for a demonstration, and signed a cheque seven minutes after the railway man had delivered the set.[116]

McMichael factory, 1930

For several years on Boat-Race day Leslie McMichael commissioned an Imperial Airways airliner and took a party of guests to view the race from the air. A McMichael receiver temporarily installed in the aircraft relayed the BBC commentary. This feat was blown up into a major publicity event, with an elaborate illuminated display in the window of the company's London showroom. These pictures date from 1934

McMICHAELS
AGAIN LINK THE BOAT
RACE WITH THE AIR.

William Lawson, of Beckenham, put realism into his display with an electrified lion, which turned its head and opened and closed its jaws in the presence of highly appreciative crowds. The trees were cut out and reproduced in natural colours, the lighting lending a startling effect of the jungle by night.

An ambitious window display mounted by a McMichael dealer, 1934

A motor-cycle combination decked out as a McMichael Twin Supervox receiver, 1934

Adey

Horace Adey made a range of portable radios which, although by no means 'state of the art' technologically, worked well enough to maintain the aura of electronic wizardry that he built up around himself and his products by a succession of well-judged gimmicks. Trained in America as an electrical engineer, Adey set up Adey Radio Ltd in 1929, in Mortimer Street, W1, with a registered capital of £25,000; two earlier ventures, Alphian Wireless Ltd and Adey Wireless Ltd, had failed to prosper,[63] although Alphian's 'Wireless Chair' had attracted some attention. His four-valve portable, shown at the 1929 Olympia show, was built round his patented 'Key' — a jack fitted with

The founders of Roberts Radio, Harry Roberts (on the right) and Leslie Bidmead, with the two sisters, Doris and Elsie Hayward, whom they married; the company's 'Aladdin's Lamp' loudspeaker fret was designed by the husband of a third sister. The model of receiver suggests that the picture dates from about 1933

'Adey' at the 1929 Olympia show. The 'New BBC Station' referred to is Brookmans Park, which inaugurated the 'Regional Scheme'

a tapped coil. This had to be plugged into a socket on the set to turn it on, thereby preventing unauthorized use, and also served as wavechange switch, rough tuner and, when twisted in its socket, reaction control. Measuring only 9" x 9" x 7", the set occupied less than quarter the volume of a typical competitor, and its performance has been assessed by a modern collector as "the equal of all but the very best".[117]

In 1930 Adey introduced a one-valve headphone portable housed in a cigar box, and used it for an inspired publicity stunt at that year's

Radio Show. The headphone was modified to fit inside a policeman's helmet, where it acted as a small loudspeaker, and the press were shown how the policeman on his beat could receive messages; it was also claimed that the arrangement had been submitted to several police forces for evaluation. Nothing came of the idea, of course, but variously garbled versions of the story appeared in national and provincial papers, and even in the *Police Review*.[118] Over the next few years numerous other portables appeared, some using valves with integral coupling coils, specially made for the company. From 1932 Adey had a factory in Marylebone employing twelve people and at times producing over 100 sets a week. Cabinets were available in several finishes, including hand-painted Chinese-lacquer designs and scenes executed in oils. The company's short-wave portable of 1935 was claimed to be the world's first, and among those exported one is believed to have been bought by Hitler for his own use. Whether Adey could have continued to succeed with a business whose whole style was more reminiscent of the twenties than the thirties must remain a matter for speculation, for late in 1935 he died, not yet 48 years old, and without his leadership Adey Radio Ltd soon went out of business.

Roberts Radio [119]

When Harry Roberts and Leslie Bidmead went into partnership in 1932 to make portable radios they were both seasoned campaigners, though only 22 and 27 respectively. After leaving school at 14, Roberts successively worked for two firms specializing in portables, and at 17 found himself with an excellent reference but no job when the second of them went into liquidation. He then worked for a freelance salesman, collecting sets from suppliers and demonstrating them to prospects in their own homes. This left his boss free to concentrate on contacting new prospects, which in practice meant spending much of the day in public houses while Roberts did most of the work. Bidmead, a keen amateur experimenter since his schooldays, had by 1927 become the 'technical' half of 'Lonsdale Radio', a setmaking company in Kilburn that built up to a work-force of about ten before going into a decline. This was largely because Bidmead's 'commercial' partner was devoting much of his effort to illicitly supplying dealers with valves which, as setmakers, Lonsdale Radio obtained at well below wholesale prices. It was at this stage that Roberts and Bidmead came together, making sets and selling them on commission for an entrepreneur who supplied the necessary capital and accommodation. The venture prospered, but on terms that the young men reckoned were too favourable to the entrepreneur, and in October 1932 they moved into the rudimentary factory they had set up with a capital of around £50 in two rented rooms in Hills Place, near Oxford Circus.

They adopted a philosophy of making a top-quality product and selling it to top-quality customers. Right at the outset, Harry took a sample receiver to Harrods, persuaded the buyer to hear it, and returned with an order for half a dozen sets, thereby beginning a most fruitful association. The company remained small throughout the 1930s, financing growth out of profits. Thus they produced barely three receivers a week during the first year and only about eight a week during 1935, and although production more than doubled following a move in March 1936 to larger premises in Rathbone Place, the registered capital was only £3,000 when Roberts Radio became a Private Limited Company in April, 1937. Roberts and Bidmead refused to cast the portable in the role of poor relation within the radio family, and nothing was stinted to justify their claim to be making "the finest of all portables". In 1939 they made their first sale to the Royal Family, when the Army & Navy Stores supplied the Queen with a Roberts set for Princess Elizabeth.

Truphonic [120]

Rounding off these accounts of various setmakers of the 1930s, the story of Jack Hester's 'Truphonic Ltd' demonstrates that some firms defy classification. Hester, born into an affluent home in 1911, became interested in radio while at public school, and by 1927 had built a short-wave set. Home for the holidays, he stayed up all night to hear the Dempsey/Tunney world-title fight from America, which enabled his father to amaze his friends by telling them the result that morning — there being no BBC news bulletin until 6.30 p.m.. However, there was no question of Jack being allowed to pursue radio as a livelihood, and on leaving school he was indentured to the Stock Exchange. He found it boring and uncongenial, and to his father's great displeasure left it at twenty-one. One of his schoolmates was Stanley Mullard's son, and Mullard gave Hester a job, selling a rather unsuccessful component-assembly system. At this point, in 1932, he came across Truphonic Radio Ltd, operating in a workshop over a garage in Putney. The company was in liquidation, with two men and a manager making up sets from its stock of components, and Hester struck a bargain with the liquidator whereby he and the manager bought up everything for £100 each; he borrowed the money from his father at 5%, repayable in a year.

The components restricted them to making an obsolete design of five-valve portable, and the manager, who turned out to understand nothing about radio beyond this one set, thought it too risky to embark on anything else. Hester solved the dilemma by buying him out, and in 1933 embarked on a range of mains receivers, using Mullard valves and circuits. He would help his two assistants to make two or three sets, put them in the back of his car, then drive off and sell them; any criticism offered when he demonstrated them was borne in mind when making the next batch. By 1935 he had established a dealer network and needed a proper factory. Driving home through Tooting one evening he saw the footings for a new factory, and stopped to investigate. The foreman told him that it was being built 'on spec', that it covered 16,000 sq ft plus offices, and that the boss would be there at 8 o'clock next morning. Hester met him and they made a deal on the spot: the factory built to his requirements and a seven-year lease at £600 p.a.. The builder threw in an empty cottage that he had been going to demolish but that Hester pointed out would make a good laboratory.

In such fashion Truphonic evolved into a well-regarded firm complete with a qualified research engineer. Production ran at about 250 sets a week, the top range being engineered for above-average sound quality and housed in period cabinets, some of which were made by Maples. Local girls, living at home and giving their mothers 10s (50p) a week, worked for 6d (2.5p) an hour. For men (who, untypically, did all the wiring) the basic rate was 1s (5p) an hour, though some earned up to £3 a week. Hester, still in his twenties, made about £1,000 a year. He and several of his key staff were in the territorials or the reserves, and were called up as war approached,

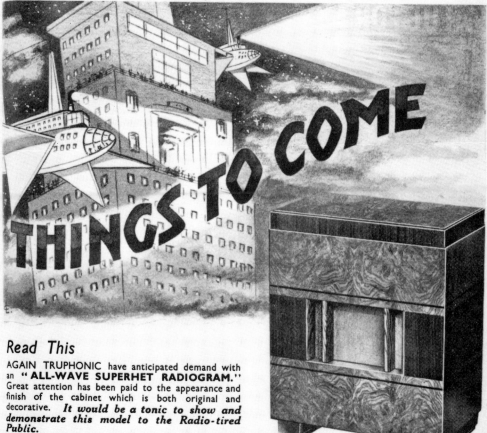

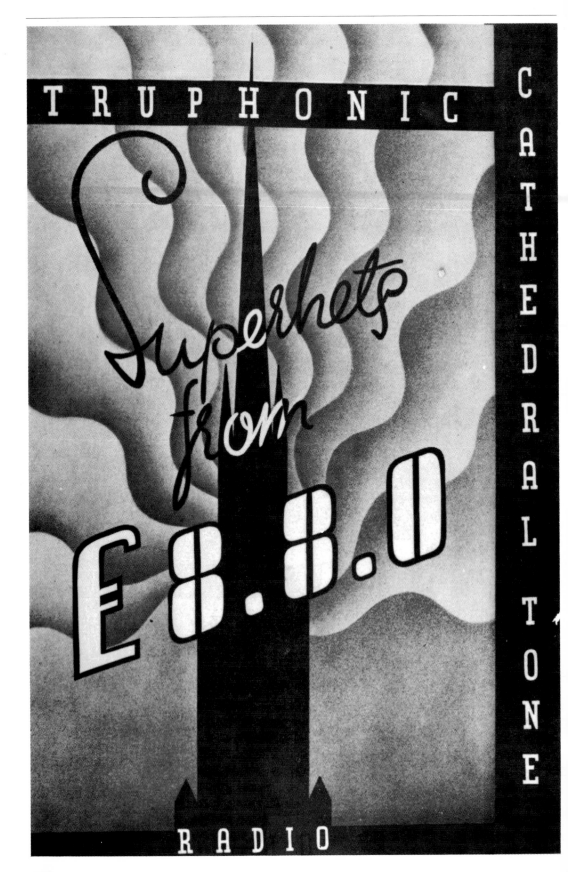

TRUPHONIC

CATHEDRAL TONE

Superhets from

£8.8.0

RADIO

above: *An early appearance of a well-known name*

left: *Leaflet of 1936*

1,000 SETS A DAY. The new Ferguson Radio factory, Cambridge Arterial Road, Enfield, has just started production. It has a floor area of 30,000 sq. ft., and is stated to have an output capacity of 1,000 sets per normal working day.

From Wireless World, *1938*

leaving the company stranded. Serving in North Africa, Hester learned that Philips had taken the factory over for war production, and he received a cheque for £500 for his shares. He blued the lot in Cairo, and never returned to the radio industry.

Battery Business

Britain was slow to electrify her rural areas, and radio batteries remained a substantial business throughout the decade, with fifteen million HT batteries sold in 1934[121] and accumulator-charging still a profitable sideline for dealers and garages. Battery valves of the 1930s had two-volt filaments, enabling a single-cell accumulator to be used, and this often incorporated some form of hydrometer; Exide's version had a large pointer indicating 'Full', 'Half' or 'Empty', and was promoted to the trade with the slogan "Tells them in time the time to re-charge". People with mains electricity who still used battery sets could save money by using an 'eliminator', of which Ekco remained the major supplier. Generally this not only supplied the HT current but included a 'trickle charger' that was left permanently connected to the accumulator.

The market leader in HT batteries was The Ever Ready Co (Great Britain) Ltd, a part of an international group that had originated in America at the turn of the century and had in 1932 been incorporated in Canada, the British company holding a substantial minority of the shares. But battery manufacture was well dispersed — in 1935 *The Wireless and Gramophone Trader* (*'The Trader'*) listed thirty-nine other 'leading manufacturers' of HT batteries, ranging from such familiar names as Chloride, GEC, Oldham and Siemens to Runwell Cycle Co (Birmingham) Ltd.

The radio retailer valued the battery highly. As a consumable item it provided a continuing and far from negligible source of income, retailing at 7s 6d (37$\frac{1}{2}$p) or more, with a discount to him of 33$\frac{1}{3}$%. Moreover, by bringing the customer into the shop several times a year it gave the opportunity to interest him in other lines. But the battery business was not regulated to the trade's best advantage. Although there was strict enforcement of the price charged for a given brand, and some uniformity of pricing amongst leading brands, there was nothing to protect the trade against cut-price unbranded batteries, or to restrict distribution to radio retailers. Initially this led to the importing of cheap foreign batteries, but soon British manufacturers started producing 'no-name' batteries, which were sold through hardware shops, cycle shops and general stores, as well as 'own brand' batteries sold through multiple stores, at retail prices of around 5s (25p). Radio retailers grew alarmed and indignant at the loss of what they regarded as a legitimate perquisite, and many themselves began to handle 'no-name' batteries. However, when action was finally taken to bring the lost trade back to them, it was not in a form that they welcomed.

In December 1934 Magnus Goodfellow, Chairman of Ever Ready, addressed a large gathering of leading wholesalers. The legitimate trade, he told them, was doing about one-fifth of the business it should — and that at a very low rate of profit — so his company was introducing, in addition to their top-price 'Winner' brand, retailing at 11s (55p), a 'Radio' brand, retailing at 6s (30p) but regrettably carrying a very low discount. He went on:

> "You will be wise to sell the new batteries and refuse support to the 'no-name any-name' batteries. If you do so, we shall be able to rid ourselves of the 'no-name' battery business which has been a curse to the trade for the last three or four years."[122]

Unfortunately for Ever Ready, however, it was well known in the trade that they themselves supplied Marks and Spencer with batteries, identical to their regular brand except for the printing on the cardboard cover, for sale at 5s (25p).[123] Meetings of the Wireless Retailers' Association (WRA) up and down the country protested that they could not tolerate the new battery's low discount, and many refused to handle it despite the extensive advertising campaign launched to support it. But after other major manufacturers had come out with six-shilling batteries, and Ever Ready had made some concessions, the storm subsided and dealers learned to live with lower discounts.

Throughout this furore Vidor, a battery manufacturer established only a few months previously, remained popular with radio dealers simply by maintaining the low prices and the 25% discount it was offering at the outset. However, it was not so much Vidor's commercial policy that excited Ever Ready's hostility as its very existence, for Vidor was the creation of Thomas Noah Cole. As has been related, Cole had formed the Lissen company in the early-1920s and had been kept on as its Managing Director after selling out to Ever Ready in 1928, on condition that he did not carry on any company competing with Lissen's business. But by 1934 this cannot have been an attractive job for a man of Cole's drive and ambition. He was not master in his own house, and demand was declining for kits and components for home constructors, which were Lissen's main products apart from batteries.

The sum of over a million pounds that he had received from the sale of Lissen enabled Cole to leave the company and start afresh on a large scale, making receivers and batteries. He bought up Burndept, which still had a good name but was moribund after resigning from the RMA in 1931;[124] ironically Burndept's founder, Witt Burnham, by now head of Ediswan, became the RMA's Chairman the following year. At the same time Cole established a new company, Vidor, as a wholly-owned subsidiary of Burndept,[125] the name reputedly being inspired by the initials of his daughters Valerie and Denise and his wife Rebecca.[126] Receivers would be marketed under both Burndept and Vidor labels,

batteries under Vidor only. To house his Vidor-Burndept venture Cole took over in April 1934 the Vickers-Armstrong light gun factory at Erith, Kent, which had stood idle since 1918 — a three-storey building with a total floor space of 135,000 sq ft, but bereft of gas, water, power or lighting cables. Within ten weeks it opened, on schedule, producing a range of Burndept receivers for the 1934 Radio Show, and the first Vidor batteries. Two months later the works employed nearly 900 people, and such was the demand for Vidor batteries (torch as well as radio) that in the spring of 1935 the original plant had to be scrapped and replaced by new machinery capable of much higher output.[127] Concurrently, Lissen reported a fall in profits, which they largely attributed to "the competing business started at Erith."[128]

As a gesture towards his agreement with Ever Ready, Cole did not run Burndept-Vidor himself but appointed a Mr R P Richardson as Managing Director, whom he would furtively meet in an out-of-the-way café to discuss company business.[84] But in the spring of 1935 Cole evidently found it irksome to continue making even this concession to the agreement, which still had over three years to run, for with impressive effrontery he brought an action appealing against it, engaging Sir Stafford Cripps and two other eminent KCs.[128] On the eve of the action Cripps approached Counsel for the Defendants with a view to settling out of court, and this was done next day, it having apparently been put to the Defendants that a man must be allowed to earn his living.[123,129] The undertaking was modified to enable Cole "...to invest or retain investments in any such competing business as herein mentioned", the restriction was limited to Great Britain and Ireland, and its term was shortened by 15 months.[130] But although the hatchet was officially buried, Magnus Goodfellow of Ever Ready ensured that Vidor was not admitted to the Association of Radio Battery Manufacturers,[123] whilst Cole continued to conduct his business furtively, his clothing puffed out with the scraps and wads of paper which he would pull out of and stuff back into his various pockets.[64] Under his direction the Burndept marque regained something of its old lustre, with some quite ambitious all-wave receivers, and in 1937 he promoted them with a publicity stunt in the best Witt Burnham tradition. The Russians had set up a transmitter at the North Pole, and a £100 prize was offered to the first Burndept listener to give convincing evidence of having picked it up; dealers would provide useful advice, and a "News-Scoop" postcard on which to report success.

An essential element of Ever Ready's commercial policy was to encourage the spread of anything that used batteries, and it was partly for this reason that the company entered the receiver business at the beginning of 1935, though one of the two models with which Ever Ready Radio Ltd was launched was an AC mains set. The chassis and cabinets were made by Pye, and merely put together and packed at the new company's factory in Finsbury Park, which was supervised by Pye management. C O Stanley was invited onto the Ever Ready board as a non-executive director, but he and Magnus Goodfellow fell out just before the war, and co-operation between Pye and Ever Ready ceased.[123]

Wholesale and Retail

Although some brands, notably Murphy, Bush and HMV, went direct and exclusively to authorized dealers, most setmakers distributed partly or entirely through wholesalers, who enabled the smaller manufacturer to enjoy nationwide distribution without the burden of a sales network. A wise wholesaler would take care not to push a retailer into over-committing himself — he might be working each of several suppliers to their credit limit. Manufacturers courted wholesalers. The RMA invited representatives of the principal companies to their monthly lunches at the Savoy, and each year GEC chartered a special train to take wholesalers and dealers up to Coventry to view their new range of models.[131]

The entire industry's year revolved around 'Radiolympia', organized by the RMA. It was held in September until 1931, but thereafter during the second half of August, and its duration increased through the decade from eight days to ten. Exhibitors, totalling around 150, would include not only setmakers and component-makers but wholesalers and trade papers, with substantial exhibits by the Post Office and the BBC, who would also broadcast a number of star-studded variety shows from the exhibition's theatre. The opportunity to see favourite radio artistes in the flesh was in fact one of the show's principal attractions, and the RMA ascribed a noticeable fall in attendance in 1938 partly to the fact that a small television studio had been substituted for the radio theatre. Total attendance reached its highest in 1934, at 238,000, and at least one daily attendance of over 30,000 was recorded every year from 1931 to 1936.

It was not until 1938 that radio-frequency feeds were distributed to the stands. Thus although the visitor in earlier years could look at all the new models, discuss them with the staff on the stands, and take away brochures, he could hear them only by going to a dealer. In shopping areas reception was often poor, but in any case the dealer knew the effectiveness of following up a shop demonstration with one in the prospective customer's home; McMichael dealers were recommended to time this to coincide with the transmission of a suitably attractive programme. If even that did not clinch the sale, the set could always be left on approval for a few days.

Some of the largest displays of radio sets were in the major department stores, although when a new buyer, John Street, took over in the mid-1930s at Whiteley's store in Bayswater he cut back on the number of different models displayed, having observed that if a prospective customer is confused by too wide a choice he says he will think it over and come back, but seldom does. Whiteley's excellent service department would probably have secured Street a Murphy dealership had he wished, but he decided that although Murphy cabinets might do for Harrod's customers they were altogether too outlandish for his own clientele.[132] Department stores often sold 'no-name' receivers and radiograms, made for them by small companies and widely advertised in the national press; although their design lacked the flair of the best products of the major manufacturers, they were well built and good value for money.[67]

There was no multiple chain devoted exclusively to radio, but Currys, who had some 200 branches in the 1930s, was one of several multiples which diversified into radio from what had been primarily a bicycle business. In the late-1930s their branches still appeared to the casual passer-by to be predominantly cycle shops, yet branch sales for the 53 weeks to 30 January 1937 totalled £765,000 for wireless and accessories as against £452,000 for cycles and accessories.[133] Low-priced sets with no frills, similar to the 'no-name' models sold by department stores, figured largely in Curry's stock, and were sold under the name 'Westminster'

The local dealer, protected as he was against price-cutting, enjoyed some advantages over the department store and the multiple. The personal touch was more valued when a radio cost several weeks' wages and needed more frequent servicing than its modern counterpart. He could usually collect, repair and return sets at short notice; if a repair was going to take a long time, the free loan of a new set would certainly create goodwill and, well managed, could result in a sale. With a well-respected name on his van, and a winning personality, he could even talk his way into people's homes, and one North London dealer of the 1930s recalls a successful sales technique exploiting this. Driving through a residential area and seeing a competitor's van outside a house he would note the address, call there later, and tactfully discover whether the competitor had left a set on approval. If so, he would ask whether he might see it, then compare it just a little unfavourably with a model that he offered to deliver, also on approval, so that the family could judge for themselves which they preferred.[74]

The standard of servicing was extremely variable. Few servicemen had any formal qualifications, although some setmakers offered training; in 1935 Ekco were running free one-week courses for registered dealers and their technical assistants, with bed and board close to the Works provided at 30s (£1.50) for the week.[134] A good serviceman was a great asset to a dealer, and liable to be 'poached' by a rival,[135] but in general pay and status were low, and were further eroded by freelance 'dabblers', some of them trade employees working in their spare time.[136]

The Valve-Makers

During the 1930s M-O V, backed by the resources of GEC's Research Laboratories at Wembley, improved their receiver-valve operation from the poor state in which HMV found it in 1929; their development of the 'beam tetrode' has already been mentioned. By 1930 M-O V had already developed their highly successful 'CAT' series of cooled-anode transmitting valves, and by substituting air-cooling for water-cooling were able to apply the same principle to a range of metal-envelope receiving valves, appropriately named 'Catkin', which were introduced in 1933. These had many advantages over valves with glass envelopes, being more robust, more uniform in their characteristics and less microphonic,[137] but they were not successful commercially. Valves for domestic receivers were often in production for only a year or two, and the tooling required by the Catkin technique was too expensive to be modified so frequently. However, the experience they provided in precision-engineering methods of valve production, and in glass-to-metal joints, was to prove valuable during the war.[138]

At the beginning of the decade Mazda were acknowledged by a competitor as having the industry's best range of valves,[45] and in 1932 they further strengthened their position by establishing at Brimsdown an applications laboratory. Known as Circuits and Measurements Department, it developed circuits using the company's valves, helped setmakers with problems, and fed back their needs to the valve development engineers. Under the leadership of Cyril Hirshman it became widely respected, and was equipped with advanced test apparatus; much of this was developed in the lab itself because nothing suitable was available commercially. Sometimes valves were specially developed for major setmakers, who then received priority in their allocation. Mazda's senior engineer, E Y Robinson, was on terms of personal friendship with Murphy's Chief Engineer, E J Power, and a fruitful relationship arose between the two companies, with expertise exchanged in both directions.[72] To keep abreast of American practice Robinson went over there each year and brought back numerous valves, which he kept in a secret room next to his office, to be tested or broken open for examination as required; the Brimsdown engineers' conclusion was that on balance they were at least level with the Americans. Towards the end of the decade the Americans standardized on a new eight-pin valve base which came to be known as the International Octal. Mazda responded by producing an octal valve base of their own, not interchangeable with the American one, and claimed a number of specific advantages for it. However, it was probably inspired equally by the wish to commit setmakers to British valves.[139]

In 1929 Stanley Mullard's resentment of his situation under Philips control came to a head, and he resigned as Managing Director of the two Mullard companies, though remaining a director of both, Chairman of the Mullard Wireless Service Company, and General Adviser to Philips on British matters. He had been prepared to make a total break, but Eindhoven appreciated the advantages of having an Englishman in a senior position, particularly since his departure might have raised awkward questions as to the ownership of the shares registered in his name. Executive control of MWSC passed to a Dutchman, S S Eriks, appointed as General Manager. Eriks was 29, and was to spend the rest of his working life with Mullard, becoming a dominant figure in British electronics, but through much of the 1930s

'The Hut' at Brimsdown, forerunner of the well-respected Mazda Applications Laboratory, in 1932. Despite its unpromising appearance, this building was extremely well-equipped. Standing outside, from left to right: Dr K R Sturley (later of the BBC), Cyril Hirshman (for many years Head of the Applications Laboratory) and Miss Nora Ridgeway (later to marry W Taylor, a senior engineer of the laboratory)

Philips' Mitcham Works, 1937

he maintained a relatively low profile. In the Mullard Radio Valve Company, however, the Dutch connection was obtrusive and, initially, chaotic. In 1932 valve production began at Mitcham, and F A Kloppert, ex-naval man and strict disciplinarian, was sent over as Production Manager. Wim Julius, who had first been sent over in 1925, was Technical Director, likeable but insufficiently assertive. The two were incompatible, and were answerable to different people in Eindhoven. Within a year or two, however, Kloppert gained full control and made Mitcham an efficient plant, with discipline tighter than was usual in British industry at that time.[140,141] It had a Technical Services Department for liaison with setmakers, but this was less effective than Mazda's applications laboratory because information on their requirements was fed back to Eindhoven, where it had to be reconciled with the possibly conflicting requirements similarly gathered from Germany, France and Italy.[142]

Early in 1933 Stanley Mullard wrote to van Walsem, who had been his first Philips contact, deploring the fact that Mullard were no longer in the dominant position of a few years previously. Much of the trouble, he thought, arose from the industry's awareness that the control and finance of Mullard was in foreign hands, at a time when nationalistic feeling was running high. Setmakers were reluctant to give business to Mullard because they felt that their profits were crossing to Holland, thereby furthering the sale of Philips receivers. They also resented the fact that new types of Mullard valve were made available to Philips first, and suspected, moreover, that they were imported. Mazda, who were fortunate in not being associated with any setmaker, had been specially active in such propaganda, and in retaliation much should be made of the fact that as part of AEI they were largely American owned. However, he was confident that the coming season's valves were first class, and would do well if available in time and vigorously pushed, adding "No manufacturer or trader will permit his national feelings to touch his pocket."[143]

S S Eriks used to say that until as late as 1939 the only British part of a Mullard valve was the vacuum inside it, but in fact moves towards making Mullard's valve production independent of Eindhoven began in 1936. Initially this reflected a general Philips policy of encouraging autonomy, but as the risk of war became stronger it became a strategic necessity, and a so-called 'X' plan was implemented. This involved not only importing the necessary machine tools but ensuring that Britain acquired the necessary expertise to carry out all the manufacturing processes, and engineers were sent over here to augment and interpret the written instructions. Early in 1937 Philips Lamps Ltd needed more production capacity than Mitcham could provide, the site by then being fully exploited. It seems to have been appreciated from the outset that Mullard would also be involved in the proposed expansion, for S S Eriks is credited with making the major decisions on the project and integrating it into the 'X' plan.[144] Eriks was anxious, on both humanitarian and practical grounds, to site the new plant in an area of high unemployment, and Blackburn was finally chosen, where owing to the decline in the cotton industry there was a large, predominantly female, labour force available. The foundation stone for a new factory was laid on 30 March 1938, and by early in 1939 it was producing radio receivers, components and lamp filaments. Meanwhile, since it looked as though the rapidly increasing demand for television receivers would soon exceed Mitcham's valve-making capacity, a second building was put up at Blackburn, and filled with both lamp-making and valve-making equipment from Holland.[140]

The Sands of Peacetime Run Out

In 1936 the Victorian house at the top of the drive at Cossor's Highbury Grove site was discreetly converted to a laboratory, where a highly specialized VHF receiver was developed by a team working under L H Bedford and O S Puckle. The engineer thereby left in charge of the firm's main research laboratory, K I Jones, lost two of his best men to the team without being allowed to know anything of what their work would be,[145] and when the development of the receiver was

PHILIPS MOTORADIO

The many advantages and special features of the new Philips Motoradio combine to make it the most practical and efficient receiver yet produced. Installation has been greatly simplified and is now a matter of a few hours work only. This has been achieved by building all necessary suppressors into the receiver itself. Philips Motoradio can in no way interfere with the car's performance, and will give results that are comparable in every way to high quality domestic receivers.

There are two types of Philips Motoradio : Type 247B-6 volt (248B-12 volt) with built-in loudspeaker, **14 gns.**, or H.P. terms from £4-6 deposit; and de-luxe model type 249B-6 volt (250B-12 volt) with separate high fidelity speaker giving large output, **16 gns.**, or H.P. terms from £6-6 deposit. Two Motoradio aerials are available, type 7302 undercar aerial, price 10/6 and type 7310 roof aerial, price £1-1-0.

PHILIPS MOTORADIO FEATURES

1. Powerful 6-valve receiver.
2. No spark plug suppressors.
3. Quick, simple installation, one bolt only.
4. Compact, size 9" x 8" x 7".
5. Long and medium wave bands.
6. Magnetic wave changer.
7. Locking device.
8. Specially designed speaker.
9. Automatic volume control.

PRICE 14 gns.

From Philips' opulent 1937–38 catalogue. However, it was not until 1955, at their third attempt, that the company finally became established in car radios

Model 655 Armchair Radio (incorporating revolving bookcase and glass topped table).

One of the new 10-valve models see page 16.

From an HMV brochure, 1938

Keates-Hacker receivers, manufactured by Dynatron in the late–1930s, were aimed at the very top of the market. The example shown is a hand-carved radio gramophone in weathered oak, built exclusively for "a well-known member of The London Stock Exchange"

The record changer used in Keates-Hacker radiograms played both sides of up to 20 records of mixed sizes

completed a large manual was published that went into the minutest detail of its specification and circuitry without revealing anything at all about its purpose.

So it was that Cossor produced the receiver for the 'Chain Home' radar stations, and the domestic-radio industry made one of its first contributions to the impending war. Meanwhile it continued to fulfil its peacetime function, right up to the 1939 Radiolympia, which closed prematurely on 1 September. In its introductory editorial to the exhibition, *Wireless World* expressed regret that the complexity of the modern receiver made it difficult to get the man in the street to take an interest in how it worked. Nowhere in that editorial is there anything about television; with only one set to every 600 people living in the service area of its single transmitter, it was still of little importance socially or economically. But by September 1939 television had made a considerable impact on the industry, and demands our attention.

Radiolympia, 1939

References

1   *BBC Yearbook*, 1933, p. 79
2   John Stevenson & Chris Cook, *The Slump* (London, Jonathan Cape, 1977) p. 18
3   BREMA Annual Report for 1948, p. 37
4   John Stevenson & Chris Cook, op. cit., p. 57
5   Ibid. p. 10
6   Information derived and made available by Gordon Bussey
7   *Wireless World*, 3 October 1928, p. 463
8   *Wireless World*, 2 November 1932, p. 243
9   *Wireless World*, 2 October 1929, p. 370
10   S G Sturmey, *The Economic Development of Radio*, (Gerald Duckworth & Co, 1958) p. 166
11   E J Hobsbawm, *Industry and Empire* (London, Weidenfeld &Nicolson, 1968) pp. 180–4
12   *Popular Wireless*, Radio Exhibition Supplement, August 1933
13   GEC Brochure, 1938: Gordon Bussey collection
14   E J Power, private conversation, 1990
15   George Edwards, private correspondence, 1989
16   Chris Pickard, private conversation, 1988
17   *Wireless World*, 16 August 1935, pp. 195–9
18   *Wireless & Gramophone Trader*, 1 June 1935, p. 152
19   Entry for Sir G V S de Ferranti, Dictionary of Business Biography
20   *Wireless World*, 15 October 1930, pp. 433ff
21   *A Brief History of Cossor* (A C Cossor Ltd, undated): Gordon Bussey Collection
22   Memorandum, Mittell to Clark, 26 June 1931: EMI Archives
23   *BVWS Bulletin*, September 1978, p. 31
24   M J Lipman, *Memoirs of a Socialist Business Man* (London, Lipman Trust, c. 1975) passim
25   *Dictionary of Business Biography*, p. 733
26   Dr Tom Going, private correspondence and conversation, 1989–90
27   *Art & Industry*, Dec 1937 p. 217
28   *Financial Times*, 25 November 1931
29   Geoffrey Dixon-Nutall, private correspondence & conversation, 1990
30   Gordon Bussey, *The Story of Pye Wireless* (Pye Ltd, 1979)
31   *The Cam*, February 1937, p. 54: Gordon Bussey Collection
32   Manuscript given by H J Pye to Gordon Bussey, 1980
33   Gordon Bussey and Robert Hawes, Sunrise to Sunset, BVWS Bulletin, Vol 7 No 3 pp. 35–6
34   Minutes of special meeting of RMA Executive Council, 19 December 1944: BREMA Archives
35   Memorandum, *re: Marconi. Summary of History of Dispute re Future Patent Rights*, 30 October 1930: EMI Archives
36   Memorandum, *Gramophone Co Ltd & MWT re Future Patent Rights: Joint Opinion*: EMI Archives
37   Report of an interview with the Sales Manager of the Marconiphone Co Ltd, 27 February 1929: EMI Archives
38   Minute to Clark, *re Marconiphone Co Ltd*, 27 February 1929
39   Minute, Whitaker to Mittell, 7 March 1929: EMI Archives
40   Memorandum of Mittell's meeting with H J Round, 11 June 1929: EMI Archives
41   Memorandum of Mittell's meeting with Mullard, 6 March 1929, and associated table *Outstanding Names*: EMI Archives

42	Memorandum of meeting held at Hayes, 16 September 1929: EMI Archives
43	Minute, Whitaker to Brown, *Valve Situation*, 31 October 1929: EMI Archives
44	Letter, E H Aird to L T Neck, 2 January 1930: EMI Archives
45	Meeting Minutes *Report on valve position*, 17 September 1929: EMI Archives
46	Letter, Clark to Sarnoff, 22 January 1931: EMI Archives
47	Cable from New York, 4 June 1930: EMI Archives
48	Clark memorandum, 3 May 1929: EMI Archives
49	Letter, Clark to E E Shumaker, 21 May 1930: EMI Archives
50	Letter, Sarnoff to Clark, 14 January 1931: EMI Archives
51	Cable, Clark to Sarnoff, 19 January 1931: EMI Archives
52	Letter, Clark to Sarnoff, 22 January 1931: EMI Archives
53	Memorandum by Clark, 17 February 1931: EMI Archives
54	Cable, Sarnoff to Clark, 27 February 1931: EMI Archives
55	Census of Production, 1930 in 'Statistics' file: EMI Archives
56	J Lodge, private conversation, 1989
57	Philips Radio Dealer's Handbook: Gordon Bussey Collection
58	*Wireless & Gramophone Trader*, 7 March 1931
59	Letter, de Jong to van Walsem, 27/11/31: Philips Archives
60	Pat Leggatt, private correspondence, 1990
61	Gordon Bussey, private correspondence, 1989
62	*Wireless World*, 8 November, 1935, p. 500
63	Publicity booklet, *The Romance of Ultra Radio*, 1935, passim
64	Ernie Marsden, private conversation, 1989
65	*Radio's Richest Voice*, May 1933: Gordon Bussey Collection
66	*Wireless & Gramophone Trader*, 15 June 1935, p. 188
67	Cecil Payne, private conversation, 1989
68	*Wireless & Gramophone Trader*, 1 June 1935, p. 150
69	Joan Long, *A First Class Job* (Sheringham, Norfolk, Joan Long 1985) passim
70	*New Scientist*, 20 July 1961 pp. 156–7
71	E J Power, private conversation, 1988
72	R C G Williams, private conversation, 1988–90
73	*Wireless World*, 6 August 1930
74	Percy Adams, private conversation, 1988
75	Sir Frederick Osborn papers, passim: Welwyn Garden City Library
76	Notes accompanying letter, C C Moore to Sir John Davis, 9 March 1978: Gordon Bussey Collection
77	*Wireless & Gramophone Trader*, 4 May 1935, p. 73
78	*RMA Monthly Bulletin*, March 1935
79	Typescript by unidentified Bush 'old-timer', 1975: Gordon Bussey Collection
80	Brochure, 1937: Gordon Bussey Collection
81	John Hester, private conversation, 1989
82	Roy Browning, private correspondence, 1988
83	*BVWS Bulletin*, September 1985, pp. 21–3
84	Letter from Frank Brittain, BVWS Bulletin, Vol. **10/2**, p. 47
85	W S Percival, private conversation 1989
86	Keith Trace, *A History of the Plessey Company* (Unpublished, c.1971), passim: Plessey Archives
87	Ernie Marsden, private conversation with Gordon Bussey
88	Bill Dalziel, private conversation, 1988

89   M J Lipman, op. cit., p. 68

90   Bernard Huntbatch, private conversation, 1989

91   Gordon Bussey, *Wireless: The Crucial Decade* (Peter Peregrinus Ltd, 1990), p. 79

92   Letter, 26 September 1931, Ferranti Archives

93   Excerpts from minutes of the Liaison Committee, BRMVA &RMA, 19 January 1931: EMI Archives

94   Memorandum, Mittell to Clark, *Your decision regarding American type valves for Philco,* 16 January 1933: EMI Archives

95   The Monopolies and Restrictive Practices Commission, *Report on the Supply of ElectronicValves and Cathode Ray Tubes* (HMSO, 1956) para 68

96   Excerpts from minutes of the Liaison Committee, BRMVA & RMA, 10 September 1931: EMI Archives

97   Letter, Mullard to van Walsem, 25 November 1931: Philips Archives

98   S G Sturmey, op. cit., pp. 225–6

99   *Wireless & Gramophone Trader*, 5 January 1935, p. 5

100   Ibid., 29 June 1935, p. 223

101   Ibid., 22 June 1935, p. 205

102   Ibid., 29 June 1935, p. 224

103   *Report of the Broadcasting Committee 1935* (HMSO Cmnd 5091, 1936) p. 42

104   Gerald Wells, private conversation, 1990

105   Monopolies Commission Report, 1956, para 68

106   BRVMA Memorandum *Importation of Radio Valves*, 24 November 1931: EMI Archives

107   Memorandum to Mr A Clark *Re Importation Duty on Radio Valves,* 28 November 1931: EMI Archives

108   Monopolies Commission Report, paras 70-1

109   Ibid., Appendix D

110   Letter, RMA to Mullard Radio Valve Co Ltd, 2 June 1932 (Copy attached to Ref 108): Philips Archives

111   Letter, S R Mullard to Anton Philips, 10 June 1932: Philips Archives

112   *McMichael Messenger*, August 1934, p. 18: Gordon Bussey Collection

113   *McMichael Messenger,* June 1935, p. 62: Gordon Bussey Collection

114   *McMichael Messenger*, April 1934, p. 48: Gordon Bussey Collection

115   Booklet *The Diamond Jubilee of McMichael Ltd* 1919–1979: Gordon Bussey Collection

116   *McMichael Messenger,* June 1935, p. 63: Gordon Bussey Collection

117   David Read, articles in *BVWS Bulletin*, March 1979, pp. 55–58

118   Robert Hawes, article in *BVWS Bulletin*, June 1986, pp. 5–7

119   Keith Geddes & Gordon Bussey, *The History of Roberts Radio* (Roberts Radio Co Ltd), 1987

120   Jack Hester, unpublished typescript

121   *Wireless & Gramophone Trader*, 12 January 1935, p. 18

122   *Wireless & Gramophone Trader*, 5 January 1935, p. 2

123   L W Orchard, private conversation, 1989

124   RMA Annual Report, 21 January 1932: BREMA Archives

125   Z M Banks, private conversation, 1989

126   Information researched by Gordon Bussey

127   Vidor-Burndept Magazine, Christmas 1953, pp. 5–9

128   *Wireless & Gramophone Trader*, 25 May 1935, p. 135

129   *Wireless & Gramophone Trader*, 25 May 1935, p. 131

130   *Wireless & Gramophone Trader*, 1 June 1935, p. 154

131   Ernest Brown, Walter Ficker, Chris Pickard, private conversations, 1988

132   John Street, private conversation, 1989

133 Harry Lerner, *Currys: the first 100 years* (Cambridge, Woodhead-Faulkner Ltd, 1984) p. 42

134 *Wireless & Gramophone Trader*, 5 January 1935, p. 3

135 Hugh Lynn, private conversation, 1988

136 *Wireless & Gramophone Trader*, 16 February 1935, p. 132

137 C J Smithells and D A Rankin, *A New Construction for Receiving Valves (GEC Journal)*, November 1933, pp. 229–235)

138 Robert Clayton Joan Algar, *The GEC Research Laboratories 1919-1984* (Peter Peregrinus Ltd, 1989) p. 121

139 Bill Taylor and Charlie Sjuberg, private conversations and correspondence,1988

140 G R M Garratt, *The Mullard Story* (Unpublished) Part 5: Mullard Archives

141 Transcripts of interviews with J D Stephenson (1982) and D Priestland (1980): Mullard Archives

142 Transcript of discussions with J M Fichter, 1986: Mullard Archives

143 Letter, S R Mullard to H F van Walsem, 31 January 1933: Mullard Archives

144 *Dictionary of Business Biography*, pp. 297–300

145 K I Jones, private conversation, 1989

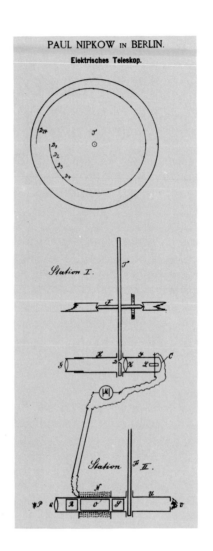

PAUL NIPKOW in BERLIN.

Elektrisches Teleskop.

3 • *Television in the Thirties*

First but Not Foremost

The story of John Logie Baird's low-definition television stands apart from the main history. Its pictures were conveyed through a BBC sound transmitter and the viewer's sound receiver, but its own technology was largely non-electronic, and apart from stimulating public interest in television it contributed nothing to the high-definition systems that succeeded it. Nevertheless Baird's 'Televisor', marketed in February 1930 and displaying a 30-line picture at $12^1/_2$ pictures/second, was the first television set anywhere in the world to be offered for sale to the public.

Throughout the late-1920s Baird had vigorously promoted television by means of demonstrations and newspaper stories, encouraging the expectation that a broadcast service was just about to begin. In 1928, those attending demonstrations mounted by Baird at Selfridges were invited to place orders for Televisors, at prices ranging from £20 to £150[1], on the understanding that the orders would be executed as soon as a service was assured. The BBC initially refused Baird's requests to transmit his signals; doing so would be interpreted by the public as an endorsement, and the Corporation's Chief Engineer, P P Eckersley, considered not only that Baird's pictures were currently well below the standard to merit this, but that they had too little potential for improvement. However, as the holder of a monopoly in broadcasting the Corporation was finally obliged to allow pictures from Baird's studio in Long Acre to be transmitted outside normal broadcasting hours, and regular transmissions began on 30 September 1929. Only one transmitter was available for the first six months, so sound and vision had to be radiated alternately.

Although it was principally to the sale of Televisors that Baird and his backers looked for their commercial reward, sets were not yet available for purchase, and when asked how many he thought had received the opening transmission Baird, a renowned optimist, could come up with no higher estimate than twenty-nine, of which twenty were the number he thought might have been home-built by amateurs.[2] Baird's companies, geared as they were to research and demonstration rather than production, had offered to issue licences to set manufacturers, but had found no takers.[3] Quite apart from yielding no revenue, this situation threatened to undermine the credibility of the whole venture, so towards the end of 1929 Baird placed orders with Plessey for the manufacture of Televisors, and these went on sale in February 1930 at 25 guineas; Plessey also produced a boxed kit of parts at 16 guineas.

The principal components beneath the Televisor's green-painted metal cover were:

> a 'Nipkow' disc, named after the German who had patented it in 1884;
> a motor to rotate it, with a toothed-wheel synchronizing attachment;
> a variable resistor for varying the speed of the motor;
> a neon lamp with a luminous electrode roughly 2" high and 1" wide;
> a magnifying lens.

The disc, 20" in diameter, was made of thin aluminium, and was perforated near its rim with a single-turn spiral of 30 tiny holes. The

Baird's first demonstration at Selfridges, April 1925

Baird demonstrates reception of 30-line pictures, transmitted by the BBC, at his Long Acre premises in about 1930. The Televisor is one of the 'production' models made by Plessey

neon lamp lay behind it, and during each revolution the spiral of holes passed in front of the electrode in 30 vertical arcs that together covered its entire area 12½ times each second. A picture was formed as the lamp's brightness fluctuated rapidly in response to the transmitted signal, as delivered by the output valve of the viewer's wireless set; the magnifying lens enlarged the picture to roughly 4" high x 2" wide.

5 April 1930   10. Downing Street,
Whitehall.

Dear Mr Baird

I must thank you very warmly for the Television instrument you have put into Downing St.. What a marvellous discovery you have made! When I look at the transmissions I feel that the most wonderful miracle is being done under my eye. I congratulate you most heartily & send you my sincerest hopes for your further success. You have put something in my room which will never let me forget how strange is the world – and how unknown. Again & again I thank you.

With kindest regards.

Yours very sincerely

J. Ramsay MacDonald

The picture was red and flickery. A performer was recognizable in a head-and-shoulders view, but anything more ambitious relied heavily on the viewer's imagination. *Wireless World*, reviewing the televisor in March 1930, commented favourably on the fact that when a clock face was transmitted it could be read to the nearest half minute, but found that for satisfactory operation the receiver's output valve should have a rating of at least five watts; relatively few receivers fulfilled this condition. From 31 March 1930 sound and vision were radiated simultaneously, using the BBC's two Brookmans

Whatever the technological limitations of Baird's system, he had nothing to learn about promoting it

Baird publicity photograph,
c. 1930

A disc Televisor with the
cover removed

BAIRD
PHONOVIS'ION
RECORD
MADE IN 1928
Shows MAN'S
Head in Motion

Park transmitters, so a second wireless set was needed to receive the sound.

For all its shortcomings, thirty-line television held great fascination for the enthusiast, who could cut out his own disc from sheet metal, mark out very precisely the positions for its 30 square holes, and himself fashion the punch and die to produce them. If he were less ambitious he could buy the Plessey boxed kit, or shop around buying cheaper components piecemeal. Half his pleasure came from building the Televisor and getting it to work, and pride in having done so enhanced his enjoyment of the results. But without this personal involvement, and considered purely as entertainment, 30-line television was too limited in scope to sustain interest, and the ready-made Televisor was a marketing failure. The order placed with Plessey is widely believed to have been for 1,000 televisors, although a document in that company's archives[4] cites 2,500, suggesting that

Baird's 30-line pictures occupied a frequency band narrow enough to be recorded on a gramophone disc, but 'Phonovision' was never really practicable, even by the standards of 1928

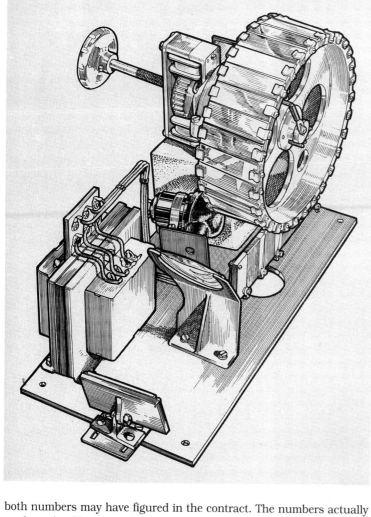

above: *The Bush mirror-drum receiver, 1933*

left: *A kit version of the mirror-drum receiver, 1933*

opposite: *Cover of a leaflet advertising the Bush mirror-drum receiver*

both numbers may have figured in the contract. The numbers actually made and sold are not known; in January 1931 Baird told the Post Office that not less than 1,000 receivers had been sold, but later he informed the Postmaster General that only about 500 were in use in December 1932.[5] What is certain is that figures of this order amply vindicated the radio manufacturers' decision not to take out licences.

In 1932 the BBC took over the running of the experimental service. With a larger studio, newly built equipment and a proper control desk, the system came closer to achieving its full potential, and the Corporation gave an undertaking that transmissions would continue until at least 31 March 1934. Baird's company was by this time under the control of the Ostrer brothers, who also controlled the newly formed Bush Radio, and in May 1933 launched a de-luxe 30-line receiver, made by Bush. This was self-contained, and gave a 9" x 4" picture. In the studio, the Nipkow disc had been superseded as a scanning device by the mirror-drum (invented in 1889), and the new receiver was based on the method of display used in the studio's picture monitors. Thirty mirrors mounted edge-to-edge around the periphery of a rotatable drum scanned a focused beam of white light from a 100-watt lamp over a ground-glass screen. The brightness of the light was varied by passing it through a Kerr cell (invented by

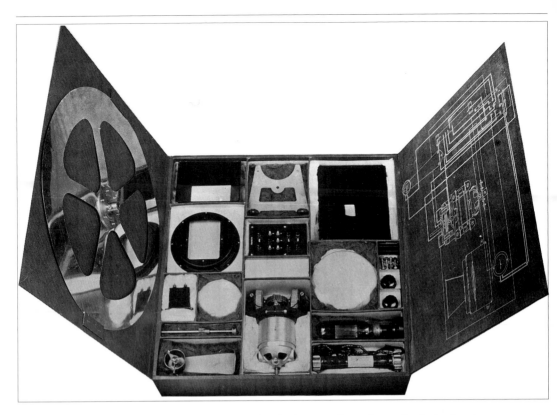

*The Baird 'Senior' kit, which
cost 12 guineas in 1931*

opposite: *Poster produced
by* The Wireless &
Gramophone Trader,
March 1935

J Kerr in 1875), which rotated its plane of polarization in response to
the transmitted signal.

Technologically this receiver was a great advance on the Televisor,
but to launch an expensive 30-line receiver in 1933 was a gross
misjudgement. It was already known within the Baird company that
EMI were developing higher-definition television for transmission on
very high frequencies, and indeed Baird were themselves also doing so,
albeit less successfully. Admittedly, these developments were not
known to the public, but the obsolescence of 30-line television was
clearly implied by the well-publicized fact that the continuation of
transmissions was guaranteed only until 31 March 1934 (though in
fact they continued until 30 September 1935). The price of the receiver
was on different occasions quoted as 75 guineas and 50 guineas.
However, very few if any at all of the 100 sets made were sold, though
some were exhibited in the foyers of Gaumont British cinemas. In their
desire to unload them, Baird even toyed with the idea of promising
buyers that they would later be exchanged for receivers suited to any
new system superseding 30 lines.[6]

In April 1934 the Post Office and the BBC agreed that the time was
ripe for a Government-appointed committee to advise the Postmaster
General on the possibility of introducing a high-definition service, and
such a committee was quickly set up under an ex-PMG, Lord Selsdon.
Its report, published in January 1935, recommended that the BBC
should begin an experimental service as soon as possible on a
standard of not less than 240 lines, and may be regarded as marking
the beginning of the high-definition era.

TELEVISION-

A PLAIN
STATEMENT

- All-day sound broadcasting will continue un-diminished for many years. Better programmes, new interest features and four new stations are planned by the B.B.C. for the near future.

- These programmes can only be received properly on an up-to-date receiver or radio-gramophone, such as you can buy to-day. You will gain nothing by waiting; you may lose, as prices are likely to rise.

- The television service will be quite separate. **When** television is available in this district, we can give you reliable advice on its reception. **Even then you will still need your ordinary receiver or radio-gramophone to get the usual all-day programmes as at present.**

Buy a new Receiver or Radio-Gram
NOW—and ensure many years of
First-class entertainment!!

Published by The Wireless and Gramophone Trader Dorset House, Stamford Street London, S.E.1

The First High-definition Receivers

Shortly after the publication of the Selsdon Committee's report a number of announcements by would-be manufacturers appeared in *The Wireless & Gramophone Trader* showing, at the most charitable interpretation, a total failure to appreciate the implications of the change to high definition. A Mr Thomas Harris "in association with a very important firm" hoped to market a receiver at only 21 guineas, while European Television Limited announced that within four weeks they would be marketing, at 33 guineas, a cathode-ray-tube 30-line receiver which could subsequently be provided with a chassis suitable for high definition at an anticipated cost of £5. Major Radiovision were proposing to market, for £16, a disc-type receiver which "could be connected for reception of the high-definition transmissions at a cost in the neighbourhood of £5."

No doubt the dealers who made up *The Trader's* readership knew what credence to give to such reports, but some of the public reacted to the prospect of television with great credulity. Whilst a broadcast statement by the Postmaster General was deemed sufficient to reassure those who feared that television would enable people to look into each other's homes, the idea that radio was about to become obsolete was sufficiently widespread to be perceived by dealers as a threat to business. *The Trader* produced and distributed a poster explaining the facts, and in an editorial proclaimed: "The public must, if possible, be made to forget all about television for the time being". The RMA circulated a confidential statement in similar vein, pointing out that to enjoy even the limited transmissions envisaged "...the televiewer will have to sit in a semi-darkened room and concentrate his vision on a small square of glass for two hours." It was against this discouraging background that manufacturers were striving to meet the technological challenge of the Selsdon report.

When sound broadcasting had begun, the technology for simple receivers had already existed. This was not so with high-definition television. Apart from its audio-frequency amplifier, the receiver's circuits had to be developed from scratch. A signal conveying a moving-picture contains so much more information than a sound signal that it must occupy a band of frequencies several hundred times wider. This in turn requires it to be transmitted in the very high frequency (VHF) band, which was unexplored territory in the early-1930s. The receiver had to amplify the VHF signal, generate line- and field-scanning waveforms in response to synchronizing pulses, and amplify the wide-band video signal varying the brightness of the cathode ray tube — all functions posing new problems.

But the biggest question-mark hung over the cathode ray tube (CRT) itself, which in the early-1930s needed to advance a long way from its current status as a somewhat exotic tool for measuring and observing waveforms. Tubes were still not fully evacuated, but relied on residual gas for their focusing, which could not be maintained over the range of beam current needed to form a picture. Screen phosphors had to be formulated that would produce white light with high efficiency and survive electron bombardment. To produce a bright trace even when spread over several hundred lines, the beam of electrons had to be made much more intense, yet remain sharply focused. This necessitated an increase in the tube's final voltage, which in turn made the beam harder to deflect, yet deflection had to be through a large angle to produce the required size of picture with a tube of manageable length. And at these large angles of deflection the beam became de-focused. It was in fact by no means certain that even the best technologists would be able to coax the laws of physics into yielding a satisfactory tube; as one of them, L F Broadway of EMI, later recalled "...at that time we believed the CRT as a display device was only an interim measure. We didn't really believe that this huge vacuum envelope, a cumbersome sort of thing, would last."[7]

Nevertheless, nine setmakers and a tube-manufacturer exhibited receivers at Radiolympia in August 1936, in readiness for the opening of the BBC's service in November; the sets were not yet for sale, pending a decision by the BBC that their transmissions could be described as a service rather than experimental.[8]

EMI: out on their own

The story of Britain's pioneering role in high-definition television tends to be told mainly in terms of EMI's studio equipment and the Marconi Company's transmitter and aerial system, with receivers largely taken for granted. This is understandable, since it was above all EMI's development of the Emitron camera that made live television practicable, while the Alexandra Palace mast, dramatically poised above North London, symbolized the heroic aspect of the venture. However, it was as receiver-manufacturers that EMI (then still HMV) embarked on television work; of necessity the company's research programme also embraced picture origination and transmission, but these came to be seen as fields for commercial activity only as it became evident, around 1933, that no-one else in Britain was pursuing them effectively.[9]

For a company that had only recently come to terms with having to involve itself in radio, HMV was remarkably quick to take an interest in television. As early as February 1929 an internal memorandum stated "I think the time has come when we should be getting to know something about what the Baird people have in the way of important patents",[10] and an active programme of work was under way in 1930, the year before the EMI merger and the appointment of Isaac Shoenberg as Head of Research.

The first objective was to determine what standards would be necessary to make television a credible form of home entertainment, and the first equipment was designed solely for this purpose. A 150-line picture was achieved by vertically scanning a film simultaneously into five 30-line signals, each portraying a fifth of the picture's width, which were sent over five separate channels then combined by mirror-drum scanning onto a common screen.[11] This apparatus was demonstrated at a scientific exhibition in January 1931, and was hailed by the press as a great advance on anything previously seen.

EMI did not finally abandon mechanical receivers until 1933,[12] but work on cathode ray tubes began in 1930, and the film-scanning gear was rebuilt for single-channel operation at a standard of 120 lines and 25 pictures/second, so as to provide test signals for receiver development. When J D McGee, who was to play a leading part in the development of the Emitron camera tube, joined EMI Research Department from the Cavendish Laboratory in January 1932, one reason for his recruitment was that the head of the television laboratory, G E Condliffe, foresaw a need to investigate the possible application of cathode rays to picture generation. Nevertheless, McGee was initially employed in assisting W F Tedham in his work on tubes for receivers,[13] and when the two of them made the first experimental Emitron in the autumn of 1932 they had to do so in secret, having failed to persuade their superiors to allow such a diversion.[14] In May 1933, another Cambridge scientist, L F Broadway, was recruited specifically to work on cathode ray tubes; they still could not be evacuated satisfactorily, nor had a satisfactory white phosphor yet been formulated.

By November 1932, EMI's policy of pressing ahead with cathode-ray-tube displays while still restricted to mechanical film-scanning had achieved results that Isaac Shoenberg, the Head of Research, judged worthy of showing to the BBC. The Corporation's Chief Engineer, Noel Ashbridge, saw a green 120-line picture, 5 inches square, that had been transmitted over a two-mile VHF link, and was distinctly impressed. Baird got wind of this demonstration, and promised to show 240 lines by the following February, but in fact they succeeded in demonstrating only an inferior 120-line picture, on closed circuit, in April. In the financial year 1932–33 EMI barely broke even, and it says much for Shoenberg's courage and powers of persuasion that he nevertheless managed to expand the research department, which at its peak had around seventy people working on television. In May 1934, the Marconi-EMI Television Company was formed which, by combining EMI's capabilities in television with Marconi's in transmission, could undertake to engineer a complete television station.

The following month, Isaac Shoenberg gave evidence to the Selsdon Committee.[15] Asked what he thought the price of a receiver was likely to be, he said "about £50 to begin with", though it is not clear how that figure followed from the episode he then related. Over Christmastide in 1933 he had relaxed the strict secrecy surrounding television work to the extent of giving a demonstration to the sales people, then asking them how many receivers they would place orders for if the price were £100. They had told him that they could easily sell 5,000 to begin with, but that afterwards he would have to come down in price. Shoenberg assured the committee that he would license other manufacturers to make receivers, that he would not attempt to impose conditions giving EMI an effective monopoly, and that if he put out a receiver at that moment it would not be liable to total obsolescence — it might, for example, be designed for 180-line transmissions but if 243 lines were adopted it would still work, though not with full definition; 243 was cited because its simple factors (9 x 9 x 3) made for ease in generating the transmitted waveform.

The Selsdon Committee's report, published at the end of January 1935, recommended the early establishment by the BBC of a trial service in the London area, with the Baird Company and Marconi-EMI operating during alternate weeks. The report did not specify a standard beyond imposing a minimum of 240 lines at 25 pictures per second, which was known to be the most that the Baird company, still tied to mechanical scanning, could manage. On 8 February *Wireless World*'s editorial, a reliable indicator of informed opinion within the industry, commented "This is indeed a high standard to demand of the service in its initial stages"; yet by that date Shoenberg had already decided to adopt 405 lines. This circumstance makes clear the excellence of EMI's security, and the courage of Isaac Shoenberg, who had been told by his management that failure would bankrupt the company. On 15 February he formalized his commitment to the 405-

line standard by submitting its basic parameters to the Technical Sub-committee of the Television Advisory Committee (which had succeeded the Selsdon Committee).

The standard used the principle of 'interlacing', patented by RCA in 1933 and used in all subsequent standards up to the present day. Interlacing enables a system transmitting 25 pictures per second to have a flicker rate of 50 per second. Provided that the standard has an odd number of lines, it is achieved simply by making the vertical scanning frequency at both transmitter and receiver 50Hz instead of 25Hz; this causes a 405-line picture to be displayed as two 202.5-line pictures having their lines interleaved. EMI adopted interlaced scanning because the flicker produced by straightforward 'sequential' scanning at 25 pictures per second had been found increasingly unacceptable as the brightness of cathode-ray-tube displays had improved.

It would seem that Shoenberg still needed to reassure himself that he knew all the implications of going to 400 lines (as the 405-line standard was still loosely termed), for early in April C S Agate, in charge of development as opposed to research, wrote to him:[16] "Re:-400 and 240 line television transmissions. In accordance with your request of a day or two ago, I have given the question of the relative advantages of these two line frequencies consideration...". Agate was a notably cautious man, considerably older than most of the Research Department people, and his reply was in character. He thought the quality currently being achieved at 400 lines was only about that potentially attainable at 240 lines. The direct cost of a 400-line receiver would not be more than 10% higher than a 240-line one, but there would be no margin of safety, necessitating a tighter tolerance on components, and more rigorous testing, installation and servicing. He continued:

> "I feel too, that this solution is likely to be made worse by attempts of other manufacturers to put out 400-line receivers which are most unlikely to be satisfactory. We might perhaps look with equanimity on the troubles of other manufacturers if we had not our similar, if lesser, troubles of our own. The prospects of television might not be badly affected by them if most makes on the market were bad, and ours were good, but there seems to me a real danger that if other makes are terrible, and ours bad, the opinion may grow that high-fidelity television is fundamentally too unreliable for practical use."

Agate went on to point out that since television would from the outset enjoy the advantages of modern production methods it could not be expected to show the same dramatic fall in cost as radio had recently done; television was thus likely to remain a rich man's hobby for a long time, but if the 240-line system were adopted, its advantages in terms of cost, complexity and reliability would help to expand the market. His final argument was that if, as he thought likely, EMI's transmissions on 400 lines would not initially be much better than Baird's on 240 lines, the unjust judgement would be formed that the EMI system was inferior because it needed more lines to achieve the same result.

Shoenberg did not find these arguments compelling; as he recalled many years later: "In deciding the basic features of our system we

frequently had to make a choice between a comparatively easy path leading to a mediocre result and a more difficult one which, if successful, held the promise of better things."[17] He allowed his decision to stand, and after the sub-committee had thrashed out the details for 405-line and 240-line transmissions with Marconi-EMI and Baird respectively, the two companies proceeded to equip the BBC's London Television Station, at Alexandra Palace. All receivers, therefore, had to be switchable between the two standards.

EMI were sufficiently confident in their Emitron camera tube to commit themselves to its exclusive use. The Emitron was identical in principle to the 'Iconoscope' tube invented in America by Vladimir Zworykin, but had been developed independently by EMI, and incorporated significant differences in manufacturing technique that gave it a performance superior to contemporary iconoscopes. It was capable of excellent definition and was sensitive enough to be used under attainable if uncomfortable studio lighting, or in full daylight.

The EMI receiver, available in HMV and Marconiphone versions that were virtually identical, had a long pedigree, and its elegant appearance reflected the fact. Available with or without all-wave radio, it used a 12-inch tube, magnetically deflected. Since this was about three feet long, it was mounted vertically and viewed via a surface-silvered mirror on the under-side of a lid opening to 45°. With the lid closed, the receiver was practically indistinguishable from a radiogram, the HMV version being veneered in piano-finish figured walnut with the loudspeaker grille in bronze expanded metal. As a finishing touch, there was a lock on the lid to prevent unauthorized use.

GEC: off on the wrong foot [18]

It was not until the formation of the Selsdon Committee early in 1934 that the Research Laboratories at Wembley began to work on television, with the establishment of a four-strong group, headed by L C Jesty, to develop suitable cathode ray tubes; work was also begun

GEC's cathode ray tube laboratory at Wembley, 1935

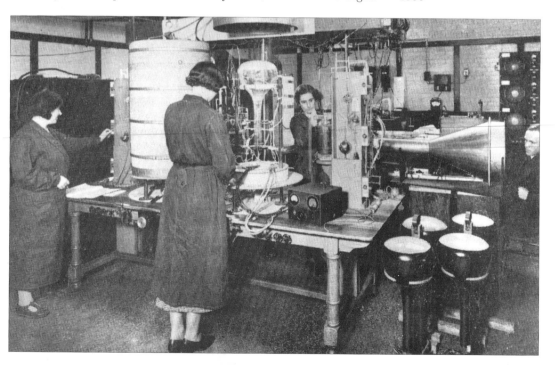

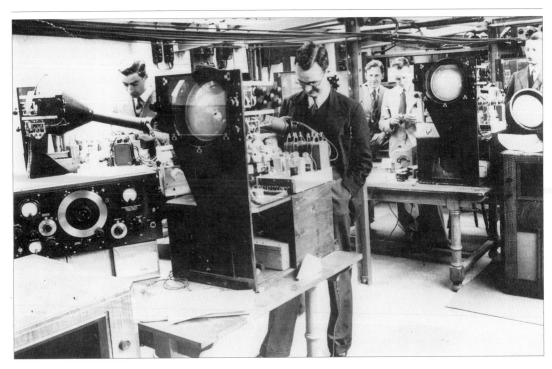

Testing GEC's first production receivers at Wembley, 1936

The GEC 12″ receiver BT3701 of 1936, on the left as originally designed, on the right after adding all-wave radio (BT 3702)

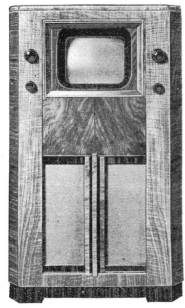

The GEC 12" receiver
BT3701, showing its three
massive chassis and the
depth necessary to
accommodate the
electrostatically
deflected tube

G W Edwards, R J Dippy &
Dr B J O'Kane at GEC's
Research Laboratories,
Wembley, c. 1938

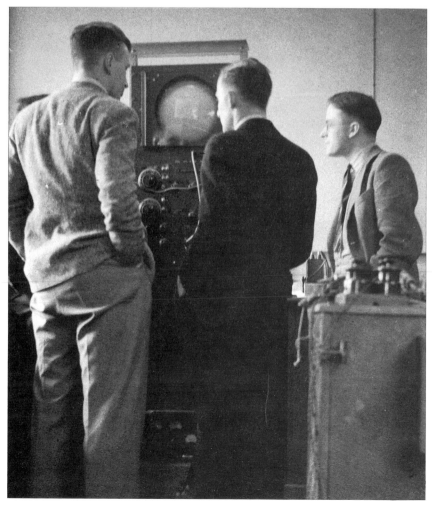

on a camera tube, but was discontinued after about a year. Later in 1934 the Laboratories began to construct a Nipkow-disc film scanner, and early in 1935, following publication of the Selsdon Committee's report, a separate television group was formed, primarily to develop receivers. Test signals were obtained by feeding the scanner's vision and sound outputs to a low-power transmitter system, but their usefulness was reduced by the fact that the scanner operated on a hybrid standard of 240 lines interlaced; it had originally been designed for the Baird standard of 240 lines scanned sequentially, and could not be adapted to 405 lines.

GEC's initial designs reflected the company's close association with a Berlin-based company, D S Loewe, which played a prominent role in developing receivers for the regular television transmissions initiated in Germany in March 1935. Because only a 180-line standard was used and receivers were installed in public viewing rooms instead of being sold to the public, Britain claims the distinction of having opened the world's first high-definition service, but the German service nevertheless generated experience and expertise that was of value to British engineers. The influence waned as GEC engineers acquired their own expertise and as Anglo-German relations became strained, though visits to Loewe continued right up to August 1939.[19]

Receivers were designed at Wembley and built at the Telephone Works, Coventry. The finished sets had then to be shipped to Wembley for final testing, since this required signals from the Alexandra Palace transmitter to be available; a special television test hut, operating as an outstation of the Coventry works, was built behind the laboratories. The receiver exhibited at the 1936 Radio Show had a 12-inch tube, with electrostatic deflection. The presence of deflector plates tends to make such tubes longer than those with magnetic deflection, but the GEC tube was made with a flask-shaped bulb, and was in fact appreciably shorter than the conical EMI tube. It was mounted horizontally and viewed directly, giving a well-proportioned receiver. However, for the variant that included all-wave radio the cabinet designer put a lift-up flap over the tube and doubled the set's frontal area, with disastrous effect on its appearance.

It would have been logical for the cathode ray tubes designed at Wembley to be manufactured by the Marconi-Osram Valve Company at its Hammersmith works, since that company was part-owned by GEC. But EMI owned the rest of M-O V, and it was deemed undesirable for so vital a component to be made by a company owing allegiance to a competitor. Instead, manufacture was entrusted to the GEC Lamp Works, also in Hammersmith, which had little background in the technologies involved, and this decision has been blamed for the fact that many production problems were experienced.

Ferranti: between two stools
Situated in Manchester, Ferranti were not well placed to receive low-definition television, and although some experimenting was begun in February 1932 material and labour costs attributable to television over the years 1932–34 averaged less than £24 a month.[20] In December 1932, however, Ferranti were approached by a television entrepreneur Solomon Sagall, and invited, as a manufacturing company, to make a modest investment in the development and holding company, Scophony Limited, of which he was Managing Director. Sagall had formed Scophony to exploit the patents of G W Walton, who had some

*Ferranti experimental
picture-tube, February 1936*

*A Ferranti production tube
of March 1937*

genuinely original and sophisticated ideas on the optics of mechanical television, and he had also recruited two other talented engineers, while his fellow directors were well-established in the film world. The claims made were impressive: "...the only solution of television as a really practical commercial proposition suitable for mass entertainment...master patents which secure for the system an absolute monopoly in the sphere of communications and entertainment."

Ferranti duly purchased £3,500-worth of shares and for eighteen months played the sponsor with generosity and forbearance, while Scophony went through financial crises and continued for far too long with 30-line television as the basis of such concrete plans as they had. However, in August 1934 Ferranti declined Sagall's invitation to invest £10,000 in a proposed restructuring of the company, and the following April learned, apparently from a press notice, that Scophony had entered into an arrangement with Ekco. Scophony's capital was to be increased to £140,000 and its board was to include W S Verrells (Ekco's Chairman & Managing Director) and John Wyborn (Ekco's Chief Engineer). Ferranti reacted with mild regret and sold their shares.[21] It must remain a matter for speculation how far the various parties to these changes were aware of the significance of a patent taken out in 1934 by one of the Scophony engineers, J H Jeffree, for a supersonic light control. As will be outlined later, this invention was to transform Scophony from a lost cause to a world leader in large-screen television.

Within a few months, Ferranti had developed a number of cathode ray tubes for television applications, but the engineer in charge of television work, M K Taylor, had clearly been influenced by Scophony's outlook, and in an internal report of January 1936[22] was looking to large-screen pictures as the most promising line of development for the company to pursue. He cited John Logie Baird's view that no-one would be content for long to watch the end of a small cathode ray tube at home, since an essential feature of being entertained was to get out and go somewhere; Taylor added, with no hint of a raised eyebrow, that Baird was enquiring for a cathode ray tube made of steel, about 8 feet in diameter, for use in Gaumont British cinemas. Taylor himself considered that television, however perfect, would not compare with radio for home entertainment: "It will necessitate careful attention on the part of the lookers-in — no chance of reading a book or going about one's affairs. It will not induce any mental relief after the day's work, or make a suitable background for hobbies or occupations." This sceptical attitude towards television did not prevent Ferranti from producing a receiver in time for exhibition at the 1936 Radio Show, but they were to remain extremely cautious.

Philips and Mullard: cross-channel television
In the 1930s both Philips and Mullard depended heavily on Eindhoven for their technology. No pre-war Philips television receivers were designed in the UK, nor were any even assembled here until 1938, while Mullard did not begin manufacturing cathode ray tubes for television until May 1937. As early as November 1934, however, a British engineer, C L Richards, was in charge of constructing a receiver at Eindhoven, where there were adequate facilities for originating and transmitting test pictures, though it was appreciated that final adjustment of production receivers would have to be carried

TELEVISION
AND
SHORT-WAVE WORLD

NOVEMBER, 1937

Progress in Television

THE MULLARD CATHODE RAY TUBE

Type M. 46-15

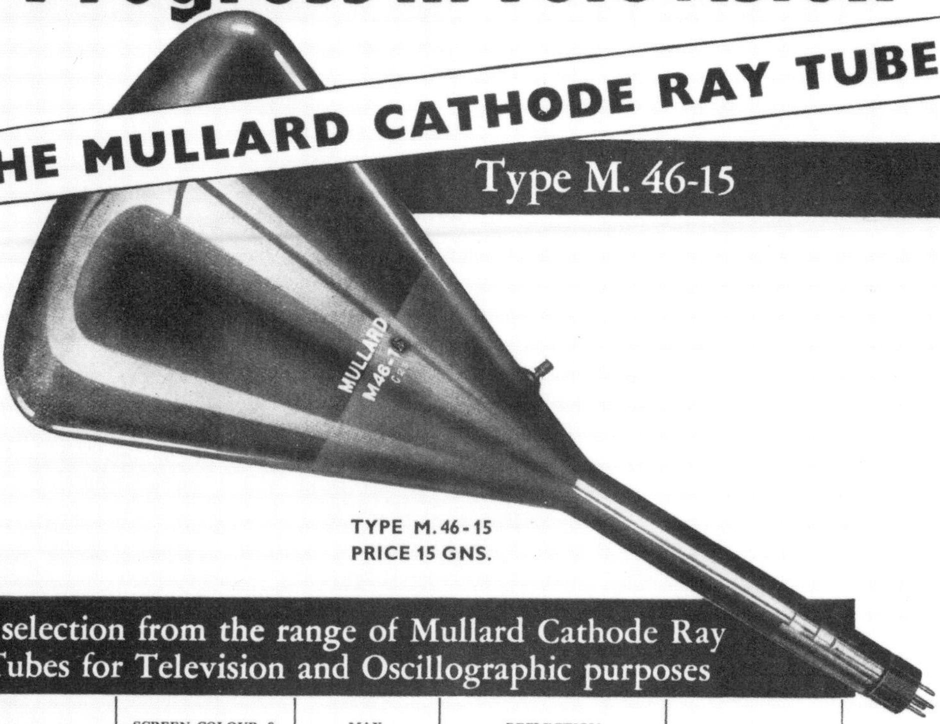

TYPE M. 46-15
PRICE 15 GNS.

A selection from the range of Mullard Cathode Ray Tubes for Television and Oscillographic purposes

TYPE NO.	SCREEN COLOUR & APPROX. DIAMETER	MAX. ANODE VOLTS	DEFLECTION METHOD	LIST PRICE
M.46-15	White 15″	5,000	Electro-Magnetic	£15 15s.
M.46-12	White 12″	5,000	Electro-Magnetic	£12 12s.
EM.46-12	White 12″	5,000	Electro-Static Electro-Magnetic	£15 15s.
E.46-12	White 12″	5,000	Double Electrostatic	£15 15s.
E.46-G10	Green 10″	5,000	Double Electrostatic	£12 12s.
E.42-B6	Blue 6″	2,000	Double Electrostatic	£ 8 8s.
A.41-N4	Green* 4″	1,200	Double Electrostatic	£ 6 15s.
E.40-G3	Green 3″	800	Double Electrostatic	£ 3 10s.
4002	Green 4″	1,000	Double Electrostatic	£ 6 15s.

★ Special Long Persistence Screen.

Write for Technical Information Sheets, giving full data, to:—

Mullard

Wireless Service Co. Ltd., Cathode Ray Tube Dept., 225 Tottenham Court Road, London, W.1.

out in England.[23] The receiver shown by the company at the 1936 Radio Show used an 11" tube, electrostatically deflected, and included an eight-valve sound receiver covering the long and medium wavebands as well as television sound.

Ediswan and Cossor: pioneers in oscilloscopes

Cathode ray tubes had been made in the 'special valve' department at Ediswan's Ponders End works since about 1925, but in the mid-1930s a separate laboratory was set up under Tommy Price exclusively to develop tubes for television. Concurrently, receiver circuits were developed at the Mazda Applications Laboratory at Brimsdown, and in 1938 Price took his laboratory there.[24] At the 1936 Radio Show Ediswan, though not a set-manufacturer, was one of the companies showing a receiver. This had been designed to attain the highest quality without regard to cost, so that it could be used as a standard against which to assess less costly circuits developed for commercial receivers.[25]

A C Cossor Ltd, founded upon scientific glassware, had made its first tubes in 1902. In 1933 two Cossor engineers, L H Bedford and O S Puckle, demonstrated an ingenious but impractical television system which portrayed light and shade mainly by varying the scanning-velocity of the electron beam rather than its intensity, thereby reducing the defocusing of their gas-focused tubes.[26] Thus it was only to be expected that they would be early entrants into the field of television receivers. Just how early, however, must have come as a surprise to the radio trade. On 9 March 1935, less than six weeks after publication of the Selsdon Committee's report and almost three months before transmission standards were finalized, *The Wireless and Gramophone Trader* announced that when the high-definition transmissions commenced ("towards the end of the year") Cossor would market a combined sound and vision receiver, Model 3622, to retail at 75 guineas; concurrently, Cossor circulated to the trade a four-page leaflet showing a photograph of the receiver. To be fair, the leaflet did state "we are refraining from making announcements to the public regarding our television receiver as we feel that such announcements at the present moment would not be to the benefit of the trade generally..."; *The Trader* commented drily "With this view traders will, we think, agree."

Notwithstanding this somewhat naïve attempt to impress the trade, Cossor did emerge as manufacturers very much to be reckoned with, and at the 1936 Radio Show exhibited a receiver featuring their own 13$\frac{1}{2}$" electrostatically deflected tube.

Pye: on the fringe

Cambridge is some 50 miles from Alexandra Palace, and the predicted range of the transmitter was only 25 miles. In practice, however, the range in favourable directions turned out to be at least 35 miles, and Pye were able to pick up an adequate signal, incidentally reaping a commercial reward from this clear demonstration of their receivers' sensitivity.

In the early-1930s the company had experimented with 30-line receivers, the engineer chiefly concerned being a young Austrian, Peter Goldmark, who was later to win fame in America as the originator of the long-playing record. As high definition approached, B J Edwards joined the company and took charge of television development.

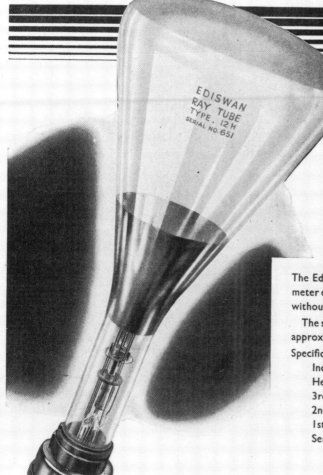

An electrostatically deflected tube of 1937

A special section was established to make valves and cathode ray tubes, and produced the 12" tube used in the company's first commercial receiver.[27] Unusually, this used electrostatic deflection for the horizontal scan but electromagnetic for the vertical.[28]

Baird: convert to cathode rays
In 1931 John Logie Baird stated that he saw no hopes for television by means of 'cathode ray bulbs',[29] but by April 1932 his company was experimenting with them and a year later demonstrated a cathode-ray display for the first time, at a definition of 120 lines. In the summer of 1933 Baird's influence within the company that bore his name decreased, with the appointment to the board of Captain A G D West, an ex-BBC engineer. Thereafter cathode-ray tubes were intensively, if belatedly, developed, and at the 1936 Radio Show a mirror-lid receiver was exhibited using a 15" magnetically deflected tube developed and manufactured at the company's laboratories at Crystal Palace. Though made and exhibited by Bush Radio, the receiver was described as a 'Televisor', which was a trade mark registered by Baird Television Limited. Being a superheterodyne receiver, it could readily be made tunable, and Bush specified it as receiving vision signals over the range 38–48MHz,[30] presumably in order to imply a degree of immunity to early obsolescence denied to the 'straight' circuits of many of its competitors. A more genuine advantage of the receiver was a guaranteed tube life of 1,000 hours[31] which, with only $2^{1}/_{2}$ hours of transmission a day, represented a reasonably long period of service.

Scophony: a radically different technology
As we have seen, until re-structured in 1935 Scophony was a small company in constant financial difficulties, and until the emergence of the Jeffree supersonic light control in 1934 was largely associated with 30-line television.

Their claims to novel technology embraced transmission as well as reception, and in July 1934 they gained an interview with the Selsdon Committee. Their technical witness, G W Walton, asserted that they were working towards a system in which the picture rate would be reduced to one picture per second, thereby enabling 240-line pictures to be transmitted in a 15kHz frequency band. The Committee expressed some scepticism as to whether his techniques would, as he claimed, allow this to be done without producing flicker, but did not question how such a system could reproduce movement. A week or two later the Committee attended a demonstration, and reported that "...nothing of obvious importance was shown".[32]

Had some catastrophe wiped out Scophony and its personnel at this point, the company would probably, and understandably, have been remembered as a shaky operation based on clever but irrelevant technology and promoted by hollow boastfulness. However, within a year the Selsdon Committee's report and the subsequent decisions on standards had forced the company to concentrate on receivers capable of operating on 405 lines, while the link with Ekco had brought a much-needed injection of practical electronic expertise. An Ekco–Scophony receiver was exhibited at the 1936 Radio Show, with a picture size of 16" x 12", and although very few, if any, domestic models were ever sold, the Scophony large-screen projector, with almost identical technology, was used with considereable success to show sporting events in West-End cinemas,

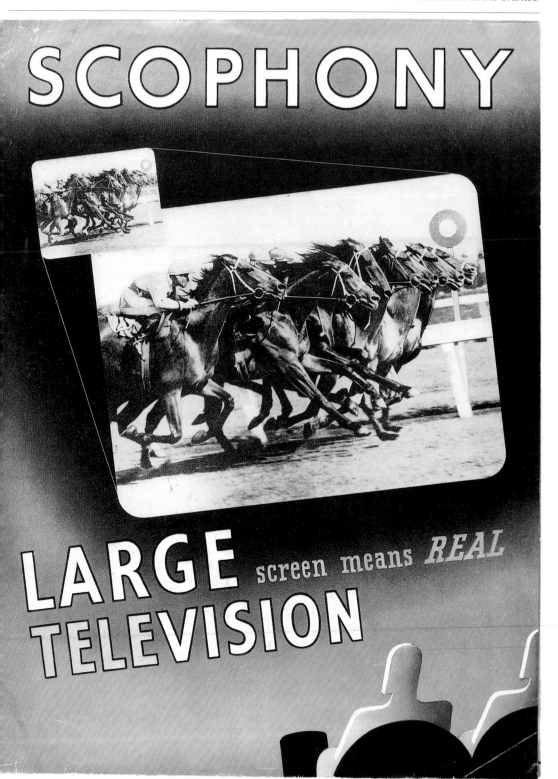

above and overleaf:
*Promotional leaflets, 1938.
Few if any Scophony receivers
were sold to the public*

TWO FOOT
RECEIVER

TELEVISION WITHOUT EYE-STRAIN

PALACE DE LUXE
RECEIVER

TELEVISION WITHOUT EYE-STRAIN

and stands as one of the peaks of pre-war television engineering.

The Scophony receiver used rotating mirrors to scan the screen with modulated light from a powerful lamp. A relatively slow mirror drum provided the vertical scanning, while for the horizontal scanning a 20-sided polygon of polished steel 2" in diameter and 0.125" thick rotated at 30,375 rpm. At each moment instead of projecting a single spot of light onto the screen the receiver projected approximately half a scanning line, thereby utilizing much more of the lamp's output. This remarkable feat was achieved by the Jeffree supersonic light control — a column of liquid along whose length the picture information sped as amplitude-modulation of an 18MHz acoustic wave; at each moment the liquid column contained the last 50 microseconds' worth of picture information, corresponding to half a scanning line. Light was shone across the entire length of the column, which was made to behave like a photographic transparency by virtue of the wave's compressions and rarefactions. The speed at which the wave travelled along the column exactly matched the speed at which the rotating polygon swept the image of the column across the screen, so no blurring occurred. Because of the rotating polygon's considerable inertia, the Scophony receiver could not tolerate any irregularities in the timing of the synchronizing pulses, whereas in conventional receivers minor irregularities produced only negligible disturbance. Scophony demonstrated to the BBC that the Corporation's equipment was badly deficient in this respect, and improvements were put in hand.[33]

Also present, and notable absentees
One minor manufacturer exhibited a television receiver at the 1936 Radio Show. Ismay Distributors of Dagenham showed a 12" set on their tiny stand under their brand name 'Halcyon', alongside two AC/DC sound receivers and a range of 'Blue Spot' loudspeakers and pickups, made for the German firm Blaupunkt. Murphy Radio (who did not exhibit at Olympia from 1933 to 1937 inclusive) designed and publicized a receiver during 1936 but did not market it. Ekco was represented only by the Ekco–Scophony receiver, while K-B and Ultra showed no television set at all.

The acid test [34]
The BBC was keen to demonstrate television at the Radio Show, although this opened almost ten weeks before the experimental service's official opening date. The RMA, who were organizing the show, were less enthusiastic, as were Baird, and the week before the show *Wireless World* was still unable to state with certainty that television would actually be demonstrated, since doubts remained both over Alexandra Palace's ability to originate adequate signals and over reception conditions at Olympia.[35] In the event a demonstration was staged, rather in the manner of a circus freak-show. A darkened booth contained some twenty sets, provided by seven manufacturers, and since the objective was solely to let the public see what television was like, and emphatically not to let them compare the various manufacturers' receivers, these were swathed in curtains so that only the screens were visible. Queues formed outside the booth, sometimes over an hour before each of the day's two ninety-minute sessions, and when visitors were finally admitted they were kept 10–12 feet from the receivers[36] and moved through at a brisk pace.[37] The BBC's Controller

(Engineering) rated the seven manufacturers' receivers in the order: Cossor, EMI, GEC, Baird, Ediswan, Philips and Ferranti. However, in several particulars Baird's transmissions failed to meet their own published specification, and this may have unfairly affected the ranking.

The demonstrations on the Baird system consisted largely of films which, being made for the cinema screen, were perceived as being too lacking in detail to sustain interest. Marconi-EMI's demonstrations included more live material, mainly variety acts from the studio and scenes from the grounds of Alexandra Palace, but their film transmissions were on the whole inferior to Baird's, notwithstanding their nominally higher transmission standard. Overall, the public seem to have been quite favourably impressed by the technical standards attained but still to have doubted whether, considered as entertainment, television had more than novelty to offer. However, receivers were not in a price range appropriate to novelties, those without sound radio costing from 85 to 105 guineas — around three months' gross pay even for white-collar workers who considered themselves quite comfortably off.

Thirty-four Eventful Months[38]
Even before the official opening of the service on 2 November 1936 it was evident that the Baird system, without a satisfactory camera for live transmission, was no match for Marconi-EMI, whose Emitron cameras were to remain in service well into the 1950s. Early in February 1937 it was announced that the 405-line standard would thenceforward be used exclusively, and that it would remain unaltered until at least the end of 1938; in retrospect this undertaking, intended to reassure potential buyers that their sets would not face early obsolescence, seems less than adequate, and early in 1938 it was announced that the standard would remain unchanged until the end of 1940.

Selling the product
The EMI sales people who three years previously had told Shoenberg that they could easily sell 5,000 receivers at £100 were soon shown to have been grossly optimistic. Although EMI cut their prices substantially in February 1937, refunding the difference to those who had already bought sets, their cheapest model still cost 60 guineas — a tenth of the price of a decent three-bedroom semi, or half that of a Morris 8 to stand outside it. The RMA's auditors reported that by 30 June 1937 total sales by all manufacturers stood at less than 1,500 — roughly one receiver for every 7,000 people living within range of the transmitter — and that sales for April to June had fallen to 347 — little more than half those for January to March. The normal seasonal decline may have been accentuated by a BBC announcement in May that for three weeks from 26 July only the demonstration film and still pictures would be radiated, to facilitate reconstruction work and to give the television staff a holiday.

The industry put much effort into making the public 'television conscious', largely through demonstrations in radio shops and department stores, but not exclusively so. Even before the opening of the service a waiting room at Waterloo station had two receivers running for the benefit of railway ticket holders,[39] and television was also on show at the Science Museum.[40] Later, an ambitious television

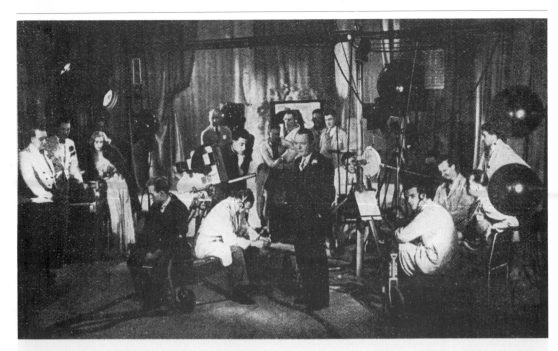

BREAKDOWN AT A.P. Artistes, producers and cameramen standing around, during a recent breakdown of the vision apparatus, patiently waiting for the " all clear." The fault, however, was not traced and the afternoon's programme was included with that for the evening. In the centre of the picture is Hyam Greenbaum, the conductor of the Television Orchestra.

From Wireless World, *11 November 1937*

exhibition staged there from June to September 1937 attracted 250,000 visitors; the public were not supposed to know whose receivers they were watching, and the author recalls seeing correspondence that referred to one manufacturer being rebuked for having a logo visible.

Television being available only in the South East, press advertising was largely confined to local papers. However, the advertising manager for HMV was able to use a national newspaper effectively by means of a simple arrangement with the *Daily Telegraph*.[41] The paper's last edition was distributed only within an area that approximated closely to Alexandra Palace's service area, so in this edition an EMI advertisement for records was replaced by one for television sets; it was never found necessary to invoke the gentlemen's agreement whereby the paper would make a refund in recognition of any enquires generated outside the service area. In April 1937 EMI issued a gramophone record for His Master's Voice dealers to use at television demonstrations.[42] Side 1, played before the demonstration, naturally stressed EMI's unique role in television but also spelt out just what television was, and how the viewer gained by being able to see as well as hear such performers as Henry Hall's dance band (who recorded for EMI and so could at this point be featured on the record). Side 2, to be played after the demonstration, reminded the audience that an HMV receiver could be obtained on hire purchase for a pound a week, before sending them on their way to the strains of Elgar. A receiver ordered from an HMV dealer was delivered direct from Hayes and installed by an EMI engineer, who aligned its vision circuits to suit the signal he found at the customer's home; bandwidth took precedence if the signal was strong, gain if it was weak.[43]

Many radio dealers, however, were not prepared to invest in

television even to the extent of installing an aerial and buying one receiver, nor did the experience of their more enterprising competitors encourage them to do so. A year after the opening of the service, Ferranti conducted a market survey in Greater London,[44] interviewing the principals of 34 retailers; these were drawn from a list of 50 who were considered, by virtue of their ability, premises, size and financial standing, to be favourably placed to handle television. Of the 34, exactly half (including Bentalls of Kingston) had not yet attempted to sell television; Sterns of Fleet Street had given up, on finding that interference was too severe to permit demonstrations. Ten of the remaining sixteen had not yet managed to sell a single set, though all had been giving demonstrations daily for many months and one had distributed 10,000 hand-bills in the neighbourhood. Only Barkers of Kensington and Selfridges had reached double figures, with sales of 25 and 50 respectively. Even with such sales, large stores did not reckon that their television departments were directly profitable, but considered that they earned their keep by attracting people in through the doors.

The Ferranti executive reporting on the survey concluded "My recommendation is that we go steady on television for some time — sit on the fence and await developments. If we take a big plunge now or even next year, we stand a chance to lose a lot of money...". The company took his advice. Tables of sales still in the company's archives show a total of three receivers as having been sold during the first 20 months of the television service, and a further 36 during the remaining 14 months of peacetime.[45] In 1939 the firm's senior television engineer approached several setmakers with proposals to supply them with cathode ray tubes, but although given some encouragement concluded "...I am afraid there will always be a tendency to buy the tube from the supplier of the valves they use and they may use offers from us merely to obtain better terms from their regular supplier".[46]

Technological progress

In the first generation of television sets, electrostatic deflection by plates within the neck of the tube was slightly more common than magnetic deflection by coils placed around it, but subsequent designs moved steadily towards magnetic deflection, and only GEC stayed with electrostatic deflection throughout the pre-war period; they showed a magnetically deflected model at the 1939 Radio Show, but it never entered production. Magnetic deflection enabled tubes to be made shorter, permitted bigger deflection angles and higher levels of beam current, and did not need a high-voltage supply for the scanning valves. But it demanded more sophisticated technology outside the tube, particularly in the design of scanning coils and line-output stages, increasing setmakers' already great dependence upon technological support from the tube and valve manufacturers.

Mullard were much less able to give such support than their main competitor, Mazda, who by the spring of 1938 were offering setmakers technical assistance in television design in exchange for exclusive contracts to supply the valves and cathode ray tubes for their television receivers. However, before Mullard were allowed to release any information it had to be checked by Eindhoven laboratories, who in turn discussed the position with the patent department, causing sufficient delay to be serious in a fast-moving field. Even worse, they

After the rejection of the 240-line system, the Baird company devoted much attention to large-screen television for cinemas. They showed this 8' x 6' picture at the Tatler Cinema in 1938

were allowed to give assistance only in approved written form, thereby preventing personal contact between supplier's and customer's engineers, essential to effective co-operation. Two of Mullard's most senior people, Eriks and Julius, wrote to Eindhoven[47] explaining the situation and seeking guidance on how to meet it, but seemingly quite resigned to it. "We realise the objections raised by Eindhoven, against a laboratory man who gets firsthand information from the Eindhoven laboratories visiting setmakers..." By this time Mullard had given a Mr Eaglesfield a budget of £1,300 a year to run a television laboratory at Mitcham, which had just begun to contribute technical information. He was therefore an obvious choice for liaison with setmakers, but Eriks and Julius conceded "...we quite understand that if we were to choose Mr Eaglesfield for this work it might involve his isolation from television information available in Eindhoven, which position is not a very satisfactory one from our own Laboratory's point of view." All they could suggest was to parallel their procedure for sound receivers by appointing a liaison engineer not in direct contact with the Eindhoven laboratory; the delay in supplying written information was simply to be accepted. For many years Mullard had managed to ensure that the Philips connection did not prevent setmakers from entrusting them with their secrets. Now, with the situation reversed, they were powerless.

At the 1937 Radiolympia Philips had, as in 1936, shown one receiver only, again entirely Dutch; it was, however, of a radically new design. The image from a 4" tube, was projected through an f/1.9 lens onto an etched glass screen 20" x 16", and to achieve sufficient brightness the tube was operated at 25kV, as against 5kV for a typical directly viewed tube. HMV also showed a projection set, although it is significant that both were removed during the course of the exhibition.[48] Philips sold some sets to the public, but by November were proposing to take them back; the tube-life was proving unacceptably low, and supplies of replacements were inadequate. This

The Philips projection set of 1937

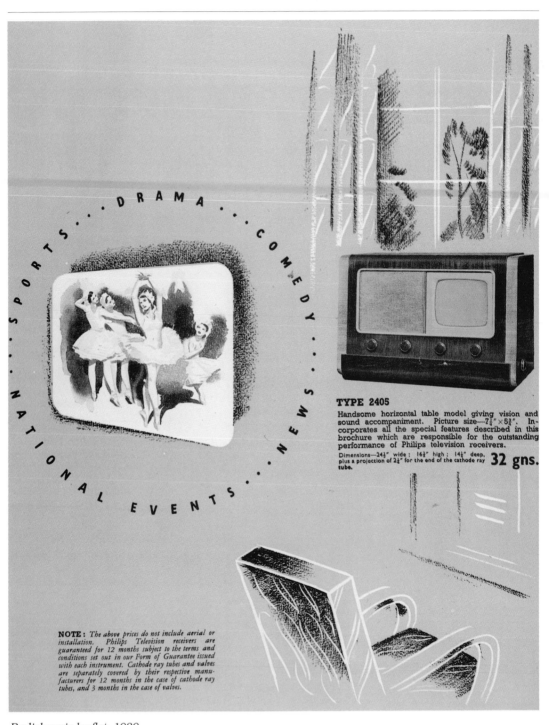

SPORTS · · · DRAMA · · · · COMEDY · · · NEWS · · · NATIONAL EVENTS · · ·

TYPE 2405

Handsome horizontal table model giving vision and sound accompaniment. Picture size—$7\frac{1}{4}'' \times 5\frac{3}{4}''$. Incorporates all the special features described in this brochure which are responsible for the outstanding performance of Philips television receivers.

Dimensions—$24\frac{1}{2}''$ wide ; $16\frac{1}{2}''$ high ; $14\frac{1}{4}''$ deep, plus a projection of $2\frac{1}{4}''$ for the end of the cathode ray tube.

32 gns.

NOTE : *The above prices do not include aerial or installation. Philips Television receivers are guaranteed for 12 months subject to the terms and conditions set out in our Form of Guarantee issued with each instrument. Cathode ray tubes and valves are separately covered by their respective manufacturers for 12 months in the case of cathode ray tubes, and 3 months in the case of valves.*

Radiolympia leaflet, 1939

On the Philips stand at Radiolympia, 1939

Assembling Ekco receivers,
Model TSC902, 1939

Arthur Askey and his family
with their Ekco television
set. The engineer who
installed it in their all-
electric flat got his assistant
to light paper in the unused
fireplace, then wandered
over the block's flat roof to
see which pot emitted
smoke. The aerial lead was
then fed down the chimney

proposal was condemned as over-hasty by the research laboratories at Eindhoven, who promised to supply tubes of improved design, and a fortnight or so later had two flown over by KLM.[49] Notwithstanding these difficulties, it was decided to proceed with a further projection model, having a slightly smaller screen, to be produced both at Eindhoven and at Mitcham. However, in February 1938 Eindhoven refused to book an order from Mitcham for six projection tubes; the explanation given — that Philips did not want to assist other setmakers before the receiver was on the market in sufficient quantities — carried the implication that Mullard were not to be trusted in such matters.[50]

In going for a large picture Philips were responding to the fact that many people introduced to television through first-generation receivers with 12" tubes found the picture disappointingly small; moreover, the projection set had a flat screen, whereas the screens of directly viewed tubes were decidedly bulbous. Nevertheless, with the high price of receivers perceived as a major reason for poor sales, there was a strong commercial pressure towards tubes less than 12" in diameter; as well as being cheaper itself, a smaller tube cheapens the receiver by requiring a lower voltage, less scanning power and a smaller cabinet. A number of manufacturers showed models with 9" tubes at the 1937 Radio Show, and GEC produced a 'vision only' model with a 7" tube for only £35, the sound signal being converted down to a medium-wave frequency and fed to the viewer's broadcast receiver. Such 'add-on' units, notably those made by Ekco, were a feature of the the 1938 show, and many of the new models had tubes of 9" or less. Prices were much lower than hitherto: a 9" Murphy console cost £30, a 5" HMV or Marconiphone table model with all-wave radio 29 guineas, a 7" Cossor 23 guineas and a 5" Pye (vision-only) 21 guineas. Lower prices were also evident at larger screen sizes: Cossor provided a 15" tube and all-wave radio for 48 guineas with their Model 1210, so named because the picture could, at a pinch, be described as 12" x 10".

Almost half the models having screens larger than 9" still used the mirror-lid technique despite its disadvantages: the surface-silvered mirror was expensive and vulnerable, specks of phosphor powder from the screen could fall onto the cathode and poison it, and tests established that the public preferred direct viewing. However, the mirror lid allowed a much slimmer cabinet than was possible with direct-viewing receivers, whose designers, like those of maternity wear, strove vainly to disguise unwelcome depth.

Commercial considerations

In December 1937 a deputation from the RMA complained to the Television Advisory Committee about the generally poor quality of the BBC's programmes. Higher expenditure had already been authorized for 1938, and during the year the range and quality of programmes improved considerably. Sunday transmissions began in April, the Outside Broadcast unit acquired more sensitive cameras, and in August a second unit was commissioned. In November, an entire play was transmitted from a West-End theatre, and by the end of the year Alexandra Palace had a second studio — the old Baird studio, completely re-equipped. Thus television became more desirable at the same time as the appearance of cheaper receivers made it more affordable, and sales at last took off. During the last quarter of 1938

Television promotion by Whiteleys of Bayswater, 1938

over 5,000 sets were sold — as against a total of less than 2,000 during the first three quarters.

Manufacturers could now begin to apply normal commercial criteria to their television operations rather than write them off as unprofitable though necessary pioneering. In February 1939 C O Stanley disclosed something of Pye's position to an executive of Ferranti,[51] then under consideration as possible suppliers of cathode ray tubes; Pye were at this time using mainly Mullard tubes. Pye had sold about 2,000 sets at an average factory price of £34, having at one time sold a 65-guinea model at the rate of 60 or 70 a week. Currently, however, sales were mainly of a 30-guinea 9" model, on which the margin on materials and labour was £7 12s (£7.60), and although he anticipated that this size and price would continue to provide his main business he would also be selling in 1940 a 5" model at £18. Stanley was of the opinion that the most successful way of trading in television and radio was to keep the manufacturing side to a minimum and to operate as far as possible wholly as an assembly plant. However, his one big fear on television was to be in the hands of the big valve-maker, and he was having a Pye-designed tube made by a small independent manufacturer. When Ferranti subsequently suggested a contract to supply Pye with, say, 12 tubes a week to establish that they could produce satisfactory ones, they were told that Pye would want around 250 per week, representing about half their total requirements.

In March 1939 Stanley convened a price-fixing meeting of setmakers[52] to prevent prices falling below their present levels, which he said were already uneconomic. Although there had been a general feeling in favour of a 5% price rise, he was able to persuade the meeting that this would be unpopular with the Government and the BBC, who were anxious to expand television, as well as with the public, and that it would be better to maintain the present prices. A list was accordingly drawn up which, however, covered only tube sizes of 9″ and above. Retail prices ranged from 28 guineas for a 9″ table model to 51 guineas for a 15″ console with radio. All prices were in guineas except that for a 9″ console, which was changed from 30 guineas to £30 at the insistence of E J Power, Managing Director of Murphy; this model was his speciality, with production running at 65 a week and expected to increase to 200, and he would not agree to increase its existing price. At a follow-up meeting, it was further agreed that dealers' discounts should be fixed, and there was provisional acceptance of the principle that any manufacturer proposing to introduce a new model between, say, 1 October and 1 June should give the RMA's secretary a certain period of notice.

COSSOR
TELEVISION CATHODE RAY TUBE

Close-of-play scores

The RMA's final score of pre-war television sales was 18,999. There are no comparable figures for individual manufacturers, but broad conclusions can be drawn from the sets surviving in museums and private collections. Small-screen EMI models with all-wave radio and Ekco vision-only 'add-on' sets seem to have been most popular, followed by Pye, EMI (12″ mirror-lid models) and Murphy, with the Cossor 1210 well ahead of any other large-screen set. Almost all the major manufacturers and a number of minor ones had television sets in their 1938/39 catalogues, giving a total of twenty marques, but Ferranti are unlikely to have been alone in achieving only negligible sales. Bush were still making sets only for sale under the Baird marque, while K-B appears in a comprehensive list published by *Television & Short-Wave World* in October 1938 but not in its successor in March 1939; the company's television operation is likely to have been a casualty of its re-formation under STC's ownership.

The 1939 Radio Show opened on 23 August and closed, a day early, on 1 September, the day on which television closed down for almost seven years; thus a whole generation of new models was exhibited but never marketed. One of some significance was designed in Pye's television laboratory, under B J Edwards.[53] It used the EF50 valve, which Mullard had initially imported from Holland, but which by the outbreak of war was under pilot production in Mitcham.[54] Designed specifically for television, the EF50 used a novel all-glass construction to allow two hitherto irreconcilable aims to be met: high mutual conductance and high input resistance at 45MHz. It enabled a stable, high-gain 45MHz amplifier to be achieved with fewer stages than hitherto, and this was compact enough to allow the entire vision unit to be built on a single chassis. The amplifier was of great and immediate value to radar, and was to contribute towards Pye's strong position in television after the war. Ironically, the contemporary Philips receivers did not use the EF50, but the EE50, which employed the phenomenon of 'secondary emission'.[55] Measured under static conditions, secondary-emission valves achieved very high gain, but could never be made to yield this in practical receiver circuits; an earlier Philips secondary-emission valve marketed by Mullard had been used, but soon superseded by a conventional valve, in the Baird receivers made by Bush in 1936.[56]

References

1   Bruce Norman, *Here's Looking at You* (BBC/RTS, London, 1984) p. 55
2   R W Burns, *British Television: The Formative Years* (Peter Peregrinus, London,1986) p. 149
3   S G Sturmey, *The Economic Development of Radio* (London, Gerald Duckworth, 1958) pp. 196–7
4   Keith Trace, *A History of the Plessey Company* (Unpublished, c.1971) p. 55
5   Ibid., p. 57
6   Burns, op. cit., p. 271
7   Norman, op.cit., p. 102
8   *Wireless World*, Vol. **39,** p. 197 (28 August 1936)
9   Burns, op. cit., pp. 257–8
10   EMI Music Archives
11   C O Browne, *Multi-channel Television*, JIEE, 1932, **70**, pp. 340–9
12   J A Lodge, *The Early Days of Television at HMV & EMI* (IEE Conference Publication 271, 1986) p. 17
13   Ibid., p. 18
14   Norman, op.cit., p. 99
15   Transcript of Shorthand Notes of Treasury Reporter, EMI Music Archives
16   Internal Memorandum, EMI Music Archives
17   G R M Garratt & A H Mumford, *The History of Television* (Proc.IEE, Vol **99**, Pt IIIa, No17, 1952), p. 41 (discussion)
18   Robert Clayton & Joan Algar, *The GEC Research Laboratories* 1919–1984 (Peter Peregrinus, London 1989) passim
19   G W Edwards, private correspondence, 1989
20   Memorandum: Ferranti Archives, Ref C8/7.8
21   Scophony file: Ferranti Archives, Ref C16/1.2
22   Television Report No 1: Ferranti Archives, Ref C8/7.8
23   A Otten (Philips Archives), letter to Gordon Bussey, 25 November 1985
24   Maurice R Bennett, private correspondence, 1989
25   *Television and Short-Wave World*, January 1937, p. 24
26   L H Bedford & O S Puckle, *A Velocity Modulation Television System*, JIEE, 1934, **75**,pp. 63–82
27   Business Document presented to Gordon Bussey by Harold J Pye
28   *Wireless World*, Vol. **39,** p. 247 (4 September 1936)
29   Burns, op. cit., p. 235
30   *Wireless World*, Vol. **39,** p. 221 (28 August 1936)
31   *Wireless World*, Vol. **39,** p. 382 (9 October 1936)
32   Thomas Singleton, *The Story of Scophony* (Royal Television Society, London, 1988) passim
33   G Wikkenhauser, Synchronization of Scophony Television Receivers, Proc.IRE, August 1939, p. 495
34   Burns, op. cit., Chapter 17, passim
35   *Wireless World*, 21 August 1936, p. 163
36   *Wireless World*, 4 September 1936, p. 271
37   *Wireless World*, 11 September 1936, p. 288
38   Burns, op. cit., Chapter 19, passim
39   *Wireless World*, 16 October 1936
40   *Wireless World*, 23 October 1936
41   Stanley Radford, private conversation, 1989
42   *The Voice* (EMI House Journal) April 1937, p. 28
43   Ivan Milliner, private conversation, 1989

44   Market survey, 1937: Ferranti Archives, Ref C8/7.8

45   Pre-war sales figures: Ferranti Archives

46   Departmental Memorandum *Cathode Ray Tubes* 1/5/39:
       Ferranti Archives, Ref C8/7.11

47   Letter Television Information for Setmakers, W O Julius & S S
       Eriks to P F S Otten, 5 March 1938: Philips Archives

48   *Television and Short-Wave World*, October 1937, p. 581

49   P.C., A Otten (Philips Archives) to Gordon Bussey, 4 July 1989

50   Philips Archives, Letter, T H P Tromp (Eindhoven) to Ir W O
       Julius (Mullard), 15 February 1938

51   Departmental Memorandum C O Stanley, Pye Ltd 27/2/39:
       Ferranti Archives, Ref C8/7.11

52   Departmental Memorandum Television from Mr Beardsall,
       10/3/39: Ferranti Archives, Ref C8/7.11

53   B J Edwards, *The Design of Television Receiving Apparatus*,
       JIEE, 1941, **88**, Pt III, pp. 191–212

54   G R M Garratt, The Mullard Story (Unpublished), Pt 5,
       pp 17–8: Mullard Archives

55   G Heller, Television Receivers, Philips Technical Review, Vol. 4,
       No. 12, December 1939, pp. 342–50

56   Bernard Rogers, private conversation, 1990

4 • *An Industry at War*

Radio as a Weapon of War

The industry that had evolved to produce competitively priced consumer goods acquitted itself with distinction when thrust into being the main provider of radar and communications equipment of crucial importance to the war effort. At the beginning of the war much of the Services' radio communication equipment was obsolete. The receiver industry possessed facilities and expertise to make a major contribution to its modernization, and by 1941 was entrusted with 98% of the development programme for aircraft radio.[1] In radar and navigational equipment, totally new both in concept and in technology, the industry's role varied widely. At one extreme a manufacturer's Chief Engineer would put an experimental unit from a Government research establishment into the back of his car and take it back to the factory to develop it into a piece of operational equipment, with the project monitored by the research establishment but the manufacturer enjoying considerable autonomy.[2] At the other, manufacturers could be mere sub-contractors working to explicit instructions, particularly if they were weak in expertise. Most companies had their share of hack work, some of it making items quite remote from radio, such as bomb racks.

It would be unfair to criticize the industry for not being ideally adapted to work much more demanding than it had known in peacetime, but some of its weaknesses, characteristic of British industry as a whole, would be of importance after the war. Compared with their German counterparts the British workforce had received less vocational training and were less well qualified.[3] A highly

Royal visit to Ultra in July 1941. E E Rosen is on the right

respected electronic engineer has recalled how, as a young man applying for a job in the pre-war industry, he was unwise enough to reveal that he knew some mathematics; he was politely shown the door, with the explanation "You see, what we want is practical people."[4] In 1941 Teddy Rosen spoke out against the low standard of training of the industry's service-men; when they entered the Forces they had to be given intensive extra training before they were able to do useful work even in their trade capacity. He warned that only by raising the ability and the status of service-men after the war would the greater demands of television servicing be met.[5] Also, the industry's productivity was low by American standards; in 1935, although Britain produced 1.9 million domestic receivers[6] her output per man hour in radio production was under a quarter of the American figure.[7]

The inevitably daunting wartime problem of matching needs to resources was compounded by the pre-war industry's lack of standardization in components. This deficiency was tackled with determination, and by March 1943 the number of types of transformer scheduled had been reduced from 1,100 to 30, and of resistors from 800 to 225.[8] But there were also inefficiencies for which the industry was in no way to blame. Urgent operational needs led to wasteful 'crash programmes' of small batches — 200 sets of a vital new equipment immediately were worth more than 1,000 in nine months' time. Finally, an arguably excessive concern with security caused production of each type of equipment to be divided amongst three or even four factories, necessitating the duplication of jigs and tools that had to be made by skilled and scarce personnel.

In one vital product, cathode ray tubes for radar, the infant television industry was the main source of relevant knowledge, and the fundamental work on tubes was mostly done in the laboratories of the manufacturers. Initially, the usefulness of the television industry's technology was rather restricted by the fact that whereas most of its recent work had been on tubes with electromagnetic deflection, the overwhelming need in radar during the early part of the war was for electrostatically deflected tubes. Thus GEC's ill-advised adherence to such tubes well after other television manufacturers had abandoned them now became an advantage, and the first development of a cathode ray tube specifically for radar was undertaken by GEC at Wembley in 1938–39, in conjunction with the Bawdsey Research Station. When electromagnetic deflection subsequently came into use, for Plan Position Indicator displays, pre-war television designs were used, and although their screens were given different phosphors little was done to improve them until the very end of the war. In consequence, Britain's post-war television tubes gained little benefit from the development work carried out here on radar tubes.[9] The situation in Germany and America was different. In 1939 Germany had already been producing television tubes with rectangular screens,[10] which would not be introduced in Britain until the early-1950s, and was somewhat ahead in magnetic deflection techniques, but was less experienced than Britain in electrostatic deflection, initially needed for radar. By the time America came into the war the emphasis in radar was on magnetic deflection, and considerable development took place there that was to be relevant to post-war television.[11]

EMI prove their patriotism

EMI were not harnessed as quickly as might have been expected, given the mass of relevant talent in their Research Department. Between 1936 and the end of 1938 Britain's entire experimental programme on airborne radar was conducted with just one receiver, operating at 45MHz, which had been taken from a first-generation EMI television set; EMI had no idea of the use to which it was being put, nor did the Government scientist using it know how it had been acquired. Towards the end of 1938 an order was placed with Cossor for half a dozen receivers, but since the EMI receiver was in constant demand it could not be spared for use as a pattern, so Cossor were given a performance specification instead. The receivers they produced were a complete failure, being insensitive and far too heavy, and were sent back; no more was heard from Cossor as potential manufacturers of airborne receivers, though they were fully loaded with receivers for other radar applications. All attempts to take the obvious course of ordering further receivers from EMI came to nought, the researchers being under some kind of restraint not to talk to the company.[12] This was probably because several senior members of the Research Department including its head, Isaac Shoenberg, were foreigners.

The first orders EMI received were for sound locators, and when they were given their first radar contract at the end of 1939 it was only to do a remedial job on existing equipment. Subsequently, however, the company was centrally involved in the development of several noted radars, including H2S; Alan Blumlein, one of Britain's greatest electronic inventors, was among those killed when a Halifax bomber crashed during flight trials of this equipment in July 1942. In addition, EMI's camera-tube department developed an infra-red image convertor, of which over 250,000 were eventually made, and the CRT team were employed both on related work and on microwave valves.[13]

C O Stanley keeps the initiative

In the spring of 1939 the scientists seeking an airborne radar receiver were guided by Professor Edward Appleton to Pye, where they found a trial batch of the 45MHz chassis using EF50 valves, which were

WS18 infantry pack set designed and manufactured by Pye

mentioned in the last chapter.[14] These were ideal for the job, and production orders were duly placed.[12]

Even making allowance for C O Stanley's tendency to embellish a story, it seems that he took a strong line with bureaucrats and brass hats. Advised to augment Pye's capacity with a large 'shadow-factory' in an industrial area, he refused. Instead, he built up a network of small village factories in the East Anglian countryside, usually in existing buildings such as church halls, and by the end of the war had a labour force of 14,000, supplying components from them. In August 1939 he refused to accept an order for an infantry set that he considered too heavy and costly, but within six weeks had two prototypes of an alternative developed. After field trials — at which he insisted that Pye engineers should be present — orders were placed for the set, and total production ran to 40,000. Pye also designed the highly successful No. 19 tank set, which was made by four companies in Britain and six in North America, and carried out the early stages of developing one of the war's most audacious devices: the 'proximity fuse'. This was a miniature radar inside an anti-aircraft shell, and to test the valve's ability to withstand the enormous accelerations encountered at firing, specimens were dropped down the lift-shaft of the University Library, Cambridge's tallest building.[15,16]

Ekco go nationwide [17]

By April 1939 Ekco, at Southend-on-Sea, had provided air-raid shelters for 3,000 people,[18] but invasion was considered at least as great a risk as air attack[19] and plans were made for dispersal. At first the pace was quite leisurely. The company paid £6,500 for an ornate nineteenth-century mansion standing in fourteen acres, just outside Malmesbury, Wiltshire, and during the 'phoney war' converted it to a small radio factory with a projected workforce of 200, though by the early summer of 1940 there were only about 60 people working there; the newcomers were not made welcome by the local gentry, who resented having their servants lured away by wages above the abysmal level they were paying. Concurrently, Ekco made preparations to take over premises for larger factories in Aylesbury, Bucks. Then came the occupation of Belgium and northern France, increasing the risk of invasion and bringing German air bases much closer to Southend. Dispersal became urgent, and the Government ordered the Ekco factory to be evacuated. Everything was stripped out except the plastics plant, whose moulding presses could not be moved, and in a remarkable exodus, accomplished in a single day, personnel and plant were transferred to Aylesbury, where the local WVS arranged for the girls to be taken to their respective billets.[19] Soon there were three factories in action at Aylesbury, with the T1154/R1155 radio equipment for bombers as the main product, and a smaller factory in Woking, Surrey. Development units designing airborne radars and infantry walkie-talkies were established behind picturesque shopfronts in Malmesbury High Street, and in the erstwhile country-house hotel near Aylesbury that also served as the company's head office. Meanwhile the deserted Southend factory had escaped bombing during the blitz of 1940–41, and the Government decided it was too valuable to be left idle. Within a year of being evacuated it was re-equipped and re-occupied. On the long benches where radios had been assembled cable forms for Lancaster bombers were made up, while the giant presses that had made bakelite cabinets now produced multiple mouldings of small articles. The company's lighting division, started just before the war in a separate building on the Southend site, had continued to operate through the evacuation period, making both lamps and microwave valves.

Not surprisingly, Ekco's management were at first unable to coordinate this complex of sites and activities, particularly in costing and other financial matters, and at one stage the company was in danger of being requisitioned and put under the management of the Ministry of Aircraft Production. Happily this was avoided. An inter-factory committee was set up with the necessary authority to achieve effective control, to such good effect that after a tour of the Aylesbury factories the Minister, Sir Stafford Cripps, referred to them as "one of the best, if not the best, units in the country producing wireless apparatus".[20] Ekco extended their operations northward with two further sites: a lamp factory at Preston, acquired in 1943, and a Government-built war factory at Rutherglen, on Clydeside, which made coils and transformers for the entire organization. Malmesbury, specializing in airborne radar, retained its country-house character despite considerable expansion, with estate-grown grapes and peaches sold in the canteen. An ex-groom taken over with the property looked after the establishment's pigs, fed from canteen waste and kept in two groups. When visitors remarked on how sleek and fat one group was, how lean and scraggy the other, it was explained that the law required half the pigs raised to be handed over to the Ministry of Food.

Making the cable-form for the pilot's panel of a Lancaster bomber at Ekco's Southend factory

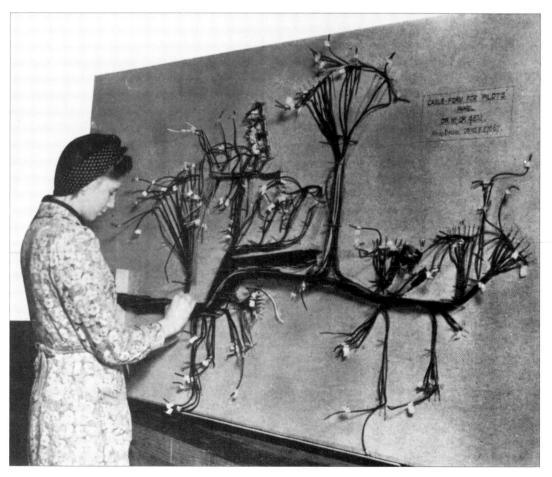

Moulding presses at Ekco's Southend factory, ranging from 10 to 1600 tons pressure

Ekco women's hostel at Malmesbury

The Green Park Hotel, a converted Rothschild mansion at Aston Clinton, near Aylesbury, became Ekco's war-time Head Office. Its Winter Garden became the clearing house for a mass of paper work

Ekco ran an officially sanctioned Pig Club at Malmesbury

GB 84 41 b c

Nur für den Dienstgebrauch

Bild Nr. F. 01093/40-082 (Lfl. 2)

Aufnahme vom 11. 10. 40

Southend on Sea

Werk für Funkgeräte „E. K. Cole"

Länge (ostw. Greenw.) · 0° 42′ 23″   Breite: 51° 33′ 17″
Mißweisung: — 9° 47′ (Mitte 1941)   Zielhöhe über NN 15 m

Maßstab etwa 1 : 12 400

Genst. 5. Abt.   August 1941

Karte 1 : 100 000
GB/E 30

500   0   500   1000 m

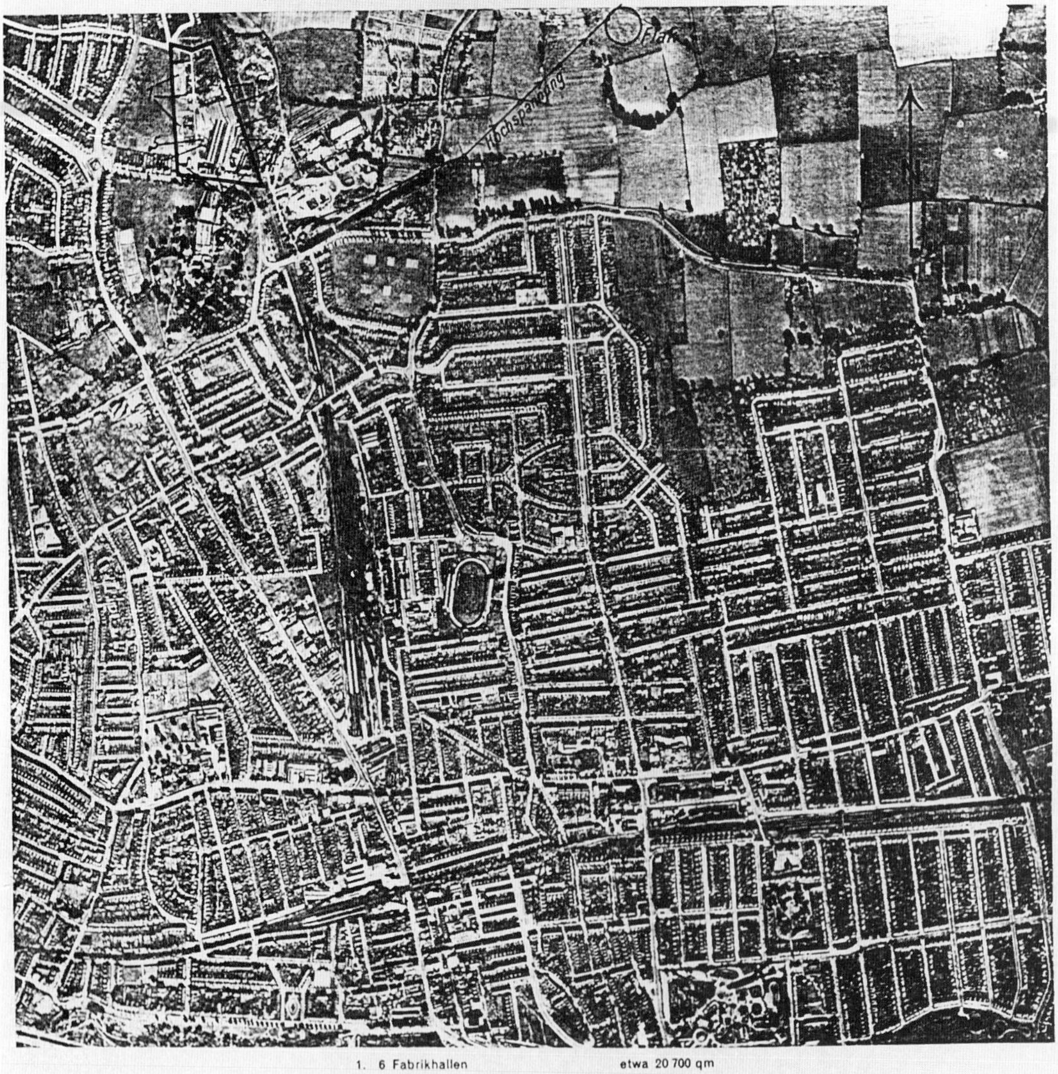

1. 6 Fabrikhallen	etwa	20 700 qm
2. Kesselhaus	etwa	200 qm
3. Verwaltungs- und Betriebsgebäude	etwa	1 800 qm
4. Lager- und Nebengebäude	etwa	1 500 qm
5. 1 Hochspannungsmast		

Bebaute Fläche etwa 24 200 qm
Gesamte Fläche etwa 62 200 qm

Gleisanschluß vorhanden

*The Luftwaffe's aerial
photograph of Ekco's
Southend works*

266

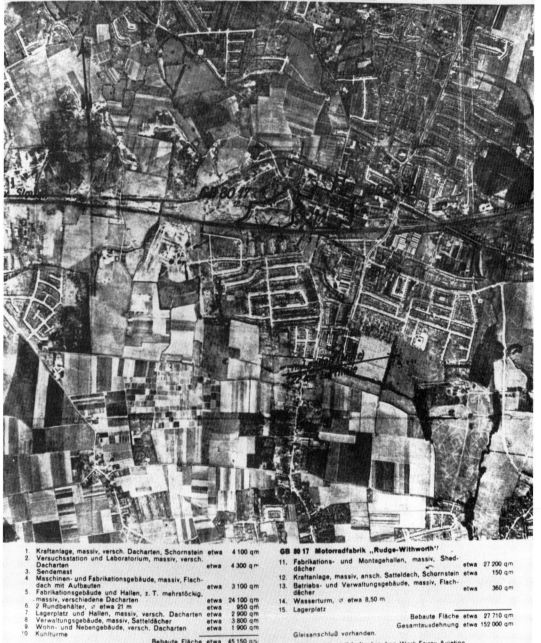

Hayes
Funkgeräte „Marconi Ltd."
mit GB 80 17 Motorradfabrik „Rudge-Withworth"

Länge (westl. Greenw.): 0° 25′ 56″ Breite: 51° 30′ 00″ (Bildmitte)
Mißweisung: — 10° 07′ (Mitte 1942) Zielhöhe über NN 30 m
Maßstab etwa 1 : 17 300

Genst. 5. Abt.   März 19..

Karte 1 : 100 000

GB/E 34

1. Kraftanlage, massiv, versch. Dacharten, Schornstein etwa 4 100 qm
2. Versuchsstation und Laboratorium, massiv, versch. Dacharten etwa 4 300 q m
3. Sendemast
4. Maschinen- und Fabrikationsgebäude, massiv, Flachdach mit Aufbauten etwa 3 100 qm
5. Fabrikationsgebäude und Hallen, z. T. mehrstöckig, massiv, verschiedene Dacharten etwa 24 100 qm
6. 2 Rundbehälter, ⌀ etwa 21 m etwa 950 qm
7. Lagerplatz und Hallen, massiv, versch. Dacharten etwa 2 900 qm
8. Verwaltungsgebäude, massiv, Satteldächer etwa 3 800 qm
9. Wohn- und Nebengebäude, versch. Dacharten etwa 1 900 qm
10. Kühltürme

Bebaute Fläche etwa 45 150 qm
Gleisanschluß vorhanden. Gesamtausdehnung etwa 79 000 qm

GB 80 17 Motorradfabrik „Rudge-Withworth"

11. Fabrikations- und Montagehallen, massiv, Sheddächer etwa 27 200 qm
12. Kraftanlage, massiv, ansch. Satteldach, Schornstein etwa 150 qm
13. Betriebs- und Verwaltungsgebäude, massiv, Flachdächer etwa 360 qm
14. Wasserturm, ⌀ etwa 8,50 m
15. Lagerplatz

Bebaute Fläche etwa 27 710 qm
Gesamtausdehnung etwa 152 000 qm

Gleisanschluß vorhanden.

GB 74 9 Verstell-Luftschrauben-Werk Fairey Aviation

The Luftwaffe's aerial photograph
of EMI's Hayes works

above: 'Cowbridge', the nucleus of
Ekco's Malmesbury factory

below: Silk mills used by Ekco to supplement the
limited storage available at 'Cowbridge'

Sir Stafford Cripps, Minister
of Aircraft Production, to
whom Ekco were
responsible

For women inexperienced in
the intricacies of wiring,
Ekco provided coloured
charts drawn by art
students

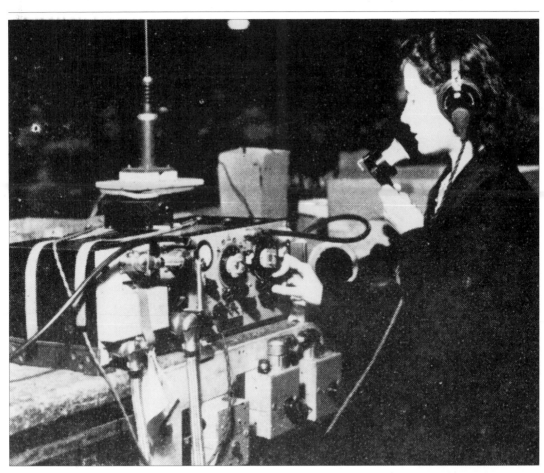

*Testing a tank set before
dispatch, at Ekco's Woking
factory*

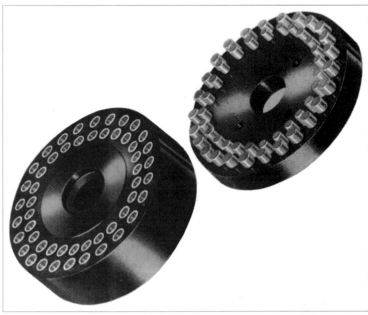

*Small precision mouldings
made on Ekco's Southend
presses*

The AI Mk VIII, an airborne interception radar developed and built by Ekco

The T1154 transmitter fitted as standard equipment in British bombers, and made by several companies, including Ekco

WS46 Walkie-talkie radio made by Ekco, in use at the Salerno beach-head, September 1943

Decca draw some winners[21]

In the 1930s Decca had been notoriously shaky financially, to the extent of having the Post Office cut off the phones and the coal merchant refuse further deliveries. When E R Lewis, a stockbroker, had bought Decca in 1928 they had been manufacturers of portable gramophones, but in 1929 he had broadened their field by adding an ailing record company, and had contrived to keep them afloat in the 1930s through a complex series of deals on both sides of the Atlantic. One of these, in 1932, was the purchase of an American record company, Brunswick, and with the company came a talented radio engineer, Harvey Schwarz, who helped Decca to establish a small presence in the field of receivers, though Lewis seems to have had little interest in radio. In 1937 Decca bought the company that made 'Embassy' records for Woolworths and 'Rex' for Marks & Spencer, and with it acquired an excellent recording engineer, Arthur Haddy; this was fortunate, for their own records were technically poor.

The war gave both Schwarz and Haddy unexpected opportunities which they exploited brilliantly, to Decca's great benefit in the post-war years. An American friend of Schwarz's, W J O'Brien, had devised a new form of radio navigation but had been unable to gain U S governmental backing. Lewis took the system under his wing and sent Schwarz over to America to develop it with O'Brien. The resulting 'Decca Navigator' made an important contribution to the success of the 1944 Normandy landings and was used world-wide after the war. Haddy was given the task of making recordings that would demonstrate the subtle differences between the sounds of British and German submarines. This demanded better techniques than currently existed, and led him to develop the recording equipment and the pick-up that would be launched after the war as 'ffrr' — full frequency-range recording.[22]

A winner from Mazda

The ubiquity of the Philips-designed EF50 valve both during and after the war, and the dramatic circumstances attending its production (see below) tend to obscure the importance of the slightly earlier valve designed and made by Mazda, which was likewise introduced for 45MHz amplification in television sets. The SP41, with a 4-volt heater, was given a 6-volt heater for military applications, and as the VR65 made a major contribution to the Battle of Britain, through its use in the R1132 VHF ground receiver; VHF radio communication between fighter aircraft and ground stations was vital to the aircrafts' deployment. The valve was also used in early airborne radar equipment and (under a different number) by the Army,[23] and was produced in great quantities at a 'shadow factory' in Baldock which in peacetime made silk stockings.[24]

Pros and cons of the Dutch connection[25]

Establishing large-scale production of the EF50 in Britain presented major problems. The valve's radically novel construction centred upon a disc-like glass base, and to produce this required both special glass and special machinery. In September 1939 Mullard still lacked the necessary equipment, information and expertise for this crucial manufacturing process, but were well stocked with imported bases, and in all other ways able to produce EF50s independently of Eindhoven, though only on a limited scale. Early in 1940

Following bomb-damage to Plessey's Ilford factory in 1940, a large factory was established in a stretch of twin tunnel built for an extension of the Central Line but not yet opened. Three stations already existed along the five-mile stretch converted, and two additional shafts were sunk and fitted with lifts. At its peak the factory employed 2,000 workers in each of the two shifts

An 18″-gauge railway was built to move personnel and materials. Allen Clark, smoking a cigar, is the second passenger from the left

Dr E A Roberts of Mullard spent three months in Eindhoven familiarizing himself with the relevant glass techniques. When Holland was invaded early in May he managed to reach the Dutch coast, and was brought back to England by a British destroyer, with detailed drawings of all the base-making machinery. Meanwhile, the Ministry of Supply needed more EF50s than Mullard's pilot-production could provide, and in March Dr Tromp, General Manager of Philips Electronic Valves, came to Britain at the Government's request and was asked for millions of EF50 parts to be sent from Eindhoven. These were shipped to England on 9 May, a matter of hours before the invasion, together with hurriedly manufactured machines necessary for large-scale production.[26] One last resource received from Holland at this unhappy time was a wooden case which had been hastily filled with industrial diamonds and brought over by Dr Anton Philips, travelling with members of the Dutch Royal Family. The diamonds were destined for Blackburn, to be used for wire-drawing dies. War or no war, they were impounded at Dover for some days, until a Board of Trade Official and an expert summoned from Blackburn had worked out the duty due on them and a banker's draft for the amount had been duly received.[27]

Cut off from Eindhoven, Mullard opened their first Research Laboratory, located at Bournemouth and headed by Bob Clarke, who had run the Technical Department at Mitcham.[28] Sadly but inevitably, the British Government's attitude to Philips Lamps Ltd changed. From being the UK arm of a valued and helpful industrial ally in a friendly neutral country, it became a company many of whose senior staff had close relatives in enemy-occupied territory, and as such it could no longer be considered totally secure. Thus when the main production of EF50s was transferred to Blackburn, in the latter part of 1940, the Mullard and Philips parts of the complex were kept strictly separate, and commissionaires were posted outside the Mullard factory with instructions to keep all Philips personnel out, though after a year or so relations became more relaxed.[29] At Mitcham, Philips' Plant Director was for a time under house arrest, being driven to and from work each day.[30] Mullard also had many Dutch staff, from Eriks downwards, but they were too vital to the war effort to be similarly treated, though they were excluded from the more secret projects,[31] and a young graduate who joined Mullard at Mitcham in 1941 found that they had not yet gone over entirely to war work.[32] As the war progressed, Blackburn overtook Mitcham both in its output of valves, with figures of 6.5 and 5 million respectively in 1944,[33] and in productivity. The plant drew its own tungsten wire, made its own metal components and its own glass, and by the end of the war claimed to be the biggest and most 'in depth' valve-making unit in the western world.[30]

Keeping the listeners going

The receiver-industry's transition from domestic to military products took some time, and as late as November 1940 Murphy were commending their stylish new 'Station Masters' to long-distance enthusiasts who could not find time to build their own sets.[34] In the early stages of the war, industry in general was urged to increase exports to the 'inexpansible maximum', to earn dollars for war supplies. *Wireless World* pointed out that although some overseas markets had been lost, in others British firms were at an advantage, since the allied blockade had eliminated competition from enemy countries,[35] and in 1940 and 1941 the receiver industry achieved annual figures of around 70,000 sets, very similar to those of the immediately pre-war period.[36] The RMA had planned to export 230,000 sets in 1941 and to produce 250,000 for the home market, which was thought to be the minimum necessary to avoid a serious reduction in listening. In the event, both targets had to be abandoned in February, when the Board of Trade cut off the supply of valves for new domestic receivers, though not for maintenance purposes. The RMA subsequently managed to negotiate some limited concessions. In so far as their commitments to the Services allowed, valve-makers would manufacture the valves needed to finish sets already 75% complete, and for the achievement of a greatly reduced export target. However, the need for exports fell in April, when 'cash and carry' gave place to 'Lend-Lease' and Britain ceased to pay America for the ever-increasing supplies of military and industrial equipment crossing the Atlantic. Indeed, it was made plain to Britain that America did not appreciate having her own exports, already diminished through supplying materials free to Britain, further prejudiced by competition from British goods using materials of the same kind. It was therefore agreed that Britain would direct its exports mainly to the Empire and would

WIRELESS WORLD

By 1944 dealers who had bought up television sets and components at the outbreak of war judged that re-opening of the service was close enough to justify advertising them

not attempt to increase them at the expense of America,[37] but in any case they rapidly diminished as the Services' demands on the industry increased, falling to fewer than 5,000 sets in 1944.[36]

As early as the summer of 1940, retailers began to fall behind with repairs, and by February 1942 it was estimated that 75% of depots were unable to keep up with demand and that 10% of the nation's radio receivers were out of use; half of these were awaiting repair and the other half short of a part not likely to be available in the near future. After prolonged negotiations the Ministry of Labour agreed that repair men over 35, though recently 'de-reserved', would be left in their jobs wherever this could be justified by their employers' work-load.[38] Even if their radios were in good condition, a third of all households were still without mains electricity and had to endure a chronic shortage of HT batteries; a Ministry of Information social survey revealed that just before Christmas 1942 one in three housewives trying to buy an HT battery failed to do so.[39] A large number of small battery-making operations sprang up to meet the shortage, mostly turning out very inferior products,[40,41] and the Government arranged for a quarter of a million HT batteries to be imported from America under Lend-Lease. Yet the established battery factories were not working to their full capacity, for batteries were predominantly a civilian requirement and did not rate highly in the allocation of manpower. The RMA pointed out to the Government that it would take at most a thousand extra operatives to make good the annual shortfall of a million HT batteries on a demand of some 10–14 million, but were told only that the Ministry of Labour would aim not to remove existing personnel where this would reduce production.[38]

One major battery plant was knocked out for the duration of the war by enemy action. On 21 April 1941 almost the whole of the Vidor-

T N Cole and his family at their home in Beverly Hills, California in 1941. Some of their names are reputed to have inspired the name Vidor. Left to right; Nigel, Cynthia, Mary, Valerie, Rebecca (Mrs Cole), Thomas, Denise, and Thomas Noah himself

Over to you - OVER!

Intensive research and experiment by scientists and technical experts in collaboration with the service departments, have resulted in important developments in design and technique. To-day the output of Osram Valves is devoted to the war effort. But Osram Valves for maintenance of existing equipments are available. Enquiries should be made at your nearest G.E.C. branch or B.V.A. wholesaler before refusing orders from your customers.

One day — perhaps soon — the progress and developments that have been made will be of the greatest interest and benefit to all. Then it will be, over to you — over !

Osram Valves
MADE IN ENGLAND

Advt. of The General Electric Co. Ltd., Magnet House, Kingsway, London, W.C.2

Burndept plant at Erith was lost in an incendiary raid; only the office block remained unscathed, and this was hurriedly converted for the manufacture of telecommunications equipment. The low priority given to battery production may account for the fact that it was not until eleven months after the raid that the company's Managing Director, R P Richardson, chose a site for a replacement factory. The Ministry of Supply had to approve the location, and insisted that it should be somewhere relatively safe from bombing. After much discussion and heart-searching Richardson decided that the place offering the best balance between present safety and future economic survival was Dundee, some 450 miles away. With a colleague, he inspected several factories, and chose one that was still operating as a jute mill. With floors on three levels it was ill-suited to a process involving long conveyors, but the necessary structural alterations were made, the 1860 steam engine that had powered the mill was moved out to provide space for a laboratory, and plant was cobbled together from bits and pieces, together with some items salvaged from Erith. The first battery came off the line on 28 October 1942, several weeks ahead of schedule, and soon the first consignment, representing six days' output, was delivered to Dundee's goods station for despatch to London. There was no southbound goods train for 48 hours, and after standing in the goods yard throughout a prolonged downpour the batteries were so much scrap.[42] In 1944 Vidor-Burndept established a factory at South Shields, on Tyneside, producing layer-type batteries for Army walkie-talkies and laying further foundations for the group's post-war prosperity.[43]

Meanwhile, the nation's receivers were inexorably ageing. About 100,000 new sets were sold in 1942 — about one for every 90 radio licences — and rather more than that number were still awaiting completion at the year's end. The idea of the industry's producing a standard 'Utility Set' to stop the rot was first raised by the BBC in June 1942, shortly before *Wireless World* independently suggested that a rudimentary two-valve 'austerity' set might meet the case.[44] With a brief to use valves and components in common production for the Services, and to make the minimum call on materials in short supply, the RMA's Equipment Technical Committee in consultation with the BBC drew up specifications for mains and battery versions, both of them superhets covering medium waves only. The design was principally due to Dr G D Reynolds of Murphy Radio,[45] but it was to some extent a joint venture, and one of the committee's members has recalled his sense of unreality at thus finding himself co-operating with people whose object hitherto had always been to drive each other out of business. The sets were to be made by several manufacturers but marketed jointly, and there was much discussion over what their prices should be.[46] At the beginning of 1943 the Board of Trade confirmed that production of the proposed receivers would be considered only after all the partially-built sets had been completed, and they did not finally go into production until July 1944. Goods sold under the name 'Utility' were exempt from Purchase Tax, so the receivers, on which this tax was to be levied, were officially designated 'Wartime Civilian Receivers'.[47] To minimize hold-ups the specifications left room for slight variations, and often it was possible to identify who had made a particular specimen not just by a code on the chassis but by its use of particular components, such as Murphy intermediate-frequency transformers.[48]

The BBC had originally asked for half a million of the sets, but in fact authorization was given for only 175,000 of the mains version and 75,000 of the battery version to be produced,[49] and it is doubtful whether demand would have justified any more. By the late summer of 1944 the war was widely believed to be nearing its end, and the *Daily Mail* published an item implying that the receivers were not a good buy, that post-war models were likely to be available soon, and that the public would be well advised to wait for them. The RMA immediately issued a press statement to counter this impression,[50] but some newspapers continued to 'write down' the receivers.[51] Whatever their merits as a buy, with 'Wartime Civilian Receiver' helpfully printed on their cartons they were an attractive steal, and after the railways had reported unduly high pilferage the Board of Trade agreed that the words should be obliterated.[52] Only two weeks before the end of the war in Europe the RMA decided to hold back the publicity about the industry's post-war reconstruction programme while it was decided whether to accept the adverse effect its release would have on sales of the uncompleted balance of the wartime-civilian-receiver programme.[53] The BBC then delivered a further blow to the receivers' prospects by announcing that certain variety programmes would be broadcast on long wave only.[54]

An attempt to relieve the shortage of receivers by importing 8,000 American sets[55] was largely unsuccessful. Adapted to work off British mains but sold without guarantee, these began to be distributed in the spring of 1944,[56] but no spares were sent and by the autumn the entire unsold stock, of some five thousand sets, was being kept for cannibalization to maintain those already in service.[52] In January 1945, there were over three thousand awaiting repair; the supply of wooden cabinets and mains-dropping 'line cords' was agreed to be entirely adequate, but still no valves had been received, while the first consignment of electrolytic capacitors had consisted of sizes not urgently required.[57]

Planning for Peacetime

It was estimated in 1944 that the radio industry had been expanded some $2\frac{1}{2}$ times for war purposes. Setmakers were aware that the transition back to peacetime production would be a difficult one, and that they would do well to take the initiative in formulating the rules under which it would take place. As early as March 1943 the RMA had decided that the interests of bona fide pre-war manufacturers would need to be protected against newcomers,[38] and by October 1944 had formulated the idea of a 'recovery period', to end on 31 March 1946, during which production of domestic receivers would be restricted to pre-war manufacturers and would be related to their pre-war share of the market; completely free trading would be re-established immediately after this date. Demand for receivers during the recovery period was estimated at 1.25 million for the home market, and the export target was set at 200,000.[58]

It was also estimated that 35,000 television receivers would be made during the recovery period, and a total of 342,000 by 31 March 1949; an official committee had recommended in 1943 that the post-war television service should retain the 405-line standard, and these estimates were based on the assumption that London's television station would re-open 9 months after the cessation of hostilities in Europe and that four provincial stations would be in service after a further 19 months.[59]

Early in 1945 the various sections of the radio industry formally inaugurated the Radio Industry Council, formed earlier in the war as a forum and as a mouthpiece for their common interests; the previous year the Radio Manufacturers' Association had been renamed the British Radio Equipment Manufacturers' Association (BREMA).[60] In February, a meeting with Board of Trade officials revealed a wide gulf between the attitudes of the industry and of Government departments. The Board of Trade officials had taken as the basis for the meeting a letter they had sent out sixteen months previously, and in consequence very little time was devoted to the resumption of civilian production. Indeed, although they expressed enthusiasm for fostering exports they thought that the question of reconstructing the industry should be deferred until the end of the Japanese war, since no major reduction of the Services' load could be anticipated until then, and that in the interim an extension of the wartime-civilian-receiver programme might be made. Understandably, the BREMA representatives opposed this attitude vigorously, and said that such a course would spell the ruin of the industry;[61] although it could not then have been foreseen that the Japanese war would end within a few months, military orders to the industry had already begun to decline. However, for a further meeting with the Board of Trade BREMA tactfully trimmed their earlier estimate of 1.25 million sets for the home market down to half-a-million, as the minimum economic figure, pointing out that expansion of exports would only be possible on the basis of a substantial home market.[62]

BREMA's forceful advocacy of the industry's interests at this period may not have been considered quite seemly by the Board of Trade, but the Government nevertheless paid the Association the compliment of entrusting it with the allocation of materials to individual companies under its own quota scheme, thereby cutting out the red tape that would have resulted from having materials doled out by the Government itself.[63] Each company's quota was based upon its audited sales during the last two years of peacetime, and 5% of the total programme was held in reserve to allow any 'hard cases' to be dealt with; it was particularly desired not to penalize companies whose pre-war sales had been reduced through early participation in military projects.

Shortly after VE day C O Stanley was at the Board of Trade, enlisting their help in tackling the industry's first post-war problem. Receiver chassis would be coming off the production line within three months, but so far there was no prospect of there being any timber for cabinets to put them in.[64]

The growth of television was not to be as spectacular as this 1945 advertisement suggests

References

1   *Wireless & Electrical Trader,* 16 August 1941, p. 73
2   R C G Williams, private conversation, 1988
3   Correlli Barnett, *Audit of War* (Macmillan, 1986) pp. 201–5
4   W S Percival, private conversation, 1989
5   *Wireless World,* July 1941, p. 171
6   Asa Briggs, *The History of Broadcasting in the United Kingdom,* Vol. **III** (Oxford University Press, 1970) pp. 67–8
7   Correlli Barnett, op. cit., p. 172
8   Ibid., p. 177
9   L C Jesty, H Moss & R Puleston, *War-time Developments in Cathode-ray Tubes for Radar, JIEE* Vol. **93** PtIIIA, pp. 149–166
10 *Television & Short-Wave World,* September 1939, p. 539
11 Bernard Rogers, private conversation, 1990
12 E G Bowen, *Radar Days* (Bristol, Adam Hilger, 1987) pp. 32–33, 76–77
13 J A Lodge (Thorn-EMI Central Research Laboratories) Phys. Technol. Vol. **18** (1987), pp. 258–68
14 B J Edwards, *The Design of Television Receiving Apparatus, JIEE,* Vol. **88** ,Pt 3 pp. 191–212
15 Publicity Brochure *The Story of Pye* (c. 1956): Gordon Bussey Collection
16 *New Scientist,* 20 July 1961, pp. 156–7
17 M J Lipman, *Memoirs of a Socialist Business Man* (Lipman Trust, c.1976) passim
18 Tom Going, private conversation, 1990
19 V P Cole, tape recording made for Tom Going, c.1987
20 Booklet *How it Changed our Lives* (E K Cole Ltd, c. 1946): Gordon Bussey Collection
21 E R Lewis, No C.I.C. (London, Universal Royalties Ltd, 1956), passim
22 John Culshaw, *Putting the Record Straight* (London, Secker & Warburg) p. 52
23 Mazda data booklet, 1972/73 edition
24 W Taylor, private conversation, 1990
25 G R M Garratt, *The Mullard Story* (Unpublished) Pt 5, passim: Mullard Archives
26 Letter, A Otten (Philips Archives) to Gordon Bussey, 4 July 1989
27 Publicity publication *PEN Souvenir Special* (Philips Electronics, 1975): Gordon Bussey Collection
28 Notes from discussions with J M Fichter, 15 July 1986: Mullard Archives
29 Transcript of interview with D Priestland, 1980: Mullard Archives
30 Bob Meens, private conversation, 1989–90
31 Transcript of interview with J D Stephenson, 1982: Mullard Archives
32 Ted Glaisher, private conversation, 1988
33 R C Winton's notes on talk with Mr Priestland on 5 July 1967: Mullard Archives
34 *Wireless World,* November 1940, p. 8 (advertisements)
35 *Wireless World,* December 1940, p. 481
36 BREMA Annual Report, 6 December 1946, p. 27: BREMA Archives
37 RMA Annual Report, 12 December 1941: BREMA Archives
38 RMA Annual Report, 5 March 1943: BREMA Archives
39 Asa Briggs, op. cit, p. 67
40 Typescript *The Story of the Ever Ready Company:* Gordon Bussey Collection
41 L W Orchard, private conversation, 1989

42   *Vidor-Burndept Magazine*, October 1953, pp. 18, 19 & 23: Gordon Bussey Collection

43   *Vidor-Burndept Magazine*, August-September 1953, pp. 4–7:Gordon Bussey Collection

44   *Wireless World*, August 1942, editorial

45   Asa Briggs, op. cit., p. 68

46   R C G Williams, private conversations, 1988 & 1990

47   *Wireless World*, August 1944, p. 228

48   Derek Dawson, private conversation, 1989

49   *Wireless World*, July 1944, p. 219

50   Minutes of RMA Council, 5 September 1944: BREMA Archives

51   Minutes of RMA Council, 11 January 1945: BREMA Archives

52   Minutes of RMA Council, 9 November 1944: BREMA Archives

53   Minutes of RMA Council, 26 April 1945: BREMA Archives

54   Minutes of RMA Council, 16 May 1945: BREMA Archives

55   *Wireless World*, December 1944, p. 367

56   *Wireless & Electrical Trader*, 25 March 1944, p. 327

57   Minutes of RMA Council, 10 January 1945: BREMA Archives

58   Minutes of RMA Council, 27 October 1944: BREMA Archives

59   Report from RMA Television Policy Committee, 9 November 1944: BREMA Archives

60   *Wireless World*, March 1945, editorial

61   Minutes of BREMA Executive Council, 2 March 1945: BREMA Archives

62   Report of 14 March 1945 BOT meeting: BREMA Archives

63   E J Power, private conversation, 1988

64   Report of Meeting at BOT, 24 May 1945: BREMA Archives

5 • *Television Takes Over*

Radio Under Rationing

Export or die

"An industry with a wartime record such as yours should turn to the tasks of peace with confidence" said the President of the Board of Trade to representatives of the radio industry in August 1945.[1] It was true that because the industry had produced vital military equipment its factories had been kept well equipped, while setmakers were particularly fortunate because they could quickly switch back to products for which there was a large pent-up demand. But just two weeks previously America had abruptly cut off Lend-Lease, and the nation's economic survival depended upon rapidly achieving a high level of exports despite a serious shortage of materials.

There had already been some agonizing within BREMA over the export target for the first year of peacetime. The original estimate had been 110,000 sets, but individual manufacturers submitted estimates totalling 500,000. This figure alerted BREMA to the risk that companies might obtain large allocations of materials for 'export' sets, then unload the sets onto the home market. The Board of Trade was warned, and after closing the loophole decided to license production of up to 400,000 sets.[2] This estimate turned out to be reasonably sound; no sets left manufacturers' warehouses for export until January 1946 but over 200,000 had done so by September, and the May–September figures corresponded to an annual rate of 390,000[3] — almost five times the best achieved before the war.

Lisle Street no great threat

Setmakers' fears that the huge stocks of surplus equipment and components would undermine full employment in the industry[4] proved largely unfounded. Some of the enthusiasts who thronged the surplus stores made television sets from bits of radar equipment, with green pictures on 5-inch tubes; others bought excellent American communications receivers at bargain prices. But few sales of domestic receivers were lost through such activities. And such were post-war shortages that setmakers were glad enough to use surplus components, from resistors and capacitors to knobs; K-B even used a flat-faced radar tube in a television set.[5] Valve-makers, however, were initially faced with considerable overcapacity, the total demand for valves in 1946 being only 45% of that for 1944.[6] The Government's huge stocks of surplus valves were disposed of gradually, by a scheme operated jointly with the BVA.[7] They were bought back by manufacturers at £5,000 per million, and those considered saleable were re-sold as new at their normal trading prices, most of the profits going to the Government. By 1954 some 27 million valves had been sold in this way,[8] and many of them found their way into domestic receivers. Two types particularly prominent were the EF50 and the SP61 (i.e. the VR65 in civilian dress), and received wisdom was that EF50s made in America by Sylvania were better than those made in the UK.[9]

A muted boom

So far as the industry's economics were concerned, the immediately post-war years were dominated by radio receivers and radiograms; as yet television had no export potential, and although the Government licensed the production of 78,000 sets in 1946,[10] fewer than 29,000 had been produced by October 1947.[11] Total production of radio receivers and radiograms for home and export markets reached the immediately pre-war rate of 1.4 million sets per annum in June 1946, but such was the shortage of materials that production continued to

From an opulent publicity booklet produced by Ultra in the late-1940s

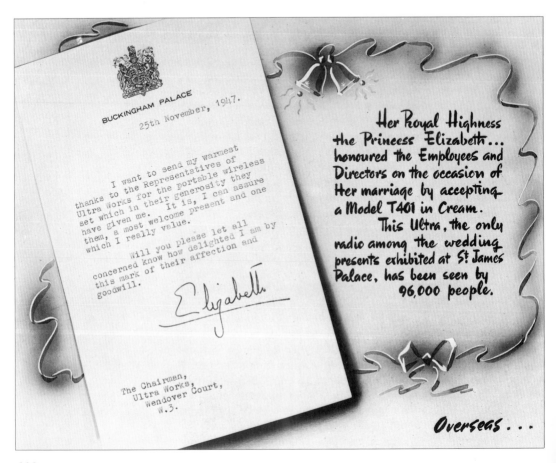

BUCKINGHAM PALACE

25th November, 1947.

I want to send my warmest thanks to the Representatives of Ultra Works for the portable wireless set which in their generosity they have given me. It is, I can assure them, a most welcome present and one which I really value.

Will you please let all concerned know how delighted I am by this mark of their affection and goodwill.

Elizabeth

The Chairman,
Ultra Works,
Wendover Court,
W.3.

Her Royal Highness the Princess Elizabeth... honoured the Employees and Directors on the occasion of Her marriage by accepting a Model T401 in Cream.
This Ultra, the only radio among the wedding presents exhibited at St James Palace, has been seen by 96,000 people.

Overseas . . .

E E Rosen with HRH The Duke of Gloucester at an exhibition, c. 1949

E E Rosen in Argentina, 1948

*Metal shop at McMichael
factory, 1947*

Radiolympia, 1947

be controlled by governmental licensing until December 1948. Demand was damped down by Purchase Tax, which fell especially heavily on radiograms because they were classified as musical instruments, and by restrictions on hire purchase, which was estimated to account for only 20–25% of total sales in 1948 compared with 70% before the war.[12]

All the major companies restarted setmaking after the war. Bush and K-B remained as purely setmaking members of groups having wider interests, but Murphy, Ultra, Ekco, EMI, and Pye took advantage of their wartime experience to maintain an involvement in non-entertainment electronics, while Cossor launched a successful radar company. Throughout the licensing period new entrants

At the British Industries Fair, 1947. Rees-Mace, pioneers in portables, made lifeboat sets during the war and in 1947 re-entered the domestic market with a wide range of products, including television sets. However, they did not survive the collapse of the seller's market in 1948

continued to be discriminated against, since the greater part of the available material was allocated by BREMA to pre-war companies in proportion to their pre-war sales. Two companies, Ferguson and Sobell, that had only been setmakers on a small scale before the war nevertheless managed to become considerable forces soon after it.

It was still possible to build up a successful business from nothing, as was demonstrated by John Street, pre-war buyer at Whiteleys of Queensway. Unfit for military service following a serious illness in 1939, Street had throughout the war held a responsible position as a temporary civil servant dealing with major radio factories, and he was not prepared to return to Whiteleys at the pay they offered. After a year or two getting nowhere, his break came when he undertook to sell off a job lot of 200 television sets on a commission of £1 a set, and succeeded in getting Currys to take all of them. The £200 enabled him to go 50/50 with a partner and set up a home-based business assembling radiograms with bought-in chassis. The coal-cellar was the office and there was no stockroom, so Street would sell in ones and twos, to independent dealers, or to Co-ops. He bought out his partner, his son joined him in the enterprise, and they acquired a shop, with a room behind and a cellar beneath. At this point, the business took off. With just four people working full-time, and a few evening part-timers, they turned out around 125 sets a week; storage space was still minimal, so components had to arrive just when required. Even when they finally moved to a small factory, they kept staff to a minimum. John Street designed his own cabinets, and conducted his own market survey before having one put into production — that is, he put the prototype in the van, parked by the kerbside in the High Street, and canvassed passers-by for their opinions. By the mid-1950s, he was producing 500–600 radiograms a week, as well as record players. He mainly supplied multiple stores, who sold the sets either under his 'Falcon' marque, or under their own brand names. Street's products had no pretensions to be other than run-of-the-mill merchandise, but they were evidently well matched to their market, for to the day he finally sold out he never had to remainder any stock.[13]

Changes inside the cabinet

To meet stringent military requirements, virtually every type of component had undergone intensive development during the war, involving a whole new armoury of plastic, ceramic and metallic raw materials. As a result, post-war components were of higher performance as well as being more rugged and compact, though their quality when measured against world standards was later to be one of the industry's major problems. One of the acknowledged weaknesses of the pre-war industry had been the multiplicity of valve types and valve bases in use. This had increased costs, both of manufacture and distribution, and had been particularly inimical to the export of receivers, making it uneconomic for overseas agents to carry a full range of spares. The war brought some rationalization, with valves for Services use produced to common specifications defined by 'CV' (common-valve) numbers and made by various manufacturers, but an attempt to standardize on the Mazda Octal base[14] for post-war domestic receivers was unsuccessful.[15] However, towards the end of the war, airborne and jungle-warfare applications created a demand for American-designed miniature valves. Plant for making them was imported,[16] and after the war setmakers moved progressively towards such valves, with fewer different types than hitherto and, latterly, a common 9-pin base.

New looks and new sounds

Notwithstanding the changes in valves and components, most of the immediately post-war sets looked and sounded very much like 1939/40 models, if less luxuriously housed, but there were one or two outstanding exceptions. Murphy's A104 of 1946 showed that they

The Decola, 1946

Ever Ready 'saucepan' radio and its battery, 1949

Romac receiver,
1946

retained their radical approach to design. A conventional table model sounds 'boxy' unless its cabinet is very rigid and padded with sound-absorbent material, so E J Power got his Designer, Dick Russell, to make a set whose chassis was mounted on the rear of a substantial baffle-board, to form a shallow table model. The set looked stylish but not outlandish, gave pleasing sound quality, and attracted much attention in the 'Britain can make it' exhibition of September 1946. Less exotic but made in great numbers over many years was the Bush DAC90, a compact AC/DC table model in a bakelite case available in several colours and with foreign-language versions of the dial for export markets.

In the summer of 1946 Decca launched an opulent record-player, the 'Decola',[17] costing over £200 and designed to do justice to their recently introduced 'ffrr' (full frequency-range recording) records, which were claimed to carry all frequencies up to 14kHz at a time when 8kHz was an optimistic upper limit for everything except television sound. Its six-watt amplifier was generously specified but unsophisticated, using PX25 output triodes dating from 1932,[18] and it had three identical 12" loudspeakers, splayed out to distribute the high frequencies over a wide angle. But there was nothing old-fashioned about Arthur Haddy's pick-up, with the sapphire stylus and its metal–rubber bonded suspension forming an integral, easily replaceable unit. There was provision for a radio tuner to be fitted as an optional extra, thereby attracting a lower rate of Purchase Tax. The author recalls attending a demonstration of the Decola. As the record changer crash-landed the pick-up on the disc, a heavy thud and a piercing hiss testified to an extended frequency range. Then Mendelssohn's 'Italian' symphony burst forth clean and bright, and we sensed that we were witnessing the birth of a new era.

For the less affluent there was Britain's first truly 'personal' portable, exploiting miniature battery valves and made by the Romac Radio Corporation, a small company in Hendon which also produced innovative car radios. The size of a small handbag, with a shoulder strap that acted as a frame aerial, the set was unusually well-styled. But the seller's market, like that of the early 1920s, fostered many unsound operations, and despite some good designs Romac was weak in discipline, skills and management. Most of the staff working on testing and alignment were of poor calibre; it took two days to diagnose a fault that arose because a component of a tenth the proper value had been fitted. When the girls assembling the handbag set were given a bonus to increase production from 50 to 60 per day, the number of repairs on production shot up from 40 to 90 a day. One of the staff was belatedly found to have been stealing handbag-radio parts for a sizeable 'cottage industry' that kept a local shop well stocked while the legitimate sets were in short supply. A later venture into television was the company's final undoing, and by 1951 it was in receivership.[19]

Of all the industry's export orders, perhaps the most unusual was the one that came Ever Ready's way in 1948 when one of their senior executives, Laurence Orchard, was visiting their South African subsidiary. He was approached by the man responsible for broadcasting in Rhodesia and Nyasaland, and asked whether his company could produce a tropicalized dry-battery set to sell for £5; this was the only way in which the great social benefits of radio could be brought to the rural population. The challenge was accepted, and a four-valve set powered by an early layer-type battery was marketed in September 1949. The problem of a cheap, durable cabinet was solved by using saucepans bought from British Aluminium and punching a hole in the bottom for the loudspeaker. The 'Saucepan Special' was sold in many parts of the world, including Malaysia, and total production ran to almost a quarter of a million.[20,21]

A brave, ingenious but forlorn venture of 1946–7 was a system known as 'ECME' (Electronic Circuit Making Equipment) for the automatic manufacture of radio receivers. It was invented by a highly versatile engineer of Hungarian descent, John Sargrove, and involved making the components integral with a moulded plastic panel, leaving only valves, electrolytic capacitors and loudspeaker to be added as plug-in elements. The panels, made with suitable grooves and depressions on both sides, were sprayed appropriately with conductive and resistive materials, then milled, to give a circuit of resistors, inductors and capacitors; the capacitors incorporated thin webs of high-dielectric material inserted during the moulding process. Production was almost entirely automatic, using a sophisticated relay control system, and the panels were electrically checked during fabrication. The maximum production rate was three panels per minute.

A two-valve AC/DC receiver suitable for the mass markets of China and India was designed, and orders for 25,000 and 20,000 respectively were received from their governments, although that from India was withdrawn following partition in 1947. A professional colour film was made showing the finished plant in operation, and the Institution of Radio and Electronic Engineers awarded Sargrove their first Clerk Maxwell Premium. However, ECME achieved only a pilot run before teething troubles, exacerbated by power cuts and material shortages, led Sargrove's financial backers to withdraw support, and his company ceased to exist; the equipment was transferred to Cossor, but never used. A major weakness of the process was its inflexibility. New tools had to be constructed for any change in product design, and the system was uncompetitive for production runs of less than 20,000.[22]

Despite its hazardous location, Ekco's Southend factory emerged undamaged from the war

A prize-winning entry in a window-display competition for Ekco dealers, 1949

Ekco tackle the Indian market, 1947

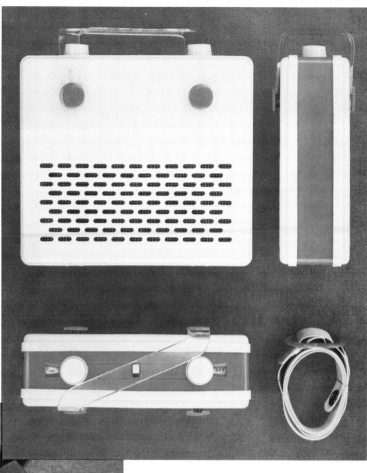

Ekco's P63 portable of 1948 typifies the compactness made possible by miniature valves and was designed by Wells Coates to exploit new plastic materials

E K Cole in 1952

*The 'second set' market
develops, 1949*

Two promising new entrants

J B Ferguson, a Canadian, founded the Ferguson Radio Corporation in
New York City in 1923 and came to Britain in the early 1930s,
establishing a small factory specializing in short-wave sets. In 1936
his company was taken over by Jules Thorn, who kept him on as Chief
Engineer until 1940, when Ferguson returned to Canada.[23] Thorn had
come to Britain from Vienna in the mid-1920s, and formed the Electric
Lamp Service Company, dealing mainly in imported electric lamps and
radio valves, before buying the Atlas Lamp Works in Edmonton in
1933. His company was re-named Thorn Electrical Industries Ltd in
1936 and went public, with a nominal capital of £150,000; the shares,
issued at a premium of 125%, were oversubscribed 36 times. The
company made net pre-tax profits of £42,000 in its first year and
continued to prosper during the war, so although Ferguson entered
the post-war scene virtually unknown as setmakers they were backed
by considerable resources.

Their rapid rise to prominence owed much to the speed with which
Jules Thorn achieved volume production when sets were still in short
supply, enabling his sales force to build up a dealer network
comparable with those of the established setmakers; there was some
truth in a colleague's jibe that they didn't have to sell, they just
allocated. Thorn's reps, too, were more in tune with the new
generation of dealers — typically two ex-service men in partnership,
one 'technical' and the other 'commercial' — than many of their rivals,
who expected the deference due to men with prestigious dealerships in
their gift. By the time the seller's market ended, Ferguson were
established as a go-ahead firm that delivered the goods.[24]

Sobell Industries Ltd evolved from a company that had employed
only about a dozen people at one point in the war, to reach a work
force of a thousand by 1950. Like Jules Thorn, Michael Sobell was a
dynamic Jewish entrepreneur from Central Europe. He had
established his first British company, Solectric Ltd, in 1934, and from
1937 had made 'Sparton' radio receivers at a small factory in
Wembley. After this was damaged by enemy action in 1940 he moved
to Amersham, and in 1941 transferred his personnel to a new
company, R.F. Equipment Ltd, which undertook contracts for the
Admiralty and the Ministry of Aircraft Production, and by 1943
employed about 180 people. He was unusually quick to get back into
civilian production, for by December 1945 his Sales Manager was
answering queries for a six-valve all-wave receiver, Model 615,
following a write-up in *The Trader*. Notwithstanding the timber
shortage, its cabinet was "in modern style of highly polished walnut
veneer with a three-quarter front panel of birdseye maple or
sycamore".

However, as a non-member of BREMA Sobell found it difficult to
gain access to the normal channels of distribution; he had
unsuccessfully tried to join the RMA in 1941, and altogether made six
applications before finally being elected to BREMA in March 1950.[25] He
therefore distributed his sets through the Great Universal Stores chain
of about 1,000 furniture shops; radiograms were after all as much
furniture as electronic instruments. Since the shops had no servicing
facilities Sobell established 'Home Maintenance', which had a fleet of
over 100 fully equipped vans and guaranteed to provide service within
48 hours of receiving a telegram from the customer.[26] As an added
attraction he gave two years' all-in free maintenance. Unfortunately

these arrangements led to his being boycotted by radio retailers well into the 1950s. They also became uneconomic; people demanded service for trivial faults,[27] and the service element in the price of the goods incurred purchase tax.

Shortly after the war Sobell had taken over a Government 'shadow factory' at Hirwaun, near Aberdare in South Wales. This was a well-judged move, for manufacturers in development areas qualified for a special allocation of materials,[28] which in Sobell's case largely consisted of valves;[26] moreover, wage levels were lower than elsewhere. However, Sobell found it difficult to get engineers to work in the area, until the lady responsible for personnel went to a resettlement camp for Poles, correctly surmising that South Wales would be no more foreign to them than any other part of Britain, and recruited a number of good Polish engineers. These were later followed by several Czechs, one of whom, Kurt Vesely, was to become the company's Chief Engineer and remain so through the mergers of the 1950s and 60s. But in 1949 he was an unknown refugee from communism, speaking poor English, and was glad enough to be engaged as a humble 'bench engineer' though he had held more senior positions in Prague both before and after the war. Initially put onto radio receivers, he found that the company's current model betrayed an alarming unfamiliarity with contemporary practice, and "looked as if it had been designed out of a physics text book."[27]

Bush head west
In 1945 Bush's links with the film industry took them into J Arthur Rank's empire. With the same enthusiasm for new ventures that had caused his ardent Methodism to involve him in films, Rank would appear unannounced at Chiswick, pull up a stool in the lab, and

From the booklet commemorating the opening of the Bush factory at Ernesettle, Plymouth, in June 1949. Note the parallel drawn between the Mayflower, and ships in the form of the Bush logo

VIPs tour the Ernesettle
factory after the opening
ceremony. From left to right:
Mr G Darnley-Smith
(Managing Director, Bush
Radio), Sir Robert Watson-
Watt, J Arthur Rank (later
Lord Rank) & John Davis
(later Sir John Davis)

Then . . .

1932

and now

1959

*From a Bush company-
dinner menu, 1959*

discuss the development of a new radio chassis with the Chief Engineer. To meet the company's rapid expansion extra space was leased in a cinema and a skating rink, both war-damaged. It was then decided that the shortage of labour would best be met by establishing a satellite plant away from London, though it was not envisaged that the site finally chosen would be 200 miles away.[29] With the encouragement of the Board of Trade, a 12-acre site was acquired at Ernesettle, on the outskirts of Plymouth, and a handsome new factory was opened in June 1949. Initially only radios were assembled there and the factory was only 40,000 sq ft. However, television production soon followed, the factory's own test gear providing a local signal of broadcast quality before television reached Plymouth,[29] and over the years the area was increased tenfold. Gilbert Darnley-Smith, Bush's Chairman and Managing Director, who had built up the company from very small beginnings, became one of the industry's most popular and respected figures. During the 1940s and 50s he served long spells as Chairman of the Radio Industry Council, and as one of the industry's two representatives on the Television Advisory Committee.

The 'contemporary' look

The Festival of Britain in 1951 shifted public taste towards a lighter and more functional style of furniture. Pye had already commissioned their first work from an up-and-coming young industrial designer, Robin Day, but not all of the company's management approved of the idea, and Day has recalled that it took some time to wean them off the high-gloss finishes, radiused corners and gilt trims that were then general. In his first designs he contented himself with achieving a broad over-all geometry, but soon established an accepted house-

The following four photographs illustrate some of the Pye products commissioned from the industrial designer Robin Day:

Radio receiver PE60, 1952. The influence of this design may be seen in the V4 television set

Television receiver CS17, 1957

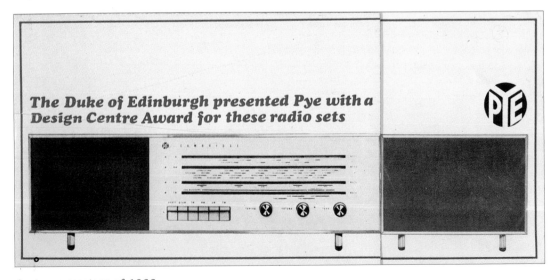

A stereo receiver of 1966,
with one integral and one
separate loudspeaker

A MASTERPIECE, EXCLUSIVELY DESIGNED
FOR PYE BY ROBIN DAY

A stereogram of 1966

style, and continued to design for Pye for the rest of the company's autonomous existence, winning awards along the way, and inspiring Pye's own designers to produce cabinets in the same tradition.[30]

Television Lifts off Slowly

On 7 June 1946 pre-war announcer Jasmine Bligh stepped before the camera and re-opened the London Television Service service by asking "Remember me?". This was more than just an effective piece of theatre, for no new sets were yet in the shops and her audience consisted of such pre-war viewers as had re-commissioned their sets. BREMA had encouraged manufacturers to contact original owners wherever possible, but the more sets they had sold the longer this took, and some components were in short supply.[28]

Pye take the lead

As C O Stanley had prophesied a year earlier, it was lack of timber for cabinets that was preventing the completion of new sets, and that now prompted him to remark "the industry has not yet got used to building houses without bricks."[31] But before the end of 1946 Pye were on the market with their first post-war set, the modestly priced but widely acclaimed B16T 9" table model; in a four-and-a-half-page test report, *Wireless World* pronounced it "very considerably superior to comparable pre-war models." Its success largely arose from its strip of radio-frequency stages using EF50 valves, which was based on Pye's 1939 design but also embodied the experience acquired in making such strips as intermediate-frequency amplifiers for radar receivers.

The B16T gave Pye some claim to be in the lead technologically. Within two years another 9" model, the B18T, put that claim beyond doubt.[23] Hitherto, the 'EHT' (extra-high tension) voltage for the cathode ray tube had been obtained from a special, and often unreliable, winding on a mains transformer that also powered fifteen or twenty valves. The transformer's strong magnetic field made its location relative to the picture tube critical,[32] while its bulk and weight made carrying even a table model a two-man job. Now, in the B18T, Pye had a 'transformerless' receiver weighing only 30lb[33] and small enough to be carried under one arm.[34] The key to this dramatic advance was a technique for generating the picture tube's EHT voltage that had first been used in the 'standard' receiver jointly designed by the five German television manufacturers in 1939 (and that had been mentioned, albeit briefly and confusingly, in a British technical magazine).[35] A Pye engineer, Dr Lax, had been with Telefunken before the war, and although he had not himself worked on the technique he remembered its principle[27] and proceeded to develop it into a practical circuit.[36] Instead of the EHT winding being on a mains transformer it was on the transformer driving the horizontal-scanning coils, and made use of the high pulse of voltage produced during the rapid flyback at the end of each scanning line; the fact that the circuit operated at a frequency 200 times higher than the mains also removed the need for a large smoothing capacitor.

Crucial though 'line-flyback EHT' was, it did not of itself enable the designers of the B18T to get rid of the mains transformer; to do that, they also had to connect the valves' heaters in series, which brought its own crop of problems. Later, virtually all television valves would be specifically designed for series operation, but at this period such valves were mixed with other types, such as the EF50, that were not designed for it but that tolerated it when they were so positioned in the chain of heaters that the heater-cathode voltage was not excessive. Heaters have a low resistance when cold, and in order to prevent a damaging surge of current when the set was first switched on they were connected in series with a thermistor — a device whose resistance was high when cold but fell to a low value as it warmed up. At that time, however, the thermistor itself was unreliable when exposed to virtually the full mains voltage at switch-on, so it in turn had to be protected, by a normal resistor shunted across it.

Pye paid a specific penalty for being first with a transformerless set, because initially the Mullard rectifier valve used was very unreliable, although designed for series-heater operation. The valve was later improved, but not before a lot of B18T sets had been sold. Although the same valve was used in the first Bush transformerless model, the TV12, a smaller proportion of the sets contained the unimproved valve, and this model and its successors won for Bush a reputation for extreme reliability. Indeed, they were reputed to be the only sets that a wise dealer would risk unpacking in the customer's home.[9,37] The TV12 and one of its successors, the TV22, used the same bakelite cabinet, so shaped that the 9" tube had a protruberant, cyclops-like appearance, and these two models have become the television sets most widely used by the media to evoke the post-war period.

Ferguson for fringe areas

Ferguson had already marketed two designs that used a high frequency to produce the EHT voltage but instead of the line-scanning circuit used a separate 80kHz oscillator. This had produced patterning on the picture until extra smoothing was introduced, and the technique proved so expensive that Jules Thorn ruefully remarked to one of the designers, Dickie Norman, "D'you know, Dick, I'm putting a £10 note in every one these receivers." But once the Pye B18T came out, every manufacturer was under intense pressure to follow suit with a similar design, which they were able to do thanks to an industry-wide patent pool.[38] Ferguson met the challenge of the B18T by producing a cheaper, less-sensitive model for use in areas of strong signal and, for viewers living in 'fringe areas', a more expensive high-sensitivity model. The noisy signal received in these areas gave the picture a trembling jaggedness that was much more objectionable than its 'snowstorm' appearance, and to combat this, Ferguson introduced a 'flywheel' line-synchronization circuit.

The flywheel consisted of a line-scanning oscillator whose frequency was voltage-controlled. Its waveform was compared with the synchronizing pulses, and mistiming between them was arranged to build up a voltage that corrected the scanning frequency and locked the two into synchronism; the correcting voltage built up gradually enough for the random mistimings of the noisy synchronizing pulses to average out and thus have no effect. The improvement was dramatic, and a valuable selling point. But unfortunately the arrangement depended upon there being no systematic mistiming of the transmitted pulses, and although by the late-1940s this was true of studio transmissions the pulse generators used on outside broadcasts suffered from 'hum'. This did not affect conventionally synchronized receivers but caused flywheel sets to bend some parts of the picture sideways; on one occasion guardsmen marching across the screen appeared to do so in a sitting position, like badly operated puppets. Ferguson were slow to appreciate the problem since it did not affect the test card, against which they judged their receivers. After a desperate argument with the BBC, and the intervention of BREMA's Technical Committee, the offending pulse generators were modified.[23] Over the years flywheel circuits became more general, and now provide part of the synchronization in virtually all receivers.

Olympia 1947. K-B were to continue to exploit their Cunard connection right through the 1950s

An advertisement of 1948

306

GEC 9" television and radio receiver, 1947. The chassis has been designed to permit a distinctive, symmetrical cabinet. The loudspeaker is behind one set of louvres, and the other is hinged to give access to the numerous preset controls it was necessary to provide in receivers at this period

An advertisement of 1950.
EMI continued to make
luxury receivers like this,
but their credibility was
undermined by the poor
reputation of the HMV 1807

SYMPTOM.	RECOMMENDED ACTION.
Instability.	Usually due to o/c ceramic condenser on R.F. unit which occurs as Model warms up. One method of tracing is to warm up chassis (with screen removed), by switching on and putting a duster over it. Wait until instability occurs, and then blow through a piece of sleeving on to each condenser in turn until it becomes stable again. The last one is the condenser to change.
Frame crushing at top or bottom.	Usually due to unsuitable Frame Output Valve KT33C. Improvement can often be made in Model 1807 by reduction in value of R38. to about 6k. Try connecting a 47k $\frac{1}{2}$w. resistance in parallel.
Microphony.	Usually unsuitable V1. Cure by interchanging similar valves in T.R.F. strip.
Blowing of Fuses.	No one cause is apparent. The trouble may be due to screen/suppressor, S/C on Z77 valves when switching on, and in some cases the smoothing condenser may also be suspected. The fuse rating is being changed to 1.5A silver type, but in difficult cases 2 A silver wire type fuses may be fitted, provided that this is noted for future reference.
Blurred Picture.	Can in some cases be due to secondary emission from the C.R.T. producing a faint unmodulated raster usually off centre and not controllable in brightness
Poor Line Synchronisation.	Usually due to unsuitable B36 valve.
Poor Framehold.	Framehold may need adjusting during the first 20 minutes after which it should remain reasonably stable. If further trouble is experienced, check R26 (R32 in 1807A) which may change value with heat. Replace by 1 watt .68 M.
Hum.	This may be due to vision on sound, in which case the fault can be cured as stated under that heading. Another cause is excessive input, in which case correct attenuation should be inserted in the aerial circuit.

-2-

Some troublesome sets

For several years line-flyback EHT was pressing against the limits of contemporary technology, and was a common cause of breakdowns. For one model of around 1950 Philips had to make three times as many line-output transformers as sets, each set requiring, on average, two replacements.[39] But such troubles are common when developing a new product, and no doubt similar tales could be told of the other major manufacturers. The public accepted that television was an exacting technology, and adjusted their expectations accordingly. On the whole they were well pleased with what the industry provided, and truly disastrous receivers like the first transformerless set produced by K-B were rare.[23] It used 'Brimar' valves, both companies being part of STC, and the first Brimar valves made for series-heater operation

The unreliability of the HMV 1807 television receiver is evident from this page of the Supplementary Information Sheet it was necessary to issue in 1950

Radiolympia, 1949

had inadequate heater-cathode insulation;[40] when a valve in the receiver failed from this cause, it often took two or three others with it.

But the most notorious set of the period came from EMI (of all companies). They had set out to design a receiver around a secondary-emission pentode claimed by its admirers to be a technological breakthrough. Unfortunately they had no more success with this type of valve than Bush and Philips had done a decade previously, and the receiver never reached the market. However, it caused the company to start from behind in the race to produce a low-priced set to compete with the Pye B18T.[41] Since it was thought essential to maintain the quality of cabinet associated with the HMV marque, the chassis had to be particularly economical, with only 14 valves. The closely spaced miniature valves in the vision strip ran very hot, causing tuned circuits to drift and produce interference between vision and sound,[42] and one of the valve-types used had particularly untrustworthy heater-cathode insulation.[43] Focus was controlled by changing the EHT voltage, which proved unsatisfactory, while the 10-inch 'Emiscope' picture tube was a redesigned radar tube[44] of indifferent quality and short life, whose sepia phosphor looked tired alongside the bluish hue of Mullard and Mazda tubes.[45] Finally, the set contained many components of EMI's own manufacture, some of which were of poor quality; EMI's devotion to vertical integration was extreme, reputedly extending to making the brass polish for the buildings' door handles. Designated Model 1807, the receiver was launched early in 1949; as a low-priced HMV model it attracted some attention,[46] thereby maximizing the damage done to EMI's reputation by its unreliability and poor performance.

Building a television set was too daunting for home-construction ever to approach the popularity it had enjoyed with radio in the 1920s. Nevertheless kits were sold, using ex-government components, that made the job easier than adapting surplus radar equipment. This is the front cover of the instruction booklet of such a kit, dating from 1949

- TELEVISION -

BUILD IT

YOURSELF

THE

PREMIER

WAY

2/6

After five weeks of using this van to demonstrate television in the prospective customer's home, Francis Radio delightedly reported that eleven out of twelve visits had produced sales

A kit of 1950 used commercial components and yielded a set more comparable to one built in a factory

The poor coordination revealed by the episode was one aspect of EMI's generally unhappy 'culture' at this period. Before the war, the close proximity of the various departments had led to fruitful cross-fertilization. Now, under Sir Ernest Fisk, they were split into separate companies. Radio and television receivers were designed by EMI Engineering Development Ltd, and although this company and EMI Research Laboratories Ltd occupied adjoining wings of the same building, staff were not allowed to enter each others' premises and the interconnecting doors were kept locked; anyone wishing to break this rule contrived a visit to the library, which was accessible from both wings.[41]

The Years of Expansion

The post-war shortage of resources affected the BBC's plans to extend the television service, and it was not until December 1949 that the first regional transmitter, Sutton Coldfield, was opened, bringing television to the Midlands and boosting production and sales figures during the last quarter of the year to over six times those of the first quarter.[47] Hitherto most television receivers had been 'straight', with vision and sound circuits permanently tuned to Alexandra Palace. Some manufacturers continued to produce straight sets, in alternative 'London' and 'Birmingham' versions, but the tendency was towards superhets, which enabled a common chassis to be used for any of the BBC network's five channels with only minor variations; the first receiver that the user himself could tune to the required channel was the Bush TV22, of 1950. By 1953 the BBC's five main transmitters were all operating and the year's sales, boosted by the Coronation, exceeded a million for the first time, outstripping radios and

radiograms combined.[48] With only about three million sets in use the market was far from saturated, and in 1955 was further stimulated by the advent of commercial television, and of a new generation of sets designed to receive both programmes.

Test table for cathode ray tubes at GEC's Research Laboratories in 1950. The company continued to market picture tubes until 1959

Into Band III

This was television broadcasting's biggest technical change since 1936. The commercial network was to be transmitted on 'Band III' (174–216MHz), and engineers had to learn how to design switchable tuners for these frequencies, which demanded a more advanced input stage than did 'Band I' (41–68MHz), carrying the BBC channels. They were hampered by the tardiness with which technical aspects of the new transmissions were defined, for the Independent Television Authority (ITA), responsible for the transmitters, could not be set up until the Television Act became law in July 1954, only 14 months before the service opened, and as late as April 1955 only two of the eight channels in Band III had been allocated for the immediate use of television.[48] In December 1953 it was already almost certain that commercial television was going to come, but manufacturers did not yet have their new models ready, though many had begun to produce 'adaptable' models; frequently this meant little more than that there was a hole in the cabinet for the shaft of the Band I/Band III tuner that would later become available for retro-fitting.[49] This situation carried the danger that normal competitiveness would tempt manufacturers into making rash claims, or even into rushing onto the market with insufficiently developed tunable models, and BREMA's members reached an agreement that would give them a breathing space. Until 1 May 1954 they would refrain from mentioning tunability or adaptability in any public advertising of their sets, and would encourage dealers to do the same. No restriction was actually imposed on introducing new models, but manufacturers would hardly be likely to do this while unable to advertise them.[50]

One major manufacturer was not covered by the agreement.

Each year the Pye Annual report gave C O Stanley an opportunity to air his forthright views on Government policy as it impinged upon his business

"...the giant of private enterprise, having at last shaken one leg free, raises its virile frame from the shackles of the midget planners that have fettered industrial endeavour during the last five years." 1950

Here Stanley attacks the manner in which profits from overseas operations are taxed. 1955

In the course of the attack against disincentives to export, Stanley takes a sideswipe at some of his competitors. 1956

'Socialist Soup': a diatribe against Luncheon Vouchers, which are likened to 'truck' payment. As an industrialist providing canteens for his workers, Stanley objected to the fact that those who instead provided Luncheon Vouchers could charge them against business expenses. 1955

Past the grave of the middle classes, exterminated by taxation, "a beautifully uniform and standardised population of hewers of wood and drawers of water, devoid of initiative," march towards destruction. 1956

Rejoicing over the success of commercial television, for which Stanley had vigorously campaigned. 1957

The National Radio Show,
Earls Court, 1954

The production line for the Pye
VT4 receiver, Christmas 1954

Pye television receiver
V4, 1953

AUTOMATIC
PICTURE CONTROL
TV

*A graphic depiction of how the V4 held
the picture at a constant black level*

C O Stanley had long been a forceful advocate of commercial television,[51] and when BREMA's Chairman expressed an 'anti-commercial' viewpoint at a meeting in July 1953 Stanley stalked out and then tendered Pye's resignation.[52,53] Six weeks before BREMA drew up its 'no-advertising' agreement, a member of Pye's Sales Department sportingly warned the Association that they were fixing a date on which to introduce sets able to receive both programmes,[54] and in March 1954, ahead of the competition, Pye duly launched the VT4, which was a tunable version of the previous year's V4. Both were compact and stylish 14" sets boasting a sophisticated automatic gain control circuit that maintained the correct black level whether the picture was of high or low average brightness. They fully maintained Pye's reputation for excellence, though the heavy demand for the VT4 outran Mullards' ability to supply cathode ray tubes and some sets were fitted with inferior tubes made by a Pye subsidiary, 'Cathodeon'; dealers tended to get sets with Mullard or Cathodeon tubes according to whether they were perceived by Pye as up-market or down-market.[37]

Pye on the rack
And then, in February 1955, Pye put out what C O Stanley described as "a really shocking bad television set". This occasioned a trauma so great that almost four years later he declared it to be only recently healed, when he assembled selected senior staff and made his first disclosure of it; a recording of his address has survived.[55] He was careful not to blame his engineers, saying that it could have happened

Views of Oulton Works,
Lowestoft, in 1960. Pye
opened the plant in 1951
and progressively
transferred all television
manufacture to it

C O Stanley (with hands
clasped in front of him)
visits the Lowestoft factory
in about 1964

to anyone, but thought it had been unwise to have had specialists for
the various areas of technology, causing any error to affect the
company's whole range of models, instead of making an individual
responsible for each model. But he said nothing of what had actually
been wrong with the sets, and from the accounts of others it is clear
that weaknesses were more widespread than he implied, and that they
embraced both design and quality-control.[37,56,57]

Model V14 and its variants had a line oscillator which, with many
specimens of the Mullard PCF80 valve employed, drifted out of the
range of the horizontal-hold control. The set contained numerous
small capacitors made by a well-known British supplier, Hunts, which

drifted in value and went open-circuit, and there were problems with electrolytic capacitors supplied by Plessey. Even the valve-holders were unsatisfactory. But dealers were slow to feed back alarm signals, and the company, at that time on top of the world, was slow to react to them, so production continued for many months before the full enormity of the problem sank in. Stanley then demanded to see all letters of complaint, and for a period saw 200 a day. A major damage-limitation exercise was mounted, with sets brought in for replacement of faulty components, and specially selected PCF80 valves supplied by Mullard, while a consumer-relations team churned out emollient letters to irate customers. So as not to undermine the confidence of the company's dealers or of its bankers, all this had to be done quietly, and without making any damaging admissions. Some dealers nevertheless gave up their dealerships, and though Pye's fortunes recovered they never regained their technological leadership.

The five-year loss-leader

In November 1955 S S Eriks of Mullard attended a Monopolies Commission hearing and showed the Chairman two of the company's picture tubes: a 9" circular one that they had sold in 1949 for £6 at a loss, and a 17" rectangular one that they were currently selling for £5 at a profit.[58] He had good reason to be proud of this contrast. Having worried during the war over how the greatly expanded company was to be sustained when the military orders ceased,[59] he had decided that television could provide the solution once it reached a sufficient scale. But current techniques for manufacturing cathode ray tubes put a brake on expansion; in 1947 the industry's output of television sets was being limited by the shortage of skilled glass-blowers.[60] Eriks made an all-out drive for mechanization and mass production, and persuaded Pilkington to undertake large-scale manufacture of the pressed glass parts that superseded blown bulbs.[59] When Mullard first went over to pressed glass, four skilled glass-workers joining screens and bulbs together by conventional techniques achieved a combined output of only fifteen units an hour; by 1950 an automatic machine developed and installed at Mitcham enabled four semi-skilled operators to produce sixty.[61] Mullard's achievement was the more remarkable in that they had no recent experience of tube manufacture, having been excluded from radar tube work during the war, nor did they receive much assistance from Eindhoven for a number of years; indeed, on several aspects of tube design they successfully opposed the parent company.[63,64]

For a time, Eriks deliberately sold tubes to setmakers below cost in order to encourage a rapid increase in receiver sales. However, Mullard's costs were not in fact known accurately, and he later admitted that they had not expected the losses to be quite as big as they were; they lost £81,000 on the 22,000 tubes made in 1947–48 and £140,000 on the 50,000 in 1948–49. Happily, the increasing sales of television receivers increased Mullard's profit from valves, which in 1949–50 balanced out the loss on tubes, and in 1951 tubes moved into profit. As Eriks wryly remarked to the Monopolies Commission "if television had not bloomed in the way it did, you would not find me sitting here any more because my decisions would have been wrong and Messrs Philips would have dispensed with my services."[65,66] As production expanded beyond Mitcham's capacity, glass-joining work was undertaken at the Blackburn plant, conveniently close to

Pilkington at St Helens, and in 1955 Mullard opened a custom-built factory for cathode ray tubes at Simonstone, which was near Blackburn and attracted financial aid from the Government through being in the East Lancashire Development Area.

Problems at Brimsdown

The Monopolies Commission noted in its report that Mullard did a much lower proportion of the maintenance trade than they did of the trade with setmakers, and since different manufacturers' tubes were not interchangeable this implied that their tubes had a longer life.[63] Their tubes certainly lasted longer than those of their principal competitor, Ediswan Mazda, who went through a bad patch in the early 1950s; it has even been asserted that the short life of Mazda tubes at this period contributed to the growing popularity of rental.[9] If the tube's heater was run at its normal voltage, emission soon fell because of 'cathode poisoning'; any increase in voltage caused a heater-cathode short-circuit,[67] and some service engineers fitted an isolating transformer to prevent this.[5] To meet the growing demand for tubes, the Brimsdown factory had gone over from 'bench-pumping', in which tubes were pumped, baked and sealed at fixed locations, to the 'in-line exhaust' technique in which tubes and their pumps travel continuously through a large oven whose various zones provide the required time/temperature cycle. Soon, however, 192 bench-pumping stations were installed at the nearby Ponders End factory. An engineer at Ponders End, whose own work on transmitting valves was disrupted by this installation, asserts that it was necessitated by severe problems with the new Brimsdown plant, and that the short life of Brimsdown's tubes was traced to a reduction of the baking time, made to increase throughput.[68] However, an engineer closely involved with the Brimsdown plant recalls that it suffered no more problems than any other new plant, and that Ponders End was brought in simply to provide additional production.[69] What is certain is that before tube manufacture was transferred to a large new plant at Sunderland in 1955, Ponders End won the accolade of pumping tubes for Mullard under contract.

The BVA loses its teeth

The primary reason for Eriks' appearance before the Monopolies Commission was that the BVA was currently under investigation, although in fact its members practised price-fixing only in their retail trade, which accounted for only 10% of their business. However, Mullard were also monopolists in their own right, since controlling over 30% of any business was deemed to constitute a monopoly, and their figures were 75% for valves and 65% for cathode ray tubes. The Commission's report was favourably inclined towards Mullard, for though their profits were high their prices were low, where they were not fixed by the BVA, while their low costs reflected their efficiency. Before the report was published, early in 1957, the Restrictive Trade Practices Act had been passed, and the BVA had already modified many of its practices to meet the Act's requirements. By the time it finally appeared before the Restrictive Practices Court in 1959, the BVA had also abandoned the 'exclusivity ' clauses confining distributors to its members' products, thereby finally emasculating itself but ensuring a clean bill of health. Individual members, however, remained largely free to make their own restrictive arrangements.[70]

Ultra looking in good shape

Before the war, Ultra's cabinets had been a weak point. Soon after it Teddy Rosen sent one of his staff on an Industrial Design course so that he could engage on more equal terms with the consultants engaged to improve the products' aesthetic appeal,[71] and in time Ultra acquired a slightly avant-garde image.[24] Rosen also secured a high standard of engineering; one of his hobby horses, at a time when television sets got very hot and were correspondingly unstable in operation, was that a receiver ought to require no adjustment during a full evening's viewing.[72] Every detail of every valve's working conditions was checked jointly by an Ultra engineer and a representative of the valve-maker, to ensure that the valve was not being abused. One of Ultra's design team, Mike Pletts, had the necessary mathematical insight to understand and exploit a sophisticated form of circuit, invented by RCA, for separating the sound and vision signals. As a result, their pictures were particularly free from 'ringing' — a fault seldom seen nowadays but then very common, consisting of a number of closely spaced black and white bands to the right of every vertical edge. It was a matter of some satisfaction to Ultra engineers that a contemporary Pye model rang rather badly.[45]

In the 1950s Teddy Rosen was in his flamboyant prime, at ease with people of all social classes; his chauffeur, Parkins, who had worked for him since the 1930s, had become a personal friend. Rosen's warmth and humour often enabled him to get away with outrageous behaviour without giving offence, as when he had Parkins pull up the Rolls Royce outside the local fishmonger's the day after receiving a delivery of dubious quality. Rosen wound down the window and flung the offending fish across the pavement into the shop, shouting "Never send me anything like that again!" before ordering Parkins to drive on.[72] But sometimes his use of unprintable language did give offence. When things had been going wrong at an exhibition in Manchester, Rosen walked into the lounge of the Midland Hotel and bore down on one of his staff with "That's the ****** I want to talk to!" Though relatively junior in the company, the man squarely told Rosen that he resented being thus addressed in a public place, then realized that he might have just earned himself the sack; instead, the episode led to a more cordial relationship between the two.[73] In 1956 Ultra opened a large, new factory at Gosport, Hants, and entered into a last, brief, phase of expansion and success.

Plessey take the peak load[74]

Plessey were hard hit when the war ended, being engaged almost exclusively on military contracts, and the work force fell from over 11,000 in 1944 to under 6,000 in 1946. A firm of consultants recommended that the company should continue to concentrate on radio components, but should strengthen its Sales Department and pay more regard to the sales potential of products before developing them. In the late-1940s sales of radio and television receivers and of components all increased rapidly, and by about 1950 together made up almost two-thirds of the company's £7 million total sales.

Sales on the receiver side of the business were still handled predominantly by Allen Clark, sole Managing Director since Bill Heyne's retirement through ill health in 1946. In 1947 Clark negotiated a three-year contract with EMI to design and manufacture Marconiphone radios and radiograms to their specification, just a

Seat in the stalls

This is the spell the DEFIANT weaves, when the twilight of your room deepens into a 'first-night' hush, before the curtain rises on the speaking likeness of reality.

And this is your DEFIANT, the 1250 Console combined TV/Radio, 10" × 8" screen, price £115 . 10 . 10 including tax; aerial equipment extra. TV only, or table models, are lower priced

DEFIANT
Television
The set you'll simply have to get!

FROM CO-OPERATIVE SOCIETIES EVERYWHERE

As the tone of this 1951 advertisement makes clear, the market at this period was still almost entirely made up of first-time buyers

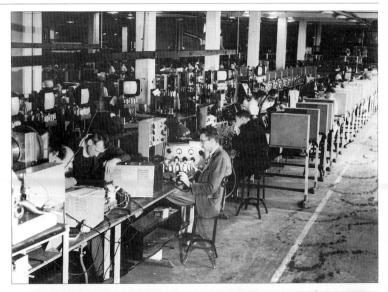

Television production at Plessey, 1949

Electrostatic spray plant on the loudspeaker line, 1949

A 'hot track' enables receivers to remain powered as they move along to successive alignment stations, c. 1959

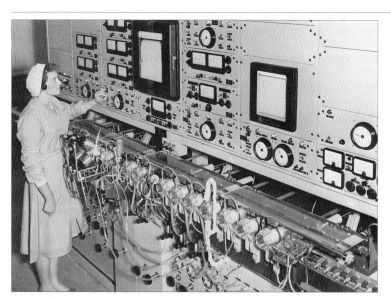

Transistors being manufactured at Plessey, c. 1959

Plessey at an exhibition, in about 1959, at which they showed over 5,000 different radio and electronic components

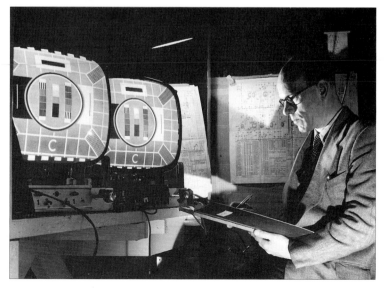

Quality control, c. 1960. Receivers taken from production lines are tested for consistency and reliability

quarter of a century after the Marconiphone contract that had set the company upon its way. Thereafter many setmakers, including major ones, sometimes had sets made by Plessey to supplement their own capacity, while sets sold under some names (most notably Defiant, sold by the Co-op) were made by Plessey exclusively. Television sets used a standard Plessey-designed chassis, possibly modified to the customer's requirements, but would be housed in cabinets specific to the customer; at one time in the 1950s, the production lines were simultaneously handling 17 different brand names. Some of these were quite obscure, but they had to be names free from any taint of price-cutting, which could threaten Clark's good standing. He once spotted in the window of a Currys' branch, and bearing their 'Westminster' brand name, a Plessey-built set currently in production for an established manufacturer, Regentone. Work on the contract was stopped immediately, and Regentone had to finish the job themselves.[75]

Providing extra capacity for an already volatile industry made Plessey especially susceptible to fluctuations in demand; they might produce 5,000 television sets one week and hardly any the next. The core of full-time workers was supplemented by daytime and evening shifts of part-timers, the latter composed largely of older women trained in Plessey methods, who could work with minimal supervision. When demand fell, the evening part-timers were laid off first, then the daytime ones, and only then the full-timers. To meet customers' ever-changing requirements, it could be necessary several times a day to switch one or other of the production lines to a different model. As a result of such stringencies, the company developed quick responses and great flexibility, and led the industry in stock-control.[76]

In the mid-1950s Plessey began to move away from 'entertainment' components into 'professional' ones, which provided a better return on the capital employed and for which demand was less volatile. As we shall see later, around 1960 the number of setmakers decreased greatly. This tended to undermine Plessey's role as a contract shop, for now the economies of scale, including the ability to produce cosmetically different models using a common chassis, were also enjoyed by the merged setmakers. From 1960 Plessey gradually withdrew from setmaking, the process becoming irreversible with the decision not to go into colour television, but they have maintained a somewhat intermittent presence as component suppliers to the industry, latterly in the field of dedicated integrated circuits.

Philips and quality-control

The first post-war television sets made by Philips were designed at Mitcham, but in 1948 a choice had to be made between another Mitcham-designed set and Eindhoven's first post-war design, produced without benefit of a television signal. The Eindhoven design was chosen as being the more nearly ready for production, despite some misgivings among engineers.[77] These proved well-founded, and despite some 50–60 modifications the set was never satisfactory. However, the episode ensured that for many years thereafter Philips UK engineers were allowed to design their own television sets. It also provided a useful baptism of fire for young Sid Perry, who had been put in charge of Mitcham's 'Factory Assistance/Post Development' laboratory a week before production started; his predecessor had seen the new project coming, and had left. Before the practice became at all

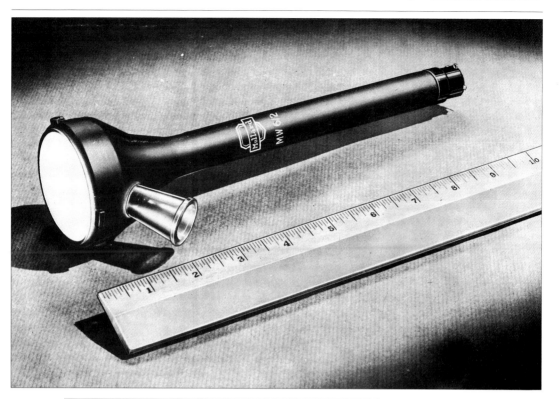

The 2¹/₂" tube used in projection sets in the early-1950s

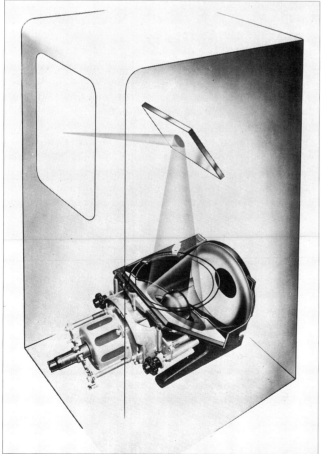

The 'Schmidt' optical system used in projection sets was much smaller relative to the receiver than appears from this stylized diagram

general in the British industry, Perry applied statistical analysis to quality control. Measuring the parameters of a small sample of receivers enabled him to predict what proportion of output would be outside of specification, and tighten up tolerances as necessary to prevent a significant rejection rate from developing; in particular, Mullard would be warned when valves were nearing the limits of their specification. By his own admission Perry was often considered exasperating and pedantic, but an enlightened management gave him their backing, even when this involved halting production for no obvious reason.[78]

Philips were the principal makers of projection receivers, which in the early-1950s offered the only means of obtaining pictures of more than about 15" diagonal. To achieve the necessary brilliance they used a special $2\frac{1}{2}$" Mullard tube, imported from Holland, and an EHT voltage of 25kV. The tube was mounted in a compact 'Schmidt' optical system employing a concave mirror, and the image was usually back-projected onto a screen of translucent plastic, although a few front-projection models with separate screens 4' x 3' were also made. At their best, the pictures given by projection sets were quite sharp, and adequately bright for viewing in subdued light, though brightness fell off rapidly as the viewer moved off-axis, while any attempt to achieve the brightness of a conventional receiver degraded the picture and shortened the tube life; this was, in any case, rather shorter than that of a normal tube, but the projection tube was considerably cheaper to replace. To protect the tube screen from damage, special circuits had to be devised to cut off the electron beam instantly if either scan failed. The optical system generally needed attention only when the tube was changed, although a Philips engineer recalls being asked by a friend to investigate why his family's projection set gave such a dim, fuzzy picture. He found the set installed in a room just behind their fish and chip shop, its entire optical system coated in condensed frying oil.[79] Although well remembered, projection sets peaked at only 2% of the market in 1952,[80] and rapidly lost ground as normal tubes increased in size.

In 1956 Philips opened a large new factory in Croydon, replete with sophisticated mechanical handling equipment. A network of six overhead conveyor systems, totalling two-thirds of a mile in length, kept work in progress continuously circulating, eliminating the need for floor storage. The conveyors dipped to a low level where necessary to allow parts to be on- or off-loaded, or to transfer television-set cabinets automatically to a system of powered roller conveyors, approaching half a mile in length, which carried them through main assembly, inspection and packing.[81]

In such matters there was little to choose between Philips and their major competitors, but in their use of printed-circuit boards (PCBs) from about 1955 they were a year or two ahead of the field. During the war a Viennese Jewish refugee, Paul Eisler, working in Britain, had pioneered a photo-etching technique for producing drilled insulated boards on which thin strips of copper defined a maze of interconnections between the holes; components soldered to the board could thus form complete circuits without any wiring. The Americans used Eisler's printed circuits in proximity fuses for anti-aircraft shells, and from 1948 made them mandatory for airborne electronic instruments.[82] One of the difficulties that had to be overcome before they yielded their obvious potential for improving reliability and

*Mechanical handling at Philips' Croydon
Works, 1957. Cabinets being loaded onto
roller conveyor, and faulty sets diverted
from the production line*

Philips' Croydon Works in 1957, shortly after its opening

reducing labour costs was that the tags of valve-holders holding high-power valves overheated, damaging the board and even melting the solder. Philips engineers designed boards in which each tag entered a considerable area of copper, extending outwards from the valve-holder, which dissipated the heat harmlessly.[79]

Ferguson and production

In exploiting PCBs for automation, however, it was Ferguson who became the industry's leaders, beginning in the late-1950s. In their first-generation equipment for the automatic insertion of components, which was of their own design, printed-circuit boards moved down a line that could be up to 120 feet long, stopping at numerous stations where one or more heads would insert particular components. A film of the equipment in action shows the impressive speed and precision with which anything from a resistor to a nine-pin valve-holder was popped into place. However, there was a fatal flaw in this approach: whenever any of the 40 or 50 insertion heads malfunctioned, the whole line had to be stopped until the fault was put right by a technician, known as the 'long-distance runner'. After persevering with the system for many months, the management reluctantly decided to go back to manual insertion.

The second generation of equipment installed was American. As a result of Italian domination of the American shoe market the demand for shoe-making machinery had collapsed, but one manufacturer realized that much of their technology could readily be adapted to component insertion. Ferguson imported their machines and, under

From a Ferguson promotional film of 1959

A draughtsman inking in the tracks on a printed circuit board at Ferguson in 1958. Note the wide spacing between tracks used in this early technique

Early automatic insertion equipment in action at Ferguson's Enfield factory in 1959

PORTABLE
NEEDS NO AERIAL

EVERYMAN
WORLD'S LOWEST PRICED
TELEVISION RECEIVER

FOUR-FOLD
ACHIEVEMENT

TOWNSMAN
NO AERIAL CONSOLE

BAIRD
THE FIRST NAME IN
TELEVISION

COUNTRYMAN
LONG-RANGE CONSOLE

An advertisement of 1950　**BAIRD TELEVISION · WEMBLEY · MIDDLESEX**

A labour-intensive operation at the Ultra/Ferguson factory, Gosport, in 1963. Circuits built as modules on printed-circuit boards still required handmade cableforms to interconnect the boards

Production Director Norman Townsend, became the world's biggest user of the technique before being overtaken by computer manufacturers. Each board now stayed in a fixed position while a versatile head moved about it inserting the various components, which had been loaded into a bandoleer in the right order. A girl watched each position, noting any isolated failures for subsequent insertion by hand; even when the machine had to be stopped for a persistent fault, no other position was affected. Ferguson engineers became especially noted for the effectiveness with which they blended different types of machine from various manufacturers in a single production line.[23,45]

The growth of rental
Renting a television set rather than buying it is a peculiarly British custom that has greatly influenced the development of the industry. Its growth was dominated by two companies, which were eventually to merge: Radio Rentals was the bigger, but DER ('Domestic Electric Rentals') had the more widespread influence on manufacture and retailing.

Radio Rentals Ltd, founded around 1930, were by 1936 renting out some 50,000 radio receivers.[83] They diversified into television just before the war, when the short life and high replacement cost of cathode ray tubes made their all-in service especially attractive. From 1948 they made their own television sets at a factory they had acquired in Bradford; initially these were simply marked 'Radio Rentals', but subsequently they became 'Baird'. The name was still a valuable asset, although in the post-war period the sets bearing it, while often innovative, had more than their share of technical problems. Through successive changes of ownership the company became Scophony Baird, Hartley Baird and finally Ambassador Baird.[67] By the late-1950s the brand was moribund and Radio Rentals bought only the name from Ambassador, renaming their manufacturing subsidiary Baird Television Ltd in 1960.[84]

Radio Rentals manufactured only for themselves, whereas DER was only one of Jules Thorn's outlets, and initially a very minor one in which he took little interest. He had taken it over before the war in settlement of a bad debt, and in 1947 it consisted of just one shop, in East Twickenham, renting out three or four thousand pre-war radio receivers. The following year Tom Ludlow, an engaging young Irishman who was to have a profound effect on the rental business, was taken on as the fifth of DER's representatives and given one of the company's plain black vans; people who rented radios did not want it known that they could not even afford the down-payment to buy one on hire purchase. Ludlow, determined to upgrade the company's image, had his van painted red, and emblazoned 'Domestic Electric Rentals'. The company now handled television sets, but offered either rental or sale. When a lady 'prospect' in Romford could not decide whether to rent or buy, Ludlow suggested she should think it over while he went to Gidea Park to get a few rental contracts signed. She looked surprised. "Gidea Park? I'd have thought they could afford to buy a set there!" "Oh they can," he replied, "but they don't just want a television set. They want the best, with constant service, and they want to change it every year. They all rent in Gidea Park." She could not sign the contract quickly enough.

A few years later, and by now head of DER, Ludlow still found it difficult to enthuse Jules Thorn over rental. He put in a budget for 25,000 sets where conventional wisdom would have decreed 3,000. Thorn sent for him, and asked him what it was all about. When Ludlow expanded on the shops he proposed to open, Thorn protested "I'm not a shopkeeper, Tom, I'm an industrialist!" Rental, he asserted, was the bottom of the market. Ludlow conceded that it had been, but vowed that he would not rest until he had put sets into the best houses in the land — and that did not exclude Buckingham Palace. In due course he made good this boast, and DER was granted a Royal Warrant.[85]

Ferguson dealers saw Thorn's rental operation as a betrayal, particularly when DER opened shops near them, and on one occasion a major retailer bluntly told Jules Thorn "either get out of TV rental, or get your sets out of my shops." Thorn literally lost sleep over this dilemma for some time before coming down in favour of rental. Retailers, he decided, were well able to look after themselves, having observed that "they would turn up in a Bentley when they owed us four months' money".[86] Nevertheless, as a concession to retailers DER sets were for a time given different cabinets from Ferguson ones, though later only the logos were different. The task of pacifying the dealers fell to Jack Wilson, Ferguson's Sales Manager (not, it will be noted, Sales Director, for Ferguson did not at that time have a separate board). He urged them to take up rental as well as sale, pointing out that unlike DER they could offer any make of set, and that many people preferred to deal with someone who ran his own shop. But the clinching argument was that whereas a sale, once made, brought in nothing more, rental brought in money week-in week-out; people stopped buying television sets whenever times were hard, but they would sell the bed before they would let a rented set go. Wilson usually won the dealers over, but on occasions DER would have to give up a site that was too close to an important dealer's premises.[24]

Rental was of profound importance to the manufacturer. Because of their steady cash flow, rental companies could afford to build up larger stocks than dealers when business was slack, thus smoothing out demand at the factory. Without this mechanism Thorn would not have been able to pursue automation so vigorously, for whereas a plant using manual assembly can simply lay off workers to cut costs when demand falls, this becomes progressively less effective as

In 1950 Philips made their first post-war entry into car radio with 'MotoRadio', but soon withdrew again. The inset shows the 344V receiver with which they finally established themselves in this field in 1955

automation increases. Finally, because a rental company gave free maintenance it could be relied upon to provide the manufacturer with more detailed information on his receivers' liability to failure than he could obtain in any other way.[87]

"An unwelcome complication"

Sound broadcasting on very high frequencies (VHF) was widely discussed during the war, in the expectation that it would begin quite soon after the war ended. In the event, the BBC did not launch its VHF radio network until May 1955. This was an extreme example of British broadcasting's tradition of tolerating delay in the interests of 'getting it right', which in this case turned on assessing the relative merits of amplitude modulation (AM) and frequency modulation (FM). On lower-frequency bands only AM was feasible, but within the 7MHz of VHF spectrum available for broadcasting there was room to make the audio signal vary the frequency of the radio wave rather than its amplitude, and thereby enable a better signal-to-noise ratio to be achieved. High-fidelity VHF broadcasting using FM had been pioneered and demonstrated in America in the late-1930s by Edwin Armstrong, while Britain had experienced high-fidelity reception on VHF through pre-war television sound, using AM. However, at the end of the war the VHF band's immediate role was seen as the more mundane one of giving the BBC better coverage by supplementing its long- and medium-wave services.

By the end of 1946 both the BBC and BREMA were on record as favouring FM[3,88] but two years later things were much less certain. The BBC were planning to erect two high-power transmitters and conduct exhaustive field trials before deciding between AM and FM, while BREMA stated that on technical aspects alone the merits of both systems were finely balanced.[12] The final decision on VHF broadcasting had to await a recommendation by the Government-appointed Television Advisory Committee, which was not free to turn its attention to the subject until 1953. By this time the BBC had opted firmly for FM and had published a full coverage plan, but the committee's task was complicated by Pye having submitted a variant of AM, involving closely spaced channels and crystal-controlled receivers, and raising more problems than it solved. Pye were represented on the Technical Sub-Committee carrying out the assessment by B J Edwards, who fought a loyal rearguard action for both forms of AM but, as a good engineer, bowed to the evidence for FM point by point, enabling the Sub-Committee to return a unanimous decision.[89] However C O Stanley, on the main Committee, wrote a minority report challenging the whole concept of VHF broadcasting as proposed by the BBC, and agreeing with little save the Committee's unfortunate statement "The introduction of VHF sound broadcasting is an unwelcome complication". In one vital matter he was to be proved right. Very few of the public, he asserted, would pay £25 or £35 for an FM set if all they received in return was the possibility of better reception of existing BBC programmes.[90]

By the end of 1956 the VHF/FM service had achieved 84% coverage but there was little or no indication that it was of itself responsible for the purchase of radio receivers,[80] and fewer than a third of the radios sold in 1957 included a VHF band, though five out of six radiograms did.[91] Even worse, those who did buy VHF sets were not always pleased with the results. During the run-up to the service

Earls Court, 1956

VHF radios and 'disc-jockey' transistorized portable record-players, 1956

the BBC had insisted that in many locations the gain and directivity of a proper outdoor aerial were essential for good reception. However, the setmakers knew that even fewer people would buy receivers if they had to buy aerials too, so they made their sets extremely sensitive but left the issue of directivity unresolved. In television, the stray reflected signals picked up by an inadequate aerial produce 'ghosts'; in FM radio they produce tinny distortion, and although this can be minimized by good receiver-design it was present in full measure in many early FM sets. A dealer anxious to make a sale was liable to assure the customer that the set needed only its internal aerial, or perhaps a 'rabbit's ears' set-top aerial. If the customer returned to complain of a rattling noise, like something loose inside the set, a popular line was that the reproduction was so faithful that he was hearing the distortion that the BBC were transmitting.[92]

Records do their bit

As a provider of good-quality sound, the BBC's VHF service had already had some of its thunder stolen by the long-playing record. In March 1949 *The Gramophone*'s editor, Compton Mackenzie, reported that the American record industry had been plunged into the worst slump it had ever known, by the advent of two new types of microgroove record, respectively playing at $33\frac{1}{3}$ and 45 rpm. He ventured to hope with some confidence that nothing like that would be repeated in this country. It was much more important for the industry to concentrate upon the removal of Purchase Tax on records than to embark upon buccaneering adventures which neither they nor the public could afford. Did readers really want to feel that their collections of records were obsolete?[93] *The Gramophone*'s attitude was sustained for many months by adverse reports on long-playing records received from American correspondents; in their anxiety to jump onto the bandwagon, some American record companies had accepted poor

Provision for $33\frac{1}{3}$ rpm long-playing records was still only optional on this luxury Dynatron radiogram of 1951

"HIS MASTER'S VOICE"

"Stereosonic"

SOUND REPRODUCTION

* * * * * * * * * * * * *

".... the one fundamental development in sound recording and reproduction which musicians have been awaiting for years."

SIR MALCOLM SARGENT

"HIS MASTER'S VOICE"

processing standards and had issued many records that were simply copied from 78s.

The 7" 45rpm disc and a record-changer for playing it were designed as an integral project by RCA.[94] The large hole in the disc enabled the disc-dropping mechanism to be housed inside the spindle, the speed of rotation was the fastest that allowed the complete changing cycle to be reliably completed during one revolution of the disc, and the playing time of just over 5 minutes was chosen to accommodate 70% of the items in the 'Classical' portion of a Victor record catalogue. In view of their strong links with RCA, EMI might have been expected to introduce both microgroove formats in Britain in 1950, in response to Decca releasing their first 33⅓rpm discs here that summer. In fact, they announced in October 1950 that until further notice they would continue to supply standard (i.e. 78rpm) records only; if for any reason they considered that records should be played at any other speed, record dealers would be given a minimum of six months' notice of their intention to introduce them.[95] Two more years were to elapse before EMI finally introduced both formats simultaneously, in October 1952. Meanwhile, they had persisted in marketing radiograms playing only 78rpm, although most manufacturers had provided for both 78 and 33⅓ (and some for 45rpm as well) at the 1950 Radio Show.[96] EMI's first machines for microgroove records, released in August 1952, were two decks for connection to a radio or radiogram; one was for 33⅓ only, the other was the RCA 45-only record changer, by then over three years old.[97] Other manufacturers had already adopted as the norm a three-speed turntable with a 'turnover' pick-up cartridge having separate styli for 78rpm and microgroove discs, although more ambitious equipment

Publicity leaflet for EMI's abortive attempt to market pre-recorded stereophonic tapes, 1956

employed interchangeable cartridges.

The microgroove disc had commercial effects beyond making existing radiograms obsolete. In conjunction with the increasing affluence of the 1950s it gave rise to a distinct 'teenage' market in self-contained record players, hitherto a very small sector, while its potential for high fidelity boosted the interest in high-quality pick-ups, amplifiers and loudspeakers. In time a specialized high-fidelity industry was to evolve, but in the early-1950s the enthusiast could find himself in a situation reminiscent of the 1920s, building circuits he didn't understand and disfiguring the family living room with home-constructed cabinets.

Having finally come to terms with microgroove records, EMI made another marketing blunder. In the mid-1950s they launched both monophonic and stereophonic pre-recorded tapes, and a range of players (some with recording facilities) to reproduce them. But there were obvious risks in buying expensive equipment dedicated to a format that there was no sign of other record companies adopting, while cream-enamelled tape decks and 7-inch spools had acquired a 'do-it-yourself' image, and somehow looked cheap and incongruous in opulent HMV cabinets. Not surprisingly, the project failed. The brochures asserted that stereophonic discs were not practicable, although within two years they would be marketed by Decca, using a technique covered by a patent granted to EMI's own Alan Blumlein in the early-1930s.

Decca continued to straddle the diverging worlds of radiograms and high-fidelity, as 'ffrr' gave way to 'ffss'(full-frequency stereophonic sound). Their highly regarded stereo pick-up, in which longitudinal motion of the stylus was inhibited by a tensioned Terylene fibre, was designed by R W Bayliff, and embodied considerable mathematical analysis.[98] Bayliff was not a Decca employee, but an Operations and Maintenance engineer with the BBC whose interest in pick-up design had started as a hobby. By the early-1950s he had made sufficient progress to submit details of his work to the BBC's Designs Department. However, at that period such 'specialist' departments of the BBC tended to regard both gramophone records and Operations

The stereo Decola, of 1958. Decca had produced an excellent stereo pickup, but were still locked into the idea of a single piece of furniture, and considered that a large number of 'tweeters' were essential

PLAYS LPs EPs and 78s

DECCA TG4

**BATTERY
OPERATED
TRANSISTOR
PORTABLE**

**4-SPEED
RECORD PLAYER**

In 1958 transistors brought back mains-free record playing, which had disappeared when the coming of microgrooves had made the wind-up gramophone obsolete

and Maintenance engineers with some condescension,[99] and no interest was shown. Bayliff was subsequently introduced to the Chief Engineer of the Decca Record Company, Arthur Haddy, and with the BBC's permission worked on the pick-up with Decca in his own time.[100]

The Portable Comes into its Own

Miniature battery-valves developed for military applications during the war needed only 50mA at 1.5V to heat their filaments, and in the early-1950s they were superseded by types consuming only 25mA, well within the capacity of ordinary torch batteries. The portable radio

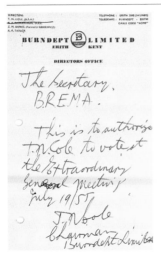

When T N Cole resumed command of his company BREMA asked for written confirmation. This was it!

Packing batteries at the rate of a ton an hour at Vidor's Dundee factory in 1953. During the year Vidor-Burndept had over 800 photographs taken in their six factories. One worker at each factory was 'ringed' and could claim a prize

A Vidor rep covering the Border country calls on the K Radio Store, Carlisle, 1954. Vidor radio batteries held a substantial share of the market, particularly in Scotland, and enjoyed a good reputation

Manufacturing batteries at Vidor's Dundee factory in 1954 was still a labour-intensive operation

The Sets *our* Dealers like to sell . . .

VIDOR 'Henley' CN 426
An AC/Battery Portable with exceptionally economical battery performance. In two - tone pastel leatherette.

VIDOR 'Royal Ascot' CN 427
An AC/DC/Battery Transportable for the modern home : in "polka-dot" blue and cream leatherette.

VIDOR CN 420

'Regatta' Portable

"The Set that cut the cost of listening" . . . the lowest-priced battery portable of its type, using the new low-consumption valves with full-size round-cell Vidor Batteries—and therefore cheapest of all portables to run.

VIDOR 'Attache' CN 396
The AC/Battery portable that has held its popularity longer than any other model.

All the year round sellers!

VIDOR
PORTABLES

From the Vidor-Burndept Magazine, March 1954

NEW! PERSONAL PORTABLE

LOVELIER THAN EVER!

THE VIDOR
"My Lady Margaret"
DE-LUXE

CN 434

12½

GUINEAS
TAX PAID
(Batteries Extra)

THE VIDOR
"VAGABOND"
PERSONAL PORTABLE

CN 439

12½

GUINEAS
TAX PAID
(Batteries Extra)

NEW slender styling . . . New colours, gay but cool . . . New sensitivity because of exclusive new aerial arrangement . . . NEW robustness with gracious line and lovely colours . . . a *personal* portable that goes with you all the way. NEW Slow Motion Dial for easy tuning.

TECHNICALLY SPEAKING
4 valve battery superhet. Two wavebands: 187-570 metres Medium & 1086 - 1986 metres Long. 5" P.M. speaker. Size 8" x 8½" x 4". Weight : inc. batteries 6½-lbs. Batteries : L.T. Vidor L5040 H.T. Vidor L.5512.

Queen of the radio world! The Vidor " My Lady Margaret" De Luxe is a more sensitive, more selective radio companion to be with you on the beach, by your fireside and in the car. You'll find all the Home and Continental stations you want and all the volume on the big 5" speaker. Accepted by the Council of Industrial Design for Design Review.

EXCLUSIVE [PATENTS PENDING] AERIAL FEATURE

Ferrite rod aerial built into retractable handle which is spring-loaded to rise at a touch 3" above the receiver.

TECHNICALLY SPEAKING :

Weight : 4½-lbs. Two wavebands. 4" speaker. Batteries : H.T.L.5500 L.T.2V0039.

VIDOR VALUE   PORTABLE   PLEASURE

Two Vidor portables of 1958

The Beverley Sisters (Teddy, Joy & Babs) on the front cover of a 1959 leaflet

gained in both compactness and economy, and at a time of increasing affluence became an affordable luxury for many more people.

Vidor

A major beneficiary was the Vidor-Burndept group, which made both receivers and batteries, and by 1953 had a total payroll of over 3,500.[101] Burndept was the manufacturing company and the brand name for the Group's non-broadcast electronics, Vidor the battery-making subsidiary and the selling organization for domestic receivers. In the mid-1950s up to a quarter of a million Vidor radio receivers, almost all portables, were produced annually by the group's factory at West Street, Erith, as well as 12,000 TeleVidor television sets.[102] Vidor made batteries for domestic, professional and military applications, with factories at South Shields and Dundee, and their own chemical plant at Brechin.

T N Cole and his family owned 90% of the shares, but since his departure for the United States in the late-1930s the group had been most ably run by R P Richardson, who owned the other 10%. However, Cole had not been idle. Shortly after the end of the war, in partnership with his son-in-law, he bought two of the laid-up Liberty ships being sold off by the U S Maritime Administration, ran them profitably enough to buy two more,[103] and enjoyed an increase in their capital value through the Korean War. He returned temporarily to Britain in 1950 and gave Richardson more money with which to develop the business,[104] and Richardson was frequently summoned to New York for consultation. Then, early in 1954, Cole returned permanently to Britain to resume control of his company;[105] he had fallen out with his daughter and son-in-law, and his wife was homesick for England. He at once began to throw his weight about, and when Richardson warned him that if he continued his dictatorial behaviour many of the management would leave, Cole suspected a plot and forced his resignation,[104] though it was publicly presented as retirement.[106]

Cole now appointed to a directorship another of his sons-in-law, Zbigniew Banks, who had been with the group for five years. As the ranks of the existing top executives thinned under the new regime he became Cole's right-hand man or, as he himself has termed it, his slave. Though now into his sixties, Cole seemed inexhaustible, talking business for hours on end then recharging himself with a 5-minute cat-nap and starting all over again; travelling in Banks's car, "he would shut the business down ten times in an hour." His mistrustfulness was now total; he signed all purchase orders himself, at home,[104] and took a suitcaseful of company papers home on the train each night in case they fell into wrong hands. An incident in the staff toilet, improbable but vouched-for by two executives who were present, showed a more attractive eccentricity. Cole walked in to find the attendant surrounded by paper towels, normally put into the dispenser in packs of 100. The man explained that since checking a pack and finding that it contained only 99 towels he had counted every pack, whereupon Cole said "Congratulations, my man, for looking after my interests" and handed him a £5 note.[107]

In the late-1950s Cole suffered personal tragedy, when his two sons were killed in separate accidents, and after that he was interested only in selling the group. Vidor's radio and television sales were declining, and production ceased around 1960. In view of their previous relationship it was rather cheeky of him to approach Ever

Ready as the most likely buyer for Vidor's battery side, and despite numerous quite cordial meetings he was unable to persuade Laurence Orchard, later to be Ever Ready's Chairman, that this was an attractive proposition; why should Ever Ready bother, when Cole already bought most of his materials from them?[20] However, there came a day when Cole and Banks left Orchard's office believing (quite wrongly, recent contact with Orchard has established) that at last a

A mink-coated Roberts RT1, c.1959; other coverings included pony skin, leopard skin, and jewel-encrusted suede. By encasing receivers in exotic materials, the Company projected the portable radio as a glamorous accessory, eventually showing an R200 receiver in a solid gold case, priced at "2000gns + battery 3s 6d"

A Roberts portable was featured in the silver-wedding article published by the Illustrated London News *in 1948*

THE ILLUSTRATED LONDON NEWS   MAY 1, 1948

A DISTRACTION WHICH THEIR MAJESTIES ENJOY AS GREATLY AS THE MAJORITY OF THEIR SUBJECTS : THE KING TURNING ON THE WIRELESS.

deal was within sight. Cole turned to Banks and declared "I'm not going to sell to those bastards!" Instead he sold out, for £1.2 million and 400,000 of their shares, to the Royston group, who needed a specialized Vidor battery for one of their products. Cole lived until 1972, long enough to see Royston fail and their many subsidiaries sold off. Burndept went to Ever Ready.[104]

Roberts: portables by appointment

Vidor made the portable big business. Roberts Radio gave it status. During the war they had moved to bigger premises, and when they resumed civilian production in 1946 they were large enough to make some impact. Harrods were pleading for increased allocations of their Model P4D ("It undoubtedly beats anything of the transportable type which has yet been placed on the market") even before it was selected as one of the twenty radios in the 'Britain Can Make It' exhibition. In 1948 use of miniature valves and a layer-type battery brought a full-specification Roberts receiver weighing only $10^1/_2$ pounds, and sold complete with a weatherproof carrying bag because people could realistically be expected to take it around with them. A variety of sets were sold to the Royal Family, and in 1955 the company was awarded the first of the four Royal Warrants it was eventually to hold.[108]

Enter the transistor

As television sets took over the nation's living rooms, portable radios gained ground at the expense of full-sized table models, being better suited to radio's residual but expanding role as a provider of 'background' entertainment in kitchen or bedroom. An increasing number of mains/battery sets were available to reduce running costs, while sensitivity was improved when frame aerials, always a weak link, were superseded by coils wound on rods of ferrite. And then came a technical advance whose immediate impact was simply that of a novel form of battery portable costing less to run though more to buy, but whose significance was immeasurably greater, marking as it did the beginning of the electronics industry's transition from thermionic valves to semiconductors.

Following the invention of the point-contact transistor at Bell Labs in 1948, valve-manufacturers had undertaken intense research into semiconductor materials and transistor manufacture, and by the mid-

An experimental radio made by GEC Research Laboratories in 1951 using 'germanium triodes', as they then termed transistors. It was stated that "numerous problems are still to be solved before large scale production can begin"

A Decca transistor portable of 1958

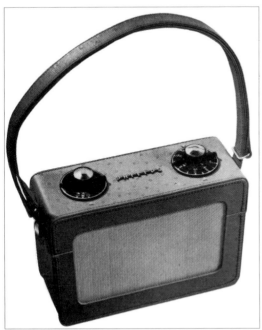

Ten hours' Play for a Penny

A TRANSISTOR PORTABLE

One of Philips' last valve portables and one of their first transistor sets, both from 1957

1950s were marketing 'alloy-junction' devices based on the hitherto-obscure element, germanium. In Britain, Mullard established a distinct lead, and it was with their OC44s, OC45s, OC71s and OC72s, using circuits developed by Mullard's Applications Laboratory, that a number of setmakers made their first transistor receivers; OC was a whimsical adaptation of Mullard's normal valve nomenclature, signifying a triode (C) with a heater voltage of zero (O).

Testing the temperature

However, the first British transistor set to be marketed, in June 1956, had a different pedigree. It was designed in Pye's Research Laboratories under Dr Lax, who built the prototype himself, but since its commercial success could not be assured, C O Stanley prudently released it through a Pye subsidiary, Pam Radio & Television Ltd, as Model 710. Its eight lozenge-shaped transistors were produced by another Pye company, Newmarket Transistors Ltd. No data sheets on them were available, their gain was subject to enormous spread, and their poor high-frequency response required the intermediate frequency to be 315kHz instead of the normal 465kHz. But the set was well received, and by the following January the company was able to market a better model using two fewer transistors, as Pye Model 123. The engineers nevertheless found it frustrating to be tied to Newmarket transistors, knowing that with Mullard ones they would be able to do a better job.[109]

A Philips transistor portable with the 1958 Cambridge West Greenland Glaciological Expedition. Good long-range reception was maintained in a deep, narrow valley, using twenty feet of flex hung from tent to tent and connected to the earth terminal

Perdio: transistors only

For several years transistor receivers remained expensive novelties; there was only one among the eight MW/LW models in Vidor's 1958/59 brochure, and at 21 guineas its price was 50% above the average of the valve sets. However, three young men saw the situation as one of great opportunity, much as an earlier generation had seen

SMALLEST RADIO IS A BIG SUCCESS

Four in a success story ... from left : Raymond Richards, Michael Heslop, Derek Wilmott and Viscount Suirdale, who says : "We have some other surprises in store."

| Blindman's guide dog | *Pocket portable draws crowds* | Doorman: Man remanded |

A production floor at Perdio's factory in Bonhill Street, EC2, 1960

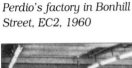

The second model of portable television receiver produced by Perdio, 1963

NEW *Perdio*

PORTARAMA

Unique Lightweight Transistor Portable T.V.

* A real go anywhere T.V.
* Runs on its own built-in rechargeable batteries (see over), Normal A.C. mains or car battery.
* 25 Transistors, 13 Diodes.
* Special 8½" Radiant Screen.
* Receives all B.B.C., I.T.A. and S.T.V. programmes.
* Built in telescopic aerial, input for external aerial.
* Two earphone sockets - one especially designed for the hard of hearing (See over).
* Finished in modern Two-Tone Grey.
* Measures only 13¾" x 10½" x 10½", weighs only 20 lbs.

P E R D I O THE TRANSISTOR SPECIALISTS
Perdio Electronics Limited   Perdio House,   Bonhill Street,   London, E.C.2

65 gns.   inc. tax   ex battery

PERDIO *NEWS*

Issued with the compliments of PERDIO LTD · PERDIO HOUSE · BONHILL STREET · LONDON · E·C·2

Telephone MOO 9546 (5Lines)

Issue No. 5 August 1961

AT YOUR SERVICE — A PERDIO MODEL

A Perdio 'Park Lane' receiver, 1961

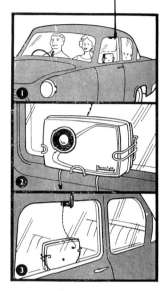

Before car radios were general, the sales appeal of a transistor portable could be increased by providing accessories such as these. A Perdio illustration from 1960

the advent of broadcasting itself, and while the established setmakers moved cautiously into the new technology they committed themselves wholeheartedly to establishing a company making transistor models exclusively.

Perdio (from 'personal radio') was originally formed in 1955 by Derek Willmott and J D Heslop. Willmott was an ex-RAF Pilot who had joined Decca Radar as a lab-boy and worked his way up to head a research group. By 1954 he had made a two-transistor receiver, and on the strength of this left Decca to pursue the idea of a pocket radio. He joined Heslop, an ex-colleague running a contract drawing business, and though no radio-frequency transistors were yet available Heslop's draughtsmen, with the help of local engineering firms, designed and adapted miniature components and a cabinet for the proposed set. By the autumn of 1956 they had a working, but by no means saleable, receiver using selected audio-frequency transistors.[110] Further finance was urgently needed, and an advertisement was placed in *The Times*. This was answered by R M J Hely-Hutchinson, the Viscount Suirdale, heir to the Earl of Donoughmore; he was 29, and qualified as a doctor, but had recently decided to go into business. Willmott and Heslop made a good impression, and he bought a controlling interest in Perdio, then made three successive injections of £500 to finance development. A production prototype appeared, and Suirdale decided to involve himself full-time as Managing Director. Heslop left the board, and his company was commissioned to produce most of the parts for 1,500 sets. A small factory was acquired just off Hatton Garden, a Works Manager was engaged, and Model PR1 went into production. By the middle of August 1957 about a hundred had been sold, and almost every one had been returned, suffering from numerous component failures and design faults.

It was, therefore, a mixed blessing when later in the month Perdio's stand at the Earls Court Radio Show drew enormous crowds, leading to euphoric press coverage of "the smallest portable radio set in Europe",[111] and a full order book. Initially production could not meet the demand, then when sets were finally delivered their lack of a long waveband made them unsaleable in some areas. The close spacing of components led to short-circuiting when sets were jolted during delivery, adding to the already-severe problems of reliability. However, Perdio's wholesalers and stockists showed great forbearance, and in May 1958 were rewarded with the first really satisfactory model, which embodied the experience gained from its predecessors. Then at the start of 1959 the 'Super 7' (re-engineered after a bad start) proved a winner, and the company could barely meet the demand for it despite building up production during the year from 150 a week to almost ten times that figure.[112]

Early in 1960 Perdio moved into a 25,000 sq ft factory near Finsbury Square, and entered a phase of very considerable success, which included creditable export performance at a time when overseas markets were already flooded with cheap Japanese receivers. By the beginning of 1961, 7,000 sets a week were being produced, some of them at a second site,[113] and a third of the company's total output to date had been exported.[114] The fact that Perdio made only transistorized receivers (including, from 1961, an all-transistor television set) gave them a reputation as specialists, which after their initial flounderings they quickly came to deserve, with a range of soundly engineered models well matched to the varied needs of the market. They had a speedy and efficient service department, and were known for straight and generous dealing; when they reduced prices they gave stockists a full rebate, although they could not claim its Purchase Tax component back from the Government.[115]

In 1962 the company went public as Perdio Electronics Ltd. With nearly 600 staff they were outgrowing their accommodation, so took advantage of a Board of Trade scheme offering purpose-built factories on advantageous terms in areas of high unemployment. In December 1962 they moved into a 115,000 sq ft factory at Sunderland,[110] confident that they could continue to hold their own against the growing competition from Hong Kong and Japan. But the number of transistor radios imported increased twentyfold between 1960 and 1963,[116] principally from Hong Kong and thus enjoying Imperial Preference as well as low labour costs. Reluctantly, Perdio resorted to having sets made there in order to remain competitive. The portable television set was successful, but shortage of special transistors restricted production, cutting down the profits which were to have financed the development of a dual-standard model for the beginning of 625-line transmissions in 1964. These factors combined to undermine the company, and in October 1965, less than three years after moving up to Sunderland, it was put into liquidation. It is difficult to see how it could have survived, given the external circumstances. Although their products were never as certain to work when taken out of the box as Japanese ones were,[117] this was not as crucial a factor as it would later be with television sets. And by 1965 it was correctly anticipated that trading conditions would soon be made harder by the abolition of Resale Price Maintenance on consumer-electronics products. The failure of Perdio symbolized the near-collapse of radio-receiver manufacturing in Britain, and augured badly for the future of the television receiver industry.

The Industry Consolidates

In the mid-1950s there were over 30 brands of television receiver on sale, and even when allowance is made for those that used a Plessey chassis or that differed only in name, such as Pye and Invicta, nearly 20 were genuinely different, with their own design, production and distribution facilities. This situation made little sense either commercially or technically, and from 1955 onwards several companies, or their setmaking divisions, were taken over by major setmakers: Cossor by Philips, McMichael by Radio and Allied Industries (previously Sobell), Pilot by Ultra, and Dynatron by Ekco, who also took over from Ferranti their brand name only; in 1960–61 K-B acquired no fewer than four brands: Ace, RGD, Argosy and Regentone.[118] Mostly, the major companies simply put their standard chassis into the smaller companies' cabinets. Dynatron, however, were something of a special case, being a family-run business that had been making high-quality radiograms and receivers since the late-1920s, and that had established a reputation for television sets of above-average performance. To maintain this reputation after the takeover, the Ekco chassis fitted to Dynatron receivers were individually checked and aligned, thereby achieving better performance than was realizable under mass production.[37] But it was not so much this absorption of small brands that caused the industry's whole structure to change within the five-year period 1957–62, as crises in the finances of many leading setmakers.

EMI bow out

In the mid-1950s EMI became so hard-pressed financially that a new chief executive's first task on taking over the reins was to go to the city to raise the following week's wages.[41] They were obliged to cut back on their range of activities, and in 1957 stopped making domestic receivers. Since the nadir represented by Model 1807 they had improved their products, notably by developing an electrostatically focused cathode ray tube, but were still hampered by poor components of their own manufacture. Thenceforward the HMV and Marconiphone brands were manufactured by Ferguson, and a new Thorn subsidiary, the British Radio Corporation, was formed to take over their distribution and sales; in the early-1970s the name would be changed to Thorn Consumer Electronics because 'British' was thought to be chauvinistic, 'Radio' incongruous for a company dealing mainly in television, and 'Corporation' unsuitable for a British Limited Company. The licence to use the brands stipulated that they were not to be used on inferior products (although in fact Ferguson engineers had some difficulty in bringing the current HMV television chassis up to standard)[119] and EMI had a right of veto on the appearance of the receivers; distinctive cabinets were designed for them by a small unit within the Ferguson organization. There was little overlap between HMV and Ferguson dealerships, so the deal gave Thorn a greatly increased network.[22] Shortly afterwards, they acquired a fourth brand name by taking over the UK activities of Philco.[120]

The stop/go syndrome

The next stage of consolidation arose from an industry-wide slump in 1960–62. Successive Governments found the receiver industry an ideal instrument for implementing 'stop/go' policies. Not only were its products subject to Purchase Tax, but television sets, which by the late-1950s accounted for four-fifths of the industry's turnover,[91] were mostly acquired either on hire purchase or rental. By changing the minimum down-payment or the maximum repayment period for hire purchase, or the number of weeks' rental to be paid in advance when a rental agreement was signed, the Government could instantly bring about large changes in costs as perceived by the consumer, irrespective of any change in the actual purchase price. And since a television set was still classified as a luxury, relatively little moral outrage was generated by making it less affordable. The main burden of the arrangement fell, of course, on manufacturers, who had to anticipate demand several months in advance and order components accordingly.

It might have been expected, for example, that 1956 would be a good year for television sales, with ITV becoming available to almost 25 million more people. However, hire-purchase deposits were increased to 50% and advance rental to nine months, and the year's turnover on television sets was 18% down on 1955.[80] Trade recovered slowly until the autumn of 1958, when all restrictions on hire purchase and rental were suddenly removed. This generated a full-scale boom. In 1959 the industry disposed of an unprecedented 2.75 million television sets on the home market, producing a turnover 33% up on 1958. No-one expected this level to be sustained in 1960, for with almost 70% of households now possessing a television set the market was at last approaching saturation. However, the downturn was much greater than anticipated, for with what Murphy's E J Power referred to as "an uncanny sense of timing"[121] the Government re-introduced hire purchase and rental controls in April. Stocks of television receivers built up to 1.2 million by August, and the year's turnover on television fell by a disastrous 36%.

A brake failure at Ekco

Surprisingly, the first casualty of this crisis was Ekco, whose post-war record had been one of unalloyed success. In 1951 they were able to claim 50% of the car-radio market,[122] and in 1955 produced a 9" portable television set. This was a thoroughly practical receiver if one ignored its poor VHF-radio facility[37] and remembered its heavy consumption when run off a 12-volt battery; a party on a motor yacht found themselves unable to start their engine after a pleasant evening's viewing.[123] By 1960 the Southend factory covered half a million sq ft and employed 5,500 people. However, when demand fell the Board were unable to prevent Eric Cole, now grown somewhat autocratic, from continuing to have television sets turned out in great numbers; it was rumoured that he was reluctant to let Jules Thorn get too far ahead of him. Stocks piled up and, inevitably, drove Ekco into financial difficulties.[124] Cole had for some months been exploring with

A de Havilland 'Dragon
Rapide' at Southend
Illuminations, 1953

Reco the clown returns to
his caravan. A photograph
issued by Bertram Mills
Circus, giving Ekco's
TMB272 portable television
set the sort of publicity that
money cannot buy

The display window of
Ekco's London Office, 1956

At the 1956 National Radio
Exhibition

Ekco's factory in 1959,
considerably expanded
since the end of the war

354

PROFITS AND DIVIDENDS—1929 to 1960

Year Ended 31st March	Issued Share Capital		Profits Before Tax	Gross Dividends Paid			Bonus Issues on Equity Capital
	Fixed Interest Capital(a)	Equity Capital(b)		Fixed Interest Capital	Equity Capital		
					Amount	Rate Per Cent	
	£	£	£	£	£		

PYE LIMITED

Year Ended 31st March	Fixed Interest Capital(a)	Equity Capital(b)	Profits Before Tax	Fixed Interest Capital	Amount	Rate Per Cent	Bonus Issues on Equity Capital
1930	150,000	30,000	62,686	15,000	30,000	100	
1931	150,000	30,000	68,654	15,000	30,000	100	
1932	150,000	30,000	115,918	15,000	37,500	125	
1933	150,000	30,000	107,804	15,000	37,500	125	
1934	150,000	30,000	51,016	15,000	37,500	125	
1935	150,000	30,000	56,581	15,000	37,500	125	
1936	150,000	30,000	77,110	15,000	37,500	125	
1937	150,000	33,800	123,477	15,000	42,250	125	I for 10
1938	150,000	185,200	101,907	15,000	46,300	25	4 for I
1939	150,000	185,200	74,309	15,000	46,300	25	
1940	150,000	185,200	99,206	15,000	46,300	25	
1941	150,000	185,200	96,440	15,000	46,300	25	
1942	150,000	185,200	96,578	15,000	46,300	25	
1943	150,000	185,200	103,905	15,000	46,300	25	
1944	150,000	185,200	104,660	15,000	46,300	25	
1945	150,000	185,200	108,399	15,000	46,300	25	
1946	150,000	185,200	115,077	15,000	54,017(c)	25	
1947	150,000	216,067	116,543	15,000	54,017	25	
1948	150,000	216,067	202,769	15,000	54,017	25	

PYE GROUP OF COMPANIES

Year Ended 31st March	Fixed Interest Capital(a)	Equity Capital(b)	Profits Before Tax	Fixed Interest Capital	Amount	Rate Per Cent	Bonus Issues on Equity Capital
1948	150,000	216,067	262,807	15,000	54,017	25	
1949	150,000	216,067	271,336	15,000	54,017	25	
1950	150,000	216,067	400,559	15,000	75,624	35	
1951	900,000	432,133	536,930	15,000	77,784	18	I for I
1952	900,000	434,061	611,039	57,531	78,131	18	
1953	900,000	602,862	743,973	52,500	126,922(c)	20	I for 18
1954	900,000	951,912	1,127,886	52,500	190,383	20	I for 2
1955	1,900,000	1,256,523	2,199,302	65,625	315,023(c)	12½	
1956	2,087,000	2,776,703	2,331,848	112,642	347,088	12½	I for I
1957	2,087,000	2,784,515	1,680,660	117,785	348,064	12½	
1958	2,087,000	2,809,077	1,693,765	117,785	351,135	12½	
1959	2,217,500	3,139,778	1,885,423	119,874	392,472	12½	I for 10(d)
1960	2,217,500	5,180,633	2,423,884	121,962	777,095	15	I for 10

Notes:—(a) Fixed Interest Capital includes the following stocks prior to their conversion into 5½% Cumulative Preference Stock in 1958:

    5% Cumulative First Preference Stock
    5½% Cumulative Second Preference Stock
    8% Cumulative Participating Preferred Ordinary Stock.

(b) Equity Capital includes the following stocks prior to their conversion into Ordinary Stock in 1958:

    Deferred Ordinary Stock
    'A' Deferred Ordinary Stock.

(c) Dividends paid on additional capital subscribed after end of year.

(d) This bonus issue was to the then Deferred Ordinary Stockholders only.

St. Clements Press Ltd., 112 Queen Victoria Street, London, E.C.4.

From Pye's Annual report for 1960

C O Stanley the possibility of a Pye–Ekco merger, but the two men were quite incompatible, and it seems unlikely that the negotiations would have been fruitful had the crisis at Ekco not forced Cole's hand. Now, however, a merger was quickly arranged, though Stanley specifically denied that it had been prompted by the slump in television sales, pointing out that through anticipating lower demand Pye had been able to make the necessary reductions in work force through natural wastage.[125] He tactfully refrained from mentioning that Ekco had recently sacked 800 workers.[126] A holding company, British Electronic Industries Ltd, was formed, with Stanley as Chairman and Cole as Vice-Chairman. At its first AGM Stanley admitted to very disappointing results and laid the blame on the Government.[127] The following year, however, he blamed the Ekco takeover, and Cole resigned. Thereafter, Southend was very much under the thumb of Cambridge. Ekco's Technical Director, Tony Martin, had the humiliation of not even being told when designs that he had vetted and approved for production were changed.[124]

Ultra over-extended

In 1961, it was Ultra that fell. Teddy Rosen had never been very interested in financial matters, and it had taken him some time to discover, in the mid-1950s, that the domestic-receiver side of Ultra was being carried by the Special Products Division, engaged in non-entertainment electronics. The prime cause was that the company's selling skills did not match its engineering excellence, but there was also inefficiency in the running of the new Gosport factory, opened in 1956. Although Rosen disliked firing people, several senior executives shortly left the company,[128] and in 1958 he administered what he termed "a dose of salts" by bringing in a notably abrasive manager, Trevor Standeven.[129] Although he amply lived up to his reputation as an autocrat,[45] Standeven also generated within Ultra great enthusiasm and a spirit of adventure, which was linked to the development and launching of the 'Bermuda' range of television receivers. The company's industrial designer, Eric Marshall, achieved a sophisticated presentation that exactly caught the spirit of the times and that sold extremely well, helping the company to achieve its target of 6% of the television market; unfortunately it also proved uneconomically expensive to produce.[130]

With hindsight, the company can be seen to have expanded too quickly in the late-1950s, culminating in the acquisition of Pilot Radio and Television Ltd at the height of the 1959 boom. Early in 1960 Rosen split Ultra's receiver and electronics interests into separate companies under the holding company. Then came the slump, and over twelve months almost £2 million was injected into the receiver company, first by a rights issue then, in April 1961, by selling 40% of the electronics company, which also paid over a dividend. But losses continued, and only a month later the entire radio and television business was sold to Thorn for £2.4 million. "What is left in Ultra now?" asked a headline in the *Financial Times* above an article deploring the fact that some 70% of the group's assets had been sold without reference to the shareholders who, it was estimated, could now expect an after-tax earnings yield of only 2.9%.[131] Rosen retired shortly afterwards — a sad end to a career of great verve and distinction. Jules Thorn, on the other hand, had got for his £2.4 million the almost-new Gosport factory, and its huge adjoining warehouse piled with saleable receivers, as well as one major and one minor brand name. But he had also rescued Ultra from a pitiable state in which manufacture had all but ceased.[45]

A calmer merger

We left Sobell in the late-1940s, established in Hirwaun, South Wales. The company was successful, but still somewhat inexperienced. Not long before August 1952, when the opening of the Wenvoe transmitter brought television to Hirwaun, Kurt Vesely was given his first television set to design. He built one with the aid of a pattern generator and a Mullard Application Report, and when it was finished he tried to pick up Sutton Coldfield, from which a signal was just receivable. It worked, and he saw a television picture for the first time in his life![27]

During one of the industry's periodic downturns in demand Sobell was left with large stocks on his hands when Great Universal Stores (GUS) cancelled their order for television receivers, and he had to borrow money on very unfavourable terms. When the terms of trade improved and GUS again wanted to buy in bulk, Sobell refused. GUS then approached EMI, who accepted the order but would only supply sets under the 'Columbia' marque. As they did not wish to make the sets themselves EMI subcontracted to Sobell, under a contract that had to be honoured even if GUS cancelled the order, which in due course they did. Sobell had not executed the full order, and was in a position to release EMI relatively painlessly from their commitment to take at least £1 million more of stock, through a complex sequence of transactions. EMI purchased Sobell Industries, then sold Michael Sobell back out of that company some physical assets and component stocks, but not its finished stock, at a net cost of £225,000; later this cost was reduced when Sobell bought back the finished stock and the trade mark. Sobell's factory continued throughout to run normally, but his company had now become Radio and Allied Industries (R & A).[26]

During these negotiations Michael Sobell, now over sixty years old, took into partnership his son-in-law, Arnold Weinstock, who was approaching 30 but had not hitherto found a worthy outlet for his evident commercial talents. The company quickly became a byword for economy and efficiency. When their production engineer, John Banner, came across a technique that opened up new possibilities for bent plywood, Weinstock did not rest until R & A were exploiting it to halve the cost of their cabinets. Financial results were outstanding, with pre-tax profits exceeding £1 million in 1956–57, yet because of the industry's known vulnerability to stop/go policies the business was valued at only £2.8 million when it was publicly floated in 1958; the profits made during the boom year 1959–60 were £1.3 million. But Weinstock and Sobell, well aware of the risks of being totally dependent on consumer electronics, were already on the look-out for an opportunity either to sell out or to diversify.

In December 1960 it was put to the newly appointed Chairman of GEC that the combination of R & A's profitability and Weinstock's managerial skills could revitalize GEC's own lacklustre performance in radio and television and in domestic appliances, which had between them lost nearly a million pounds over the preceding nine months; R & A, even under slump conditions, were still comfortably in profit.[132] Within three months GEC had bought R & A for a little over £8 million

An early Sobell television
receiver, 1949

Sobell development laboratory, c. 1954

Murphy Radio in 1956

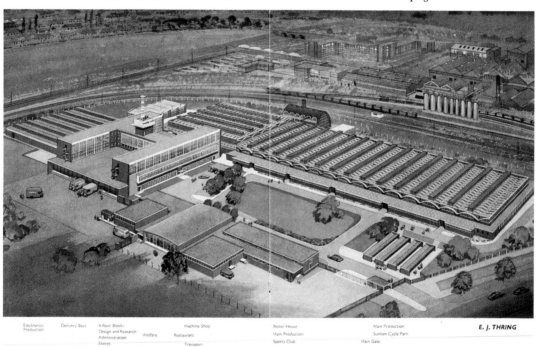

Electronics Production | Delivery Bays | 4-floor Block: Design and Research Administration Stores Plating Shop behind | | Welfare | Machine Shop Restaurant Transport | | Boiler House Main Production Sports Club | | Main Production Sunken Cycle Park Main Gate | | E. J. THRING

Headquarters and Main Factory of Murphy Radio Ltd at Welwyn Garden City

— some three times its valuation three years previously — to form a radio and television business commanding almost a sixth of the home market.[133] Weinstock became joint managing director of domestic appliances in addition to radio and television. He visited the television factory at Coventry, which was on four floors and, though more highly mechanized than R & A's Hirwaun factory, much less efficient. He judged the television sets being made there to be unsaleably ugly, and gave orders that, after existing commitments had been met, production should cease and the sets be cleared by making price cuts of around 20%, with full rebates to the trade.[26] The press interpreted these cuts as merely a more extreme version of what other companies had been doing for some months.[134] Rationalization of the group followed. Although GEC had never made much impact on the post-war radio and television scene it contained a great deal of engineering talent, and a number of engineers from the Coventry factory became valued members of the new organization's radio and television laboratories;[27] these were at Slough, in the premises of the McMichael company, which R & A had acquired in 1956. Trevor Standeven, who had been at R & A before Rosen had employed him to purge inefficiency at Ultra, now returned from Thorn to take overall charge of the radio and television operation.[135]

Two suitors for Murphy

Through the post-war years Murphy maintained their tradition of good engineering and stylish cabinets; they extended the principle of their 'baffle' set to console radios and, later, made television sets in moulded plywood cabinets wrapped around the picture tube so that the screen filled the entire frontal area. The cabinet was a major item in the costing of a receiver, and this technique enabled them to produce a competitive set without lowering their technical standards. In common with their competitors they expanded to meet growing demand, and laid plans for a custom-built factory on an industrial estate in Skegness, having already taken over two sections of the town's Winter Gardens. Although the new factory, with a projected work force of around 600, did not represent a major expansion of the company, which held about 6% of the television market, its timing was singularly unhappy. No sooner had Skegness Council agreed to its being built[136] than Murphy announced a £76,000 loss for 1960, following a £660,000 profit in 1959,[137] and in February 1962, only three months after the factory opened, Power was negotiating to sell out. He had decided that no television manufacturer could survive in the 1960s without a strong presence in the rental field, and at 62 had no wish to dispose of a large portion of his holdings in the company to acquire one. Initially, Power entered into discussions with Jules Thorn,[138] but being unable to discern just why Thorn should want Murphy, feared that negotiations might be prolonged and perhaps inconclusive. Accordingly, when the Rank Organisation subsequently made a more positive approach,[139] Power and his family agreed to their buying control of the company.

Murphy was to run in harness with Bush, which had been part of the Rank Organisation since 1945. Dealers were assured that Murphy's separate identity would be "jealously guarded", while staff were told that they still worked for Murphy Radio — only the top management structure had changed.[140] The Murphy brand was indeed retained after the two companies were merged, as Rank Bush Murphy, but although Murphy had good design and production staff, within a year very few of them were left in the company apart from the Industrial Design unit, which had been responsible for cabinets.[141]

Deals in devices [40,142]

Consolidation also took place in the early-1960s among valve and semiconductor manufacturers, with varying degrees of success. In 1960 Jules Thorn, wishing to have a valve-making company within his group, took over Brimar Valves and Tubes from Standard Telephones and Cables. It proved a disappointing acquisition. Brimar applied less rigorous test procedures than Mazda even to the 'industrial' range they

Early transistor manufacture at Salford Electrical Instruments, Stockport, 1958

Lord Chandos, Chairman of AEI, visits their semiconductor factory at Tottenham in the mid-1960s

Valves and tubes within the AEI group, 1916–1966

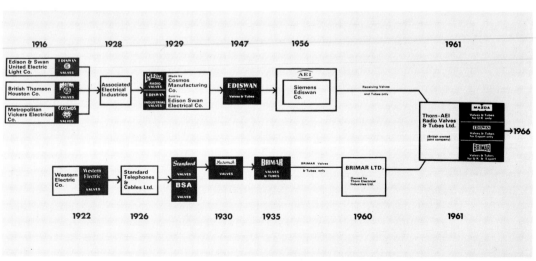

supplied to such users as the Post Office, and only one of their 'entertainment' valves was judged good enough to go into Thorn receivers. To retrieve the situation, Thorn took over in 1961 the management of AEI's valve and semiconductor interests, in a jointly owned company Thorn-AEI Radio Valves and Tubes Ltd; an unfortunate aspect of this sequence of events was that it gave Brimar's staff seniority over Mazda's.

Prior to the Thorn merger, Mazda had developed a range of germanium transistors at Brimsdown, but under the new regime the high-frequency types were discontinued and for a time Thorn-AEI made only low-frequency transistors for use in Thorn receivers. Mullard, meanwhile, had produced a new generation of germanium transistors capable of amplifying VHF. Mazda now attempted a leap-frog operation by negotiating with American General Electric to manufacture plastic-encapsulated silicon transistors, but were unable to secure the rights on terms that would have been competitive, and the exercise was abandoned when another American manufacturer, Fairchild, flooded the European market with an all-conquering range of cheap high-performance transistors made by silicon-planar technology; having invested a lot of money in germanium, Thorn was not prepared to re-engineer for silicon. The tradition of the Mazda Applications Laboratory was extended to transistors in a new laboratory at Brimsdown, which pioneered the considerable changes in domestic-receiver design made necessary by the move from germanium to silicon transistors, but as the company were never a significant supplier of either type, this yielded little commercial benefit.

Mullard managed the transition from germanium to silicon more successfully. In 1961 they pooled their semiconductor resources with those of GEC to form Associated Semiconductor Manufacturers Ltd (ASM),[143] and thereby gained access to American work on silicon-planar technology.

Crisis at BREMA

When BREMA was formed in 1944, its constitution was designed to maintain an equitable balance of power among its forty or so member companies. Voting power at General Meetings was related to turnover, as were subscriptions, and the Association was governed by an annually elected Council of twelve members, who were either heads or senior executives of twelve companies that gave a fair representation of the industry as a whole. Each was entitled to a single vote, and although in fact formal voting seldom took place the Council's decisions obviously tended to reflect majority opinion among members attending its meetings. This arrangement worked well enough until consolidation upset it. By 1962 some 75% of the setmaking industry's turnover came from five major groups: British Electronic Industries Ltd (i.e. Pye/Ekco), Rank Bush Murphy, GEC/Radio & Allied Industries Ltd, Philips Electrical Ltd and Thorn Electrical Industries Ltd. And no group was willing to have two or possibly three important executives, representing separate trading companies, devoting time to BREMA affairs merely to ensure its due influence on the twelve-man Council.

As a result, GEC/Radio and Allied Industries Ltd tendered their resignation, while Pye, currently outside the Association, declined to re-join. BREMA's Director, S E Allchurch, thought that the constitutional changes required to meet this situation would be so radical that it would be best to wind up the Association and start afresh.[144] However, the necessary changes were made without going to this extreme, and everyone duly returned to the fold. Reconciliation had come about through private meetings of the heads of the five groups, under Jules Thorn's leadership,[145] and the Association's governing body was now to consist simply of these five people. Its day-to-day business was in the hands of a nine-member Executive Council comprising representatives of each of the five groups and of four companies elected annually from the rest of the membership[146]; subsequently, in 1965, full powers were given to the Executive Council, and the five-man body became purely advisory.[147]

405 lines under notice

In 1960 the Postmaster General appointed a Committee, under Sir Harry Pilkington, to consider the future of broadcasting, and a bewildering range of possibilities came under examination. Foremost were the creation of a third television network, colour television, and the extension of television broadcasting into Bands IV & V, in the ultra-high-frequency (UHF) spectrum. Britain's massive commitment to 405 lines, with over ten million licences in force,[89] added unwelcome complication at every turn. The 625-line standard was by then firmly established in Europe and many other areas, and the prospect of perpetuating Britain's isolation by embarking on major new developments with the world's lowest line-standard was unattractive. The high visibility of its scanning lines was already setting a limit to picture size; in 1958 five-sixths of the receivers being sold in Britain had 17" tubes, but sales of 21" sets had actually fallen, from 8% the previous year to a mere 5%, whereas this tube size predominated overseas.[148]

Recommendations submitted to the Pilkington Committee by the Television Advisory Committee, and favouring a progressive change-over to 625 lines, were based on exhaustive tests by the BBC, the ITA,

An exhibition at the headquarters of the wholesalers Brown Bros, in Great Eastern Street, 1963

Pye's 1958–59 Annual Report ridicules Britain's continuing adherence to 405 lines

K-B were still using hand-wired tag-board assembly in this dual-standard receiver of the mid-1960s, here undergoing test and alignment

the Post Office and the industry, but were confined to technical considerations. The Memorandum submitted in December 1960 by the Radio Industry Council (RIC), representing BREMA members and component manufacturers, was mainly about commercial aspects. It recommended introducing a third network on 405 lines at VHF, and using 405 lines at UHF for any further networks, thereby avoiding the expense of dual-standard receivers and minimizing the problem of obsolescence.[149] Of all possibile paths forward this was the least likely to put people off buying new 405-line sets, at a time when warehouses were full of them, and there were allegations in the Press, strongly denied by BREMA, that this consideration had influenced the recommendation.[150]

Christmas at K-B in the mid-1960s

*At the last Radio Show, held at Earls Court in 1964.
Left to right: Lord Hill (Postmaster-General),
C O Stanley, Dennis Bates (Exhibition Officer),
S E Allchurch (Director of BREMA) and Harry Roberts*

DECCA DR122

New Price—99 gns.

DR122 23″ Television complete with UHF tuner and matching stand— 109 gns

A dual-standard receiver,
1965

Pye, who had not been members of BREMA since 1953, rejoined the Association in 1960, in the belief that it was going to promote the 625-line standard, of which C O Stanley was a passionate advocate.[151] Almost immediately the RIC Memorandum showed otherwise, and

Stanley re-resigned. As unwilling to refrain from rocking the boat on this issue as he had been on tunable receivers in 1954, he got Ekco to withdraw their support for the RIC Memorandum, thereby destroying the unanimity of BREMA members' backing. A month or two before the 1961 Radio Show he told its organizers that he refused to accept the restrictions they were trying to impose on the demonstration of 625-line television,[152] thereby obliging the rest of the industry to follow suit.[89] In the interests of secrecy, Pye had not done their 625-line work in their Television lab; a UHF/VHF tuner was developed by a 'Special Projects' engineer, and everything else by a German engineer who was engaged specially and attached to the Radio lab.[56] The upshot was that at the Radio Show Pye and Ekco showed a fully engineered dual-standard receiver, whereas other setmakers could only show 625 lines on sets allegedly demonstrating how their 405-line models could later be adapted to that standard, while praying that no-one would ever actually insist that this be done.[153]

The Pilkington Committee's Report was published in June 1962, followed by White Papers to enable its recommendations to be implemented. These were that the BBC should provide the next additional television programme, that it should be transmitted in UHF Bands IV & V on 625 lines, and that the two existing networks should continue on 405 lines VHF but be duplicated on 625 lines UHF as soon as possible. There would be room for a fourth network on UHF, and eventually for two more on VHF when the 405-line service was withdrawn. No decision was reached on the introduction of colour beyond the fact that it should be on 625 lines and should be "compatible" — that is, satisfactorily receivable on black-and-white receivers.

Setmakers duly produced the necessary dual-standard receivers. The '405/625' switch was of great complexity, for changing over from 405 to 625 affected most of the set's functions. A UHF tuner was substituted for the VHF one, different tuned circuits were used throughout the intermediate-frequency stages. The video signal modulated the carrier negatively instead of positively, and the sound signal used FM instead of AM. Finally, the line output stage and its EHT circuitry had to run half as fast again. All this only increased the pre-tax price of a typical set, now with a 19" tube, from about £50 to £60.

The new network, BBC2, opened from Crystal Palace on 20 April, 1964, after a publicity campaign unaccountably centred on a pair of toy kangaroos, 'Hullabaloo' and 'Custard'. It was sheer ill luck that Greater London suffered a massive power failure on the opening night, but it soon became apparent that BBC2 lacked the thrust to launch 625-line television successfully. The BBC had assured the Pilkington Committee that its new network, while complementing its existing one, would not be given a minority character, but since BBC1 continued to compete with ITV it was inevitable that BBC2 should acquire a highbrow image. Some wag christened it "the great unwatched", and BREMA reported that "public reaction to BBC2 had proved apathetic."[154] At the beginning of 1964 it had been expected that there would be a second commercial network within two or three years, but with the return of a Labour Government in October this expectation faded. Only the prospect of colour television gave the industry any grounds for optimism.

References

1   *Wireless World*, June 1946, editorial
2   Report from Export Policy Committee, 18 June 1945: BREMA Archives
3   BREMA Annual report dated 6/12/46
4   Minutes of Executive Council meetings, 21 February &
    21 March 1945: BREMA Archives
5   Gerald Wells, private conversation with Gordon Bussey, 1990
6   Monopolies & Restrictive Practices Commission *Report on the Supply of
    Electronic Valves and Cathode Ray Tubes* (HMSO,1956), para 78
7   Michael Mason, The BVA: A Personal Memoir (Unpublished, 1986) p. 6
8   Monopolies Commission, op. cit., paras 61(c), 235–6
9   Bernard Rogers, private conversation, 1990
10 *Wireless World*, June 1946, p. 193
11 BREMA Annual Report dated 19 December 1947
12 BREMA Annual Report dated 25 February 1949
13 John Street, private conversation, 1989
14 E Brian Munt, A Short History of Ediswan, Brimar and Mazda
    (Unpublished, 1989)
15 Monopolies Commission, op. cit., para 340
16 Correlli Barnett, *The Audit of War* (Macmillan, 1986) p. 179
17 *The Gramophone*, September 1946, pp. 54–5
18 Thermionic Valves 1904–1954 (IEE, 1955) p. 49
19 Dennis Lisney, private correspondence, 1989
20 Laurence Orchard, private conversations, 1989-90
21 Rosaleen Smyth, *The Saucepan Special* (*BVWS Bulletin*, Vol. **2,** No. 3, p. 42)
22 K G Beauchamp, *John Sargrove — Innovator and Pioneer of Automation,*
    (Eighth I EE Weekend Meeting on the History of Electrical Engineering,
    Imperial College, July1980)
23 Dickie Norman, private conversation, 1989
24 Jack Wilson, private conversation, 1989
25 Old members' file, BREMA Archives
26 Lord Weinstock, private conversation, 1990
27 Kurt Vesely, private conversation, 1989
28 BREMA Annual Report dated 6 December 1946
29 Historical notes and covering letter, C C Moore to Sir John Davis, 9 March
    1978: Gordon Bussey Collection
30 Robin Day, private conversation, 1988
31 *Wireless World*, June 1946, p. 193
32 Peter L Mothersole, *The Evolution of the Domestic Television Receiver* (Royal
    Television Society, 1988) p. 9
33 *Wireless World*, September 1948, p. 338
34 Stuart McCrerie, private conversation, 1980
35 *Television & Short-Wave World*, September 1939, p. 538
36 Norman Leaks, private correspondence with Gordon Bussey,1988
37 Gerald Wells, private conversation, 1990
38 S G Sturmey, *The Economic Development of Radio* (London, Gerald Duckworth
    & Co Ltd, 1958) pp. 231–2
39 A G Priestley, private conversation, 1988
40 Bill Taylor, private conversation, 1988
41 Jim Lodge, private conversation, 1989
42 John Brace, private correspondence, 1988

43   Gordon Bussey, private conversation, 1990

44   Derek Martin, *Thorn EMI: 50 Years in Radar* (Thorn EMI plc, 1986) p. 19

45   Doug Topping, private correspondence, 1989

46   *Television*, Spring 1949, pp. 36–7

47   BREMA Annual Report for 1949

48   BREMA Annual Report for 1954

49   Syd Westwood, private conversation, 1990

50   Circular, *Television Publicity*, 22 December 1953: BREMA Archives

51   *Daily Herald*, 20 June 1952

52   *The Observer*, 21 August 1960, p. 3

53   Letter, C O Stanley to P H Spagnoletti, 21 July 1953: BREMA Archives

54   Letter, C G Rieck to Secretary of BREMA, 4 November 1953: BREMA Archives

55   Taped copy of disc recording made at the close of business, 1958, lent by Norman Leaks

56   Norman Leaks, private correspondence and conversations, 1988–90

57   James Gildea, private correspondence and conversations, 1988–90

58   Transcript of evidence, pp10–11: Mullard Archives

59   Notes on a discussion with Miss Perkins, 1969: Mullard Archives

60   BREMA Annual Report for 1947

61   Monopolies Commission Report, para 288

62   *Television and the Viewer*, September 1950, pp. 16–17

63   Monopolies Commission Report, para 290

64   Transcript of talk with Mr van Hoorn, 1967: Mullard Archives

65   S S Eriks, transcript of evidence to the Monopolies Commission: Mullard Archives

66   Monopolies Commission Report, para 292

67   Frank Pack, private correspondence, 1989

68   Maurice Bennett, private conversation, 1990

69   Peter Degan, private conversation, 1990

70   Typescript *The Monopolies and Restrictive Practices Commission (Basic Facts)* (Undated): Mullard Archives

71   Cecil Payne, private conversation, 1989

72   Dr Alan Rose, private conversation, 1989

73   Edwin Birch, private conversation, 1989

74   Keith Trace, *A History of the Plessey Company* (Unpublished, c.1971), passim: Plessey Archives

75   Maurice Eley, private conversation, 1988

76   Bill Dalziel, private conversations, 1988–90

77   R C G Williams, private conversation, 1989

78   Sid Perry, private conversation, 1990
      Alfred Priestley, private correspondence and conversations, 1988–90

80   BREMA Annual Report for 1956

81   K Mumby, *Dynamic Approach to Handling in TV and Radio Manufacture - Part II, (Mechanical Handling*, November 1957)

82   New Scientist, 30 January 1986, p. 67

83   Monopolies Commission Report on the proposed merger

	between Thorn Electrical Industries Ltd and Radio Rentals Ltd, 1968
84	Memorandum *RE: 'AMBASSADOR'*: BREMA Archives
85	Tom Ludlow, private conversation, 1989
86	"The house that Jules Thorn built", Financial Times, 24 November 1970
87	Reg Gray, private conversation, 1989
88	*Wireless World*, September 1946, editorial
89	Keith Jones, private conversation, 1990
90	Second Report of the Television Advisory Committe, 1952 (HMSO,1954)
91	BREMA Annual Report for 1959
92	R V Harvey, letter in the IEE's *Electronics & Power*, c.1986
93	*The Gramophone*, March 1949, editorial
94	B R Carson, A D Burt & H I Reiskind, A record changer and record of complementary design (RCA Review, June 1939, pp. 173–190)
95	*Wireless World*, October 1950, p. 340b
96	*Wireless World*, September 1950, p. 307
97	Ruth Edge, private correspondence, 1990
98	R W Bayliff, Some aspects of gramophone pick-up design (Proc.IEE, Vol 109, Pt B No 45, May 1962, pp. 233–43
99	Keith Geddes, personal recollection
100	R W Bayliff, private correspondence, 1989
101	*Vidor-Burndept Magazine*, Christmas 1953, p. 9: Gordon Bussey Collection
102	Information supplied by Percy Chapman
103	John E Lentakis, private correspondence, 1990
104	Zbigniew Banks, private conversations, 1989-90
105	*Vidor-Burndept Magazine*, March 1954, p. 9: Gordon Bussey Collection
106	*Wireless and Electrical Trader*, 18 September 1954
107	Information supplied by Gordon Bussey
108	Keith Geddes & Gordon Bussey, *The History of Roberts Radio* (Roberts Radio Co Ltd, 1987)
109	Alec Jones, private conversations, 1989/90
110	Derek Willmott, private correspondence, 1989
111	*The Star* , 30 August 1957
112	*Perdio News*, Issue 1 (February 1960): Gordon Bussey Collection
113	*Sunday Dispatch*, 5 February 1961
114	*Perdio News*, Issue 4 (January 1961): Gordon Bussey Collection
115	Letter from C E Pickard of Lugton & Co, quoted in Perdio News Issue 7 (January 1963): Gordon Bussey Collection
116	BREMA Annual Reports for 1961 and 1964
117	Chris Pickard, private conversation, 1990
118	Roy Browning, private correspondence, 1988
119	Sid Jones, private conversation, 1990
120	*Financial Times*, 29 October 1960, p. 7
121	Murphy Radio AGM, 26 May 1961
122	Silver Jubilee booklet published by Ekco in 1951
123	Information supplied by Gordon Bussey
124	M J Lipman, *Memoirs of a Socialist Business Man* (Lipman Trust, c.1976) pp. 178–9

125   *The Observer,* 30 October 1960
126   *Financial Times,* 29 October 1960
127   *Evening Standard,* 10 November 1961
128   Letters in 'Old Members' file: BREMA Archives
129   Alan Bamford, private conversation, 1990
130   David Hewitt, private conversation, 1990
131   *Financial Times,* 15 May 1961, p. 1
132   Robert Jones and Oliver Marriott, *Anatomy of a Merger* (London, Jonathan Cape,1970) pp. 209–13
133   *Financial Times,* 1 March 1961
134   *Financial Times,* 7 April 1961
135   *Electrical & Radio Trading,* 9 September 1961
136   *RBM News,* July 1971: Gordon Bussey Collection
137   *Financial Times,* 5 May 1961
138   *Financial Times,* 23 February 1962
139   E J Power, private conversation, 1990
140   *Murphy News,* Special Edition, July 1962
141   Wally Hull, private correspondence, 1989
142   Dennis Harvey, private conversation, 1989
143   Robert Clayton and Joan Algar, *The GEC Research Laboratories 1919–1984* (London, Peter Peregrinus Ltd, 1989) pp. 219–20
144   Memorandum on BREMA Organisation 5 June 1962: BREMA Archives
145   Minutes of Special Meeting of Executive Council, 25 June 1962: BREMA Archives
146   BREMA Annual Report for 1962
147   BREMA Annual Report for 1965
148   BREMA Annual Report for 1958
149   *Memorandum to the Committee on Broadcasting,* The Radio Industry Council, 30 December 1960: BREMA Archives
150   Letter, Allchurch to Stanley, 30 June 1961: Pye file, BREMA Archives
151   Pye Annual Report, 1958–59
152   Letter, Stanley to Radio Industry Exhibition Co Ltd, 21 June 1961: Pye file, BREMA Archives
153   Sid Westwood, private conversation, 1990
154   BREMA Annual Report for 1964, p. 5

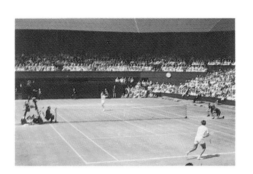

6 • *Broadening Horizons*

Colour research at Ekco in the early-1960s, after the company had been taken over by Pye

Getting into Colour

Britain did not rush into colour television any more than she did into VHF radio. When the Pilkington Committee reported in 1962, there had been colour broadcasting in America for eight years, but it had not yet 'taken off'. Although the basic techniques were sound, the receivers of the period had neither the performance nor the stability to encourage widespread ownership, and under a regime of commercial broadcasting this produced the vicious circle that there were few colour programmes because there were few colour receivers, and vice versa.

Practical colour television had depended upon getting round two seemingly insoluble problems: transmitting the extra information required without overflowing the existing channels or upsetting monochrome receivers, and producing a compact display device that could reproduce any colour at any point. The first had been tackled in 1950 by the combined efforts of leading companies in the American radio industry, which placed generous resources at the disposal of its own National Television Systems Committee.[1] In an outstanding *tour de force* they produced the 'NTSC' system which, together with its derivatives, has remained the principal basis of colour television worldwide. Judiciously exploiting the human eye's limitations, it adds a low-definition colouring signal to the black-and-white signal; this colouring signal is decoded by colour receivers but is visible on monochrome receivers only as a fine dot-pattern in highly coloured areas. The display problem was solved by a single company. RCA mounted a massive assault, developing several ideas concurrently, and produced the 'shadow-mask' tube, from which most present-day colour tubes are directly descended. Early types, however, had a very narrow scanning-angle and thus were inordinately long; indeed, it was only after seeing RCA's first rectangular-screen tubes, on one of his annual visits to America, that Jules Thorn told his staff that he was now prepared to consider making colour sets.[2]

The choices

The success of colour would depend above all on setmakers producing receivers whose performance, stability and reliability would persuade the public to pay three or four times the price of a black-and-white set. Thus the receiver-industry's views on how colour should be introduced in Britain carried a lot of weight in the Television Advisory Committee's Technical Sub-Committee (TAC/TSC). That influence was enhanced by BREMA having as its principal representative a skilled and forceful advocate, Keith Jones, and by the considerable technical support he received from member companies. Although Jones worked for Thorn Electrical Industries, it was mainly through collaboration with Bernard Rogers, of Bush Radio's Advance Development Laboratory, and with Dr A J Biggs, of GEC's Hirst Research Centre,[2] that he derived the experimental data that enabled BREMA to make a contribution comparable with those of the broadcasting authorities and the Post Office.

By the time Britain needed to make its decisions on colour, in the mid-1960s, the NTSC system was under challenge from two European derivatives, designed to overcome the colour errors that it often produced under operational conditions. 'SECAM', from France, differs quite substantially from NTSC, and ran through numerous modifications before finally being adopted by France, Russia and East European countries; it concerns us only insofar as France's relentless advocacy of it tended to obscure the technical issues at international meetings convened to establish a common standard. A year or two after SECAM, but differing much less from NTSC, came 'PAL'. This was a German invention, although the UK made significant contributions to the specification as finally adopted. The coding of the colouring signal is changed on alternate scanning lines, in such a way that any distortions imposed on the signal produce, during successive lines, errors of equal magnitude but opposite sign. A glass delay-line makes the two signals available simultaneously, enabling them to be averaged so that their errors cancel.

In the TAC/TSC deliberations on the choice of colour system, the BBC initially favoured NTSC rather than PAL, primarily because it produced a less disturbing dot pattern on monochrome receivers, but also because the additional circuitry in a PAL receiver, and especially its glass delay-line, would make it more expensive. However, BREMA soon developed a strong preference for PAL. The visibility of dot patterns was less of a problem in the home than in the laboratory, because few black-and-white receivers reproduced the dots at full intensity. BREMA conceded that PAL receivers would initially cost 3.5% more, but held that this would be partially offset by lower maintenance costs[3] and would in any case fall rapidly once sets were in mass production.[2] The cost to the setmaker of a PAL receiver's glass delay line did in fact fall from £1 to 30p over a ten-year period despite inflation.[4] But far more important to BREMA was the fact that PAL receivers were highly immune to colour errors. Broadcasters, they felt, did not sufficiently understand the problems of producing receivers of adequate and stable performance, particularly as it was anticipated that initially these would use valves; whereas broadcasters can keep signals within tight tolerances through constant monitoring and adjustment, a domestic receiver is expected to run for years without attention. The presence of an arbitrary 'hue' control on NTSC receivers, moreover, inevitably undermined broadcasters' incentive to maintain strict standards from camera to transmitter, and in America had prompted the cynical observation that NTSC stood for "Never twice the same colour".[5] Britain's eventual change to wholehearted support for PAL was based partly upon such technical considerations, and partly on the desirability of using the same coding system as most other European countries, in order to facilitate exports and the exchange of programmes. The international discussions that led to the adoption of PAL by all European countries except France and the Soviet bloc involved much wheeling and dealing, and Bernard Rogers' fluency in German proved a considerable asset to the British delegation.

In 1965–66, concurrently with the international discussions on colour systems, there was a strong lobby for adding colour to BBC1 and ITV on their existing 405-line VHF services rather than duplicating them on 625 lines UHF as recommended by the Pilkington Committee. In part this simply reflected a loss of nerve, as early indications from reception of BBC2 confirmed that it would take many years and many hundreds of transmitters to give UHF anything like the almost total coverage already achieved at VHF.[6] But the ITV companies were also keen on 405-line colour for the purely commercial reason that it would give them an immediate mass audience for colour, while the BBC's Director General, Hugh Carleton Greene, saw it as a way of getting colour started in 1966 to mark the twentieth anniversary of the re-opening of BBC television. The TAC/TSC was divided,[7] with Keith Jones firmly against the idea; it was essentially a makeshift which would have carried long-term penalties, committing the public to inferior pictures on the two networks they watched most, and to receivers made more expensive and less satisfactory by having to produce colour pictures on two different line-standards. Jones secured the backing of his employer, Jules Thorn, who let it be known that he would refuse to make the necessary receivers,[2] while he himself refused to associate BREMA with a Committee Paper favourable to 405-line colour. Rather than have the paper go forward to the TAC with a note of BREMA's dissension, the Chairman invited Jones to co-operate with the Secretary in producing a revised version,[6] and as a result the TAC advised the Postmaster General in November 1965 that colour should be transmitted on 625 lines only.[8] However, in less official circles the idea of 405-line colour refused to lie down, and it was not until February 1967 that the Government made a statement finally disposing of it, so that the industry could get on with designing sets.[9]

Colour at half cock: 1967–69

It was finally announced in March 1967 that BBC2 would begin a colour service — Europe's first — later in the year. The official opening on 2 December was preceded by a launching period that began with the Wimbledon Tennis Championships in July and included films and occasional studio broadcasts. This established the excellence of the BBC's pictures, but came too soon after the final decision on standards for the industry to have made many sets. By the end of the year only 32,000 had been produced,[9] and many of the first models marketed were of somewhat immature design.[10] As with any other new and prestigious product, there was an initial demand from those who had to have colour receivers almost regardless of cost, but once this was satisfied the rate of disposal actually declined; in 1968, colour

From breadboard to
showroom: the evolution of
the Ferguson 2000-series
all-transistor colour
receiver of 1967

*The 2000 receiver was
totally new in every
particular, and the
designer's bench was even
more precarious than usual*

*The bench prototype, with
a lot of tidying up still
to be done*

*The completed set and its
ten plug-in circuit boards*

Topping out the 2000

Ready for the customer

Sir Jules Thorn takes HRH The Duke of Edinburgh on a tour of Ferguson's headquarters at Enfield, 1970

sets accounted for only one in fifteen of manufacturers' disposals.[11] Since only the least popular of the three networks was available in colour, acquiring a dual-standard colour set was an inherently unattractive proposition, particularly as single-standard models would obviously be cheaper, and in fact turned out to be so by 15–20% when they appeared in Autumn 1969.[12] One manufacturer, K-B, which had made a notably successful dual-standard monochrome portable, bypassed the dual-standard colour set altogether.[13]

The dual-standard interlude nevertheless enabled manufacturers to gain useful experience of colour sets before moving into top gear in 1969. Two Ferguson engineers, John Bussell and Sid Jones, were sent over to America in 1966 to study current American practice and then to decide whether Ferguson should use valves or transistors in their own sets. Bussell and Jones had a preference for transistors, but this was not shared by their colleagues and they suspected that they were being sent over to cure them of it; the sets had to be in production within two years, so there was a strong case for using well-established technology. They found the American consumer-electronics industry at a low ebb, its engineering talent drawn into military projects by the Vietnam war. Colour sets used valves exclusively, and most still used hand wiring, not printed-circuit boards. Semiconductor manufacturers, however, were producing a range of transistors and diodes that seemed capable of covering every function in a colour receiver. The engineers came home and announced that they would make an all-transistor colour set, conscious that by doing so they were throwing away any excuse for failure.

At one point things did go badly wrong. The receiver's line-output stage and its separate (though synchronized) EHT generator both used a type of transistor designed and made for a military radar by the British arm of Texas Instruments (TI), who had assessed its rating only for this one application. Although the television engineers were operating it within that rating it was in fact being over-run, and one of them recalls steadily filling glass sweet-jars with burnt-out transistors at £14 a time. Fortunately there was excellent collaboration between the two firms, and when the problem was finally identified TI changed the transistor's design to overcome it. The resulting '2000 series' receiver, launched in 1967, was the world's first large-screen all-transistor colour receiver, and well up to contemporary standards of performance and reliability. It was, however, expensive to produce, and Jules Thorn (*Sir* Jules since 1964) repeated his grumble of twenty years previously, though it was now quite a sheaf of £10 notes that he was putting into the back of every set. The power supply was one of the design's costlier features, and Ferguson's Chairman, Dickie Norman, ordered the engineer responsible, Sid Jones, to produce for the next generation of receiver something at half the volume, half the weight and half the cost. The switched-mode circuit that Jones developed to meet this requirement became the standard configuration for power supplies world-wide, and remains so in 1990.[14]

Concurrently Rank Bush Murphy, in collaboration with Plessey, were pioneering the next stage in the evolution of the television receiver: the development of analogue integrated circuits (ICs), each carrying out some function hitherto requiring a substantial number of transistors and other discrete components. In June 1968 they announced the first IC in the world to carry out the complex functions of decoding a PAL colour signal. It was to be used in that autumn's new models, and would replace 65 discrete components occupying an area of 36 square inches.[15]

Events of the Dual-Standard Years (1964–69)
Pye lose control
Early in 1966 a number of Pye's Directors, uneasy over the group's finances, elected to the Board F B Duncan, Chairman of one of the group's subsidiary companies, and shortly appointed him Deputy Chairman. Finding the Radio and Television Division making serious losses and the financial position critical, he arranged for a firm of consulting accountants to investigate Pye's affairs.[16] It was under these unhappy circumstances that on 4 May C O Stanley, now 67, retired as Chairman and became Honorary President. The following day he took the chair at the Annual Dinner of the Radio and Television Industry, a starry occasion with guests ranging from Quintin Hogg to Bud Flanagan, which naturally turned into a celebration of his career. Most people in the room knew that Pye were in trouble, but that

merely added to the affection with which Stanley was regarded. He had always been a maverick, often a prima donna, and sometimes a braggart, but few could resist his Irish charm, and for forty years the industry had been the richer for his vision and enthusiasm. Stanley received many compliments from his peers, including Sir Jules Thorn, and paid one in his turn, referring to Harry 'Portable' Roberts as "one of the best-loved and certainly the biggest-hearted man in the Industry".[17] But the strains of "For he's a jolly good fellow" at the Dorchester were only a bitter-sweet interlude in the sustained discord at Cambridge.

Duncan took over as Chairman, and the Board immediately dismissed Stanley's son John from his position as Deputy Managing Director. John Stanley issued a writ for wrongful dismissal but refused to leave the Board, and a resolution to remove him from office was put on the Agenda of the AGM in November. Meanwhile, the accountants had submitted their report. Ironically, Pye had made the same mistake that had delivered Ekco into their hands a few years previously: maintaining television-set production at a higher level than demand justified. But they had made matters worse by their attempts to dispose of the sets. They had acquired a number of rental and retail businesses, then poured money into expanding them (in one case from 20 to 140 establishments) without ensuring that their managements were up to the task, and had granted them large amounts of credit on unduly generous terms without exercising proper financial control. As a result, far more sets had left the factories than had gone out to paying customers.[18] Most damning of all, Pye had lent one of these businesses funds to buy more shares in its own subsidiary, at what the accountants considered an altogether excessive price, and some of the purchase consideration had been received by directors and employees of the Pye group.[16] At the AGM the shareholders duly unseated John Stanley. A few days previously he had circulated to shareholders a letter exculpating himself from blame for the company's troubles, but Duncan had countered with another letter pinning it back onto him;[19] three years later, he settled out of court for what he described as a "very substantial" payment, and a statement that at no time had the boards of the Pye companies doubted his integrity and honour.[20]

Within a week of the AGM Philips had made an opening bid for Pye shares, soon countered by Thorn, who were keen to acquire the group's profitable Telecommunications side, and GEC's Arnold Weinstock also made an approach, though it came to nothing.[21] But by the end of the year Philips had built up a commanding stake through brokers, and had made a firm offer that led to their gaining a 60% shareholding early in 1967. To obtain governmental approval for the takeover Philips had to give the Trade Secretary, Anthony Wedgwood Benn, an assurance that Pye's separate British identity would be preserved,[22] and that the group, Britain's largest exporter of radio and television sets, would continue to maintain a surplus of exports over imports. As a result, Pye retained a considerable degree of autonomy, and television receivers continued to be designed and built at their Lowestoft factory.[18] The Ekco factory at Southend had been closed early in 1966, in belated recognition of the group's over-capacity. It was gutted, then lavishly re-built by Philips for a projected high-technology venture. Before this could be implemented, however, changing market conditions caused Philips to sell it to the Access

Bank Credit Card Consortium as their computer centre and offices.[23] The factory was largely a casualty of successive Governments' manipulation of demand through credit restrictions; it now became the headquarters of an organization that was to make such restrictions much less effective.

Sacrifice of a pawn

In November 1967 GEC took over AEI, which had been seriously under-performing for some years.[24] The take-over, vigorously opposed by AEI, received governmental blessing as a means of rationalizing the heavy-electrical industry, which was facing over-capacity as CEGB orders tailed off.[25] Its consequences for the Thorn-AEI component operation were mere incidentals, though none the less devastating for that. Only five months previously, Thorn and AEI had themselves rationalized their joint semiconductor activities by establishing a new company, AEI-Thorn, which transferred manufacture of Mazda transistors from Brimsdown to AEI's Lincoln factory, where AEI already produced devices for professional use. But Arnold Weinstock did not wish to make entertainment devices, and asked Thorn to remove the Mazda plant from Lincoln; it was in production for just eight months.[26]

Rental under review

Tom Ludlow left DER in 1964, and started up a new rental company, Vista; as Managing Director of the company producing 60% of Thorn Electrical Industries' profits, he had resented being left out when Jules Thorn bestowed executive directorships of TEI on a number of senior staff.[27] Rental continued to expand rapidly — by 1966 there were eleven times as many rental shops as in 1957[28] — and could be expected to become still more popular with the advent of colour, because sets would cost much more, would be more likely to go wrong, and would be obsolescent as soon as BBC1 and ITV were available on 625-lines.

Every major manufacturer except GEC now had an interest in a rental chain. Arnold Weinstock had stayed out of the field quite deliberately, despite his father-in-law's keenness to enter it. His Sales Director in the late-1950s, Bentley Jones, had left Thorn partly because he considered the operation of DER in competition with Thorn's dealers to be improper, and Weinstock respected and to some extent shared this sentiment. Even after Bentley Jones died, in 1960, Weinstock continued to regard rental companies simply as highly valued customers for his receivers, and supplied sets on generous credit terms to Ludlow's new Vista company. An additional reason for his unwillingness to invest in a rental chain was his belief, mistaken as it turned out, that the law allowing rental sets to be considered for income-tax purposes as fixed assets of the owning companies[29] was indefensible and would soon be changed.[30]

DER and Radio Rentals had each taken over other chains, and remained the largest companies in the field, but with very different profiles. Although Radio Rentals had 1,400,000 rental subscribers to DER's 900,000, their manufacturing subsidiary, Baird Television, made only 7–8% of the industry's receivers as against the 25–28% made by Thorn. It became evident to the two groups that both would gain from a merger. This would enable Thorn to expand manufacture, notwithstanding their recent failure to acquire Pye. Sir Jules Thorn's desire for expansion at this particular time reflected his awareness that only through efficient mass production could the British television industry hope to survive the coming onslaught of foreign imports, as it lost the protection conferred by the 405-line standard. For their part, Radio Rentals stood to gain by combining their manufacturing resources with those of Thorn, whose prime cost for a typical monochrome receiver was at least £4 less than Baird's,[31] primarily because of their much greater volume of production and the higher degree of mechanization it permitted. Both parties would benefit from co-ordinating their research, servicing and administration, and from closing uneconomic shops where catchment areas overlapped, though all the trading names used by the various rental outlets would continue to be used.

In January 1968 their boards announced that terms for the purchase of Radio Rentals by Thorn had been agreed, and the Board of Trade referred the proposed merger to the Monopolies Commission. Six other manufacturers submitted their views to the Commission, but three of them offered no objection to the merger and only GEC were implacably opposed to it, since they supplied 35,000 sets a year to Radio Rentals,[32] and stood to lose that business. Many witnesses, from all sides of the industry and from the consumer lobby, expressed fears that the merger would intensify undesirable tendencies already evident. There was currently a shortage of receivers, and retailers and rental chains not linked to manufacturers thought that they had been discriminated against in the supply of sets; however, the two companies were able to produce figures refuting this accusation. One manufacturer, while not suggesting that Thorn would do anything so dishonourable, argued that the proposed group would be able to eliminate all competition; by taking its profits only from distribution it could undersell and eliminate other manufacturers, and could then support itself on manufacture while pricing other distributors out of business. The consumer lobby noted that dominance by the rental chains had already narrowed the range of price and quality offered to the British public relative to what was available abroad. Thorn countered this last objection by taking the Commission down to their Gosport factory, where a special exhibition was mounted to show the great variety of receivers that could be made from a common chassis.[33]

The companies could credibly claim that society as a whole would benefit from the merger. They proposed to divert much of the manufacture of television components to Baird plants in the Bradford area, where employment was currently suffering through the contraction of the textile industry. A merger would also assist exports. Finally, they pointed out, if the merger were *not* allowed, control of Radio Rentals would very possibly pass to a foreign-controlled company, unspecified but not difficult to identify. The Monopolies Commission decided that the enlarged Thorn group would not have undue commercial power, was likely on past form to use that power responsibly, and would in any case be kept in check by foreign competition. Accordingly it gave the proposed merger its unqualified approval. One member, Professor T Barna, submitted a note of dissent that was closely reasoned but flawed by a misapprehension about the way the industry was heading. "Television manufacturing" he asserted "is an assembly industry using very little fixed capital, where design and marketing matter at least as much as size."[34] One notable consequence of the merger was that Thorn not only put much-needed resources into Radio Rentals' factories in the Bradford area but upgraded the laboratory there into a substantial unit with a staff of around a hundred; being located well away from the group's television-assembly factories, the Bradford laboratory became its centre for fundamental and advance-development projects.[33]

Shortly before the merger, Ludlow's Vista chain had been bought out by Radio Rentals in order that he might take over that company, which for a short time he did. But Ludlow had not spent four years attaining this commanding position just to find himself again working for Jules Thorn, notwithstanding the "profound affection"[27] he retained for him. He left Radio Rentals and took a year off planning his third rental operation, Spectra. Sir Arnold Weinstock, badly hit by the loss of his sales to Radio Rentals, decided he could no longer maintain an 'arms length' relationship with rental, and took an 80% stake in the venture.

The end of Resale Price Maintenance

BREMA construed the Resale Prices Act, 1964, as "a threat to traditional, well-tried business practice which had operated to the advantage of both the industry and the consumer", and briefed Solicitors to advise on preparing the industry's case for exemption.[35] A case was submitted in 1966, but by the end of the year the Association, having been advised that this stood no chance of success, reluctantly abandoned it, and RPM duly became unlawful for the industry's products in March 1967, manufacturers quoting only a 'recommended' resale price.[36] The independent dealer had always received a lower discount than the multiple dealer; now he was to be undersold as well. His sole advantage was the better service he could offer, and he tended to discourage anyone who bought a set at cut price from a vendor with inferior service facilities then brought it to him to repair when it went wrong; at least one dealer charged such customers steeply enough to wipe out the savings they had made.[37]

An early consequence of the abolition of RPM was the appearance of a form of retailing totally new to this country: the discount warehouse, pioneered by Comet in 1968.[38,39] Comet Battery Services had been founded in Hull by George Hollingbery and Walter Honor in 1933, and had charged submarine batteries during the war. By the time George Hollingbery died, in 1958, he and his son Michael had built Comet up into a retailing and television rental business with several branches, all in Hull; Honor had sold out his interest in 1953. Michael Hollingbery held his own against the rapidly expanding rental multiples thanks to the support of Philips, who enabled him to offer new sets bearing their prestigious brand name at a very competitive rental. In 1960 he opened his first branch away from Hull, in Bridlington, and by 1967 had expanded Comet into a 'mini-multiple', beginning to spread from the East Riding to the West Riding, but also beginning to find the rental market saturated. He therefore decided to diversify into 'white goods' (refrigerators, washing machines, etc.) and, lacking expertise in this field, recruited a man with wide experience of electrical retailing, Gerry Mason. Both Hollingbery and Mason had seen American discounting at close quarters, and Mason also knew a lot about hi-fi equipment, so Comet did not launch their white goods through their shops, but through a discount warehouse that also handled radio, television and hi-fi, and that offered good servicing through their existing organization.

The place was truly a warehouse, sited on one of Hull's industrial estates and piled with merchandise in cardboard boxes. There was sawdust on the floor, and anyone who misbehaved was apt to be sent to the back of the queue of customers awaiting their turn outside the door. Thus overheads were minimal, and the operation's main expense lay in its heavy newspaper advertising, which listed every product and showed the saving on the manufacturer's recommended price, typically amounting to 20%. The public could scarcely believe their luck. No matter that the ambience was seedy; together with the lingering perception of RPM as a mark of commercial propriety, that merely added a spice of naughtiness to visiting the warehouse. Moreover, people had often driven some way to get there, so were reluctant to return home empty-handed and would accept a substitute if the exact model they wanted was not available.[40]

A second warehouse was opened in 1969, in Leeds, and from 1970 Comet grew explosively, establishing branches near all major centres of population. Understandably they were extremely unpopular with other retailers, and hence also with manufacturers, although when they hit a bad patch in the mid-1970s manufacturers chose to provide vital support rather than see a major outlet fail. Michael Hollingbery was conscious that by neither displaying nor demonstrating goods he was going beyond the accepted limits of competitiveness. The consumer was visiting retailers' showrooms and choosing a model with the help of their assistants, then going to Comet to buy it. The company therefore smartened up their premises and displayed their goods, although it was usually only television sets that were demonstrated. Retailers were also placated by some manufacturers' practice of producing slight variants with different model numbers specifically for Comet and other discount houses. When the consumer asked retailers their price on such a model, he could truthfully be told that they did not stock it. In the mid-1980s Hollingbery sold a controlling shareholding in Comet to Woolworth Holdings plc, which subsequently became Kingfisher, and soon afterwards left the company. Eighteen years on from the opening of the first warehouse, hostility towards Comet had decreased but not entirely disappeared; when the new Chairman joined he found that one or two manufacturers would not even talk to him.[39]

The Golden Years of Colour: 1970–73

From 15 November 1969, BBC1 and ITV programmes were originated on 625 lines and almost all were in colour; they were also electronically converted to 405-line monochrome for the existing VHF services, which carried on as before with negligible loss of picture quality. At this time BBC2 had 80% coverage, and by the end of the year 50% of the population could pick up all three networks on UHF,[12] using a single-standard colour or monochrome receiver. With some encouragement from BREMA[2] the BBC and the ITA had co-sited the three transmitters serving each area, so the single-standard viewer now needed only a single, relatively compact aerial, and could get rid of two much larger ones. The environment benefited, but Belling-Lee, who ever since television began had held a large share of the aerial market, had already decided that UHF aerials were too cheap to be profitable, and had sold off that side of their business.[41]

By the end of 1969 it was already clear that the British public had taken colour to its heart, and that with rental accounting for 85% of disposals the price of receivers was not restraining demand as much as had been anticipated. The industry hurriedly revised its plans,[42] and production of colour sets reached an annual rate of 1.25 million by the end of 1971. At £116 million, that year's turnover in colour sets alone was almost 50% more than that of the entire industry in 1967,[43] and financing their distribution had become a problem; dealers looked to manufacturers for guaranteed credit facilities, but they were already burdened with investment in new production plant and had to bring in finance houses.[44] It proved impossible to increase production fast enough to meet surges in demand, such as occurred in July 1971 when all credit restrictions were suddenly removed, and imports were sucked in by recurrent shortages. Total colour deliveries to the trade in 1973 approached 2.7 million, equalling 1959's all-time record for monochrome, and there was a colour set in almost a third of all households.[45]

The Philips G8 receiver, launched in 1971, was a good example of current practice. A British-designed all-transistor model with a 22" screen, its circuits were divided between a number of modules on separate, plug-in printed-circuit boards. This simplified the work of service technicians, few of whom were able to cope fully with the complexities of colour receivers, while the demarcation between the various modules was carefully worked out to allow them to be individually updated as technology advanced, enabling the G8 to be kept in production for almost ten years.[4] When it first appeared it required on average over 3 service calls per year; the version produced five years later required less than one call every two years.[46] As originally designed, the colour decoder in the Philips G8 employed two Mullard ICs, and its designers were forcibly reminded of the space such components saved when, six weeks before the set was due to go into production, high strategy within the Philips organization obliged Mullard to withdraw one of them, thereby rendering the other unusable. The circuit hurriedly designed to replace them contained 98 discrete components. There was no way in which it could be fitted into the 3" x 3" space that the two ICs had occupied, so it was built on a separate board that sat above the original panel and overhung other components.[4]

An Industry under Invasion

In October 1973 Thorn announced that they planned to make at least 20% more colour sets in 1974 than in 1973.[47] Within weeks, the colour bonanza was abruptly halted as Britain ran into a winter of economic troubles, from the Arab oil crisis to the miners' strike and the three-day week, and stringent credit controls were re-imposed. The fall in demand brought a crumb of comfort by reducing the risk of the market becoming saturated before there had been time for a replacement market to develop,[48] but only intensified a growing concern over imports, which in 1973 amounted to a quarter of total deliveries for colour, and almost a third for monochrome.

Coming to terms with Japan

In 1972–73 Japanese imports were rising rapidly, and already perceived as the principal threat to the British industry. Japan had the largest television industry in the world,[49] producing colour sets at the rate of over 8 million a year.[50] Her domestic market was approaching saturation, with colour sets in 80% of homes,[51] and was

further depressed as a result of the rise in oil prices in 1973. In a relentless export drive she had already caused great damage to the American television industry despite increased import duties. However, under a 1962 treaty Britain was allowed to restrict imports from Japan only if they were "in such increased quantities and under such conditions as to cause or threaten serious injury to producers of like or competitive products in the United Kingdom." It was highly unlikely that these conditions could be considered to exist, and in any case British Governments, of whichever party, were advocates of free trade and reluctant to invoke them.[52] In 1972 the Radio Industry Council had put the industry's case for a limitation of Japanese imports to the Secretary of State for Trade & Industry,[53] who had advised industry-to-industry talks as a means of negotiating voluntary restraint, and the following year talks were instituted between the RIC and the Electronic Industries Association of Japan (EIAJ), to agree and where necessary update annual quotas. Talks were held several times a year and are widely regarded as having been remarkably successful, given the two industries' very real conflict of interests. Indeed, in about 1980 the Government advised the Machine Tool industry's trade association to visit BREMA in order to learn how to set up similar talks.[54] Not everyone takes such a favourable view of the RIC/EIAJ talks, however; Lord Weinstock likens them to a deer talking to a tiger, and considers the simile to have been borne out by events.[30]

The talks produced their first effects in the late-summer of 1973, when the Japanese Ministry for International Trade and Industry (MITI) instructed EIAJ to keep within stated limits for that year's exports to the UK of both monochrome and colour receivers; for colour sets the limit gave Japan a 10% share of the total market, and a 40% share of imports.[49] Relations became strained in 1974 when the EIAJ were reluctant to reduce the year's quota to accommodate the sudden drop in demand,[50] and later in the year talks came very close to breakdown over the quotas for 1975. Discussion on colour receivers lasted for ten hours, and EIAJ had to return to Tokyo with a figure lower than they had submitted the previous year. This was unprecedented, and threatened EIAJ's good standing with the MITI.[55] Nevertheless agreement for 1975 was reached, and though the Japanese stated their intention of abandoning voluntary restraint thereafter, they resumed it from 1977 onwards; in 1976 colour

*Poster advertising Sony
1320UB receiver, c. 1970*

television sets had remained within their customary limit of 10% of the market but there had been an alarming rise in the figures for monochrome sets and for some audio products.[56]

Over the years the EIAJ/RIC talks became broader in scope, and although there were sometimes harsh things to be said, trust and friendship developed between the two teams; talks were held annually from 1979 until 1988, after which the European Association of Consumer Electronics Manufacturers (EACEM) took over from the RIC as the western organization. For most of the fifteen-year lifespan of the talks the same men headed the two delegations, establishing an excellent rapport[57] and deserving much of the credit for their success: Lord Thorneycroft was made a Life Peer in 1967 after a long parliamentary and ministerial career, and went on to serve with great distinction as President of BREMA from 1968–85; Noboru Yoshii, originally a banker, was a senior executive of Sony, described in a history of the company as "a peppery, bouncy man",[58] but possessed of great charm.

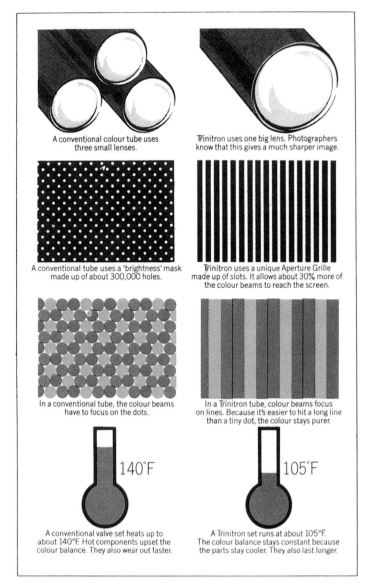

A conventional colour tube uses three small lenses.

Trinitron uses one big lens. Photographers know that this gives a much sharper image.

A conventional tube uses a 'brightness' mask made up of about 300,000 holes.

Trinitron uses a unique Aperture Grille made up of slots. It allows about 30% more of the colour beams to reach the screen.

In a conventional tube, the colour beams have to focus on the dots.

In a Trinitron tube, colour beams focus on lines. Because it's easier to hit a long line than a tiny dot, the colour stays purer.

140°F

105°F

A conventional valve set heats up to about 140°F. Hot components upset the colour balance. They also wear out faster.

A Trinitron set runs at about 105°F. The colour balance stays constant because the parts stay cooler. They also last longer.

From a Sony brochure of 1970

Threats from other quarters

Japan was not the only source of worry over imports. By 1965 cheap radio receivers from Russia and East European countries were perceived as a potential threat,[59] and over the next few years they were joined by radiograms and monochrome television sets, at manifestly 'dumped' prices; in 1973 Russia was landing small monochrome television sets at an average price of £11.59.[60] Communist countries are particularly given to dumping, the pressure to win export markets being intensified by their need for hard currency, while they can charge high prices on the home market because there is no competition. But though imports from these sources caused irritation in the industry, they were of less significance than those from Far Eastern countries with which Britain did not have voluntary agreements. The Japanese refused to discuss the question of their companies' production outside of Japan, and in 1977 Hitachi Singapore refused to place any restraint on exports of monochrome receivers, whereas Philips' Singapore subsidiary had agreed to a reduction. Hitachi's action was seen by the RIC as an attempt to circumvent the understanding reached at the RIC/EIAJ talks; concurrently, Hitachi were planning to open a plant in the UK, as will be described later, and each of these two episodes reinforced the resentment generated by the other.[61] Exports of monochrome receivers from Taiwan were already restricted by Government quota, and after unsuccessful attempts to negotiate a voluntary limit with South Korea, a quota was imposed on that country too. But despite all these steps, home production failed to retain the 50% share of the monochrome market reckoned to be the minimum required for a profitable level of production.[62]

European manufacturers of colour receivers enjoyed some protection through the PAL patents, which as a result of a long-standing patent-sharing agreement were administered jointly by AEG-Telefunken and EMI. From the early-1970s Japanese manufacturers were licensed to produce a quota of PAL receivers but were restricted to small tube sizes, and it was not until 1974 that even 20" tubes were allowed.[63] Other Far Eastern countries were denied licences altogether, but their competition had to be faced after 1979, when the first of the patents expired.

A new breed of colour tube

The first Japanese colour set to make an impact in Britain was a Sony model with an 11" 'Trinitron' tube, substantially different from the shadow-mask tube. A preoccupation with transistorized monochrome sets had prevented Sony from giving any serious attention to colour until 1961, by which time other Japanese makers were already marketing sets with shadow-mask tubes. But Masaru Ibuka, Sony's co-founder, disdained merely copying fully developed ideas, and the company looked around for an alternative technology. They settled on the 'Chromatron' tube, an American invention used in military applications, but after several years of experimenting and the launch of an unsuccessful receiver they were forced to admit that it was quite unsuitable for development into a consumer product, and the autumn of 1966 found Sony as far as ever from having a viable colour tube.

It was out of this desperate situation that the Trinitron was conceived by a young Sony engineer, and marketed within two years. It used a single electron gun with three cathodes side by side, a screen with the three colours in vertical stripes, and an 'aperture grille' of vertical slits instead of a shadow mask. Because its geometry was simpler than that of a shadow-mask tube it needed less 'convergence' correction to bring its red, green and blue images into registration, while the vertical stripes of phosphor covered the screen more effectively than the dots of the shadow-mask tube, giving a brighter picture. However, its screen was a portion of a cylinder, not a sphere, and fears for its strength initially restricted the Trinitron to small screen sizes.[64] When the first Trinitron models were exported, no Japanese company had been granted a PAL licence, so Sony designed the receivers to convert the signal to NTSC before decoding it. This ploy meant sacrificing the error-correcting properties of the PAL system and fitting a manual 'tint' control, used in normal NTSC receivers but inherently incapable of correcting most colour errors. Had all Japanese manufacturers followed suit the reputation of the PAL system could have been undermined to no purpose, so AEG-Telefunken bowed to the inevitable and began issuing licences.[5] In fairness it must be reported that despite the PAL/NTSC conversion the Trinitron receivers gave good pictures. They were also extremely reliable,[65] and quickly became something of a cult.

Establishing a colour-tube industry

By the early-1970s both Mullard and Thorn had large colour-tube plants, the latter after an expensive diversion up a blind alley. The shadow-mask tubes of the 1950s were sufficiently fraught with problems for a lot of effort to be put into 'beam-indexing' colour tubes, which operated on a different principle and promised to be simpler. In these the screen bore red, green and blue phosphors in vertical stripes, as in a modern shadow-mask tube, and was scanned by a single electron-beam, as in a monochrome tube. As the beam crossed each stripe, its intensity was switched to correspond to the appropriate colour signal. Thus as well as being simpler the beam-indexing tube was free from the shadow-mask tube's inherent disadvantage that the mask intercepts and wastes at least two-thirds of each electron beam. The American valve-maker Sylvania invented the 'Zebra' beam-indexing tube, and in the late-1950s Sylvania and Thorn jointly built a special laboratory and pilot production plant on Thorn's site at Enfield to develop it. The project was abandoned in 1963, when it became clear that the simplicity of the tube was more than offset by the quantity and the complexity of circuitry needed to switch control of the beam's intensity between the three colour signals.[14]

In 1964 the company began production development of Mazda shadow-mask tubes at Brimsdown. Taking out a licence to use the RCA patents did not cover the techniques to implement them, and although Thorn-AEI had access to Sylvania's technology this was still for round tubes with 70° deflection, whereas the British setmaking industry would require rectangular tubes with 90° deflection. By April 1966 Brimsdown was ready to produce a 25" tube, but in a plant limited to 1,000 tubes per week, which was clearly not going to be enough for very long.[26] However, the Radio Rentals group owned a one-third share[66] in an experimental colour-tube plant set up with RCA (Great Britain) Ltd in 1966, and when Thorn took over Radio Rentals in 1968 this link with the inventors of the shadow-mask tube was seen as offering an ideal basis for a major move into colour tubes. In

1969 Thorn Colour Tubes Ltd was set up, with 51% of the equity held by Thorn and 49% by RCA, who had technological control. A green-field site was secured near the experimental plant, at Skelmersdale, near Liverpool, and £10 million invested in building a copy of RCA's American plant, with an inital capacity of 300,000 tubes a year.[67] Its situation within a Development Area qualified it for Government grants and loans, but also meant that the manual workforce consisted mostly of redundant workers from Liverpool docks, with matching industrial relations; on the day in October 1971 when Sir Jules Thorn was due to perform a ceremonial opening the entire manual workforce was on strike and the event was cancelled.[26] Between 1971 and 1973 another £4.5 million was spent on increasing the plant's annual capacity, first to 600,000 then to 900,000 tubes, [67] on the strength of the booming colour-set market.

Philips went straight to the shadow-mask tube, taking out a licence from RCA, and splitting the development effort. The screen/shadow-mask combination was dealt with by Mullard at Mitcham, everything else by Philips at Eindhoven.[68] Mullard began their colour-tube production at Simonstone, then in 1972 opened a purpose-built factory at Durham. In 1974 they launched the 20AX range of 'self-converging' tubes, mostly imported from Holland, and based on an idea conceived by Philips engineers twenty years earlier. Like other shadow-mask tubes of its generation a 20AX had its three electron-guns side by side instead of in a triangle, and the screen-phosphors in vertical stripes instead of in triads of dots. Its originality lay in using deflection coils that produced a precisely calculated degree of astigmatism, and thereby cancelled many of the registration (or 'convergence') errors inherent in the tube's geometry. Thus like the Sony Trinitron, though by different means, it achieved a dramatic reduction in the number of corrections needed, and of their magnitude. The neck of a classical shadow-mask tube carried an elaborate array of coils supplied with various waveforms that had to be adjusted to stretch, squeeze, bend and twist the three coloured images into registration. Even if optimized when the receiver was new, these adjustments drifted, and in practice few early sets were free from quite noticeable errors. The development of tubes such as the 20AX and its successors has contributed greatly to the economy, performance and reliability of the modern colour receiver.

Colour tubes in crisis
Because a colour-tube plant is more capital-intensive than a receiver factory it is even more vulnerable to a fall in demand, and Britain's colour-tube makers reached crisis point in 1975. In April the colour licence was increased by 50% and shortly afterwards VAT on receivers, whether bought or rented, was put up from 8% to 25%. Even fewer colour sets were made than in 1974, and many of those that were made contained low-price imported tubes. It was believed in the British industry that Japanese prices were too low to be explicable as anything other than 'dumping', and representations were made to the Board of Trade. A team of civil servants went out to Japan to investigate, but reported that the low price of their tubes reflected long production runs and high efficiency, and in October 1975 the Government stated that there was no evidence to justify anti-dumping duties.[69,70] However, it was contended by British manufacturers that this conclusion showed the futility of defining dumping simply as

selling at a higher price in the producing country than in the importing country. Vertical integration in the Japanese television industry made it impossible to establish a meaningful 'home market' price for tubes, against which to compare the export price, covering only labour and materials, that a manufacturer could charge for tubes produced surplus to his own setmaking needs.[71,72]

Although British setmakers used British tubes for most of their 22" sets, which size accounted for almost half of total deliveries, no British tubes were available in the 18"–20" sizes that accounted for almost another third,[73] until Thorn started small-scale production of a 20" tube in August 1975.[74] Thus to compete in this market setmakers had to use imported tubes, thereby lowering the base that supported the entire price structure of colour receivers, and leading to the use of American and European tubes, again cheaper than British ones, in half the industry's output of 26" sets.[69]

The first casualty of the slump in demand was the plant that Pilkington had established specifically for colour-tube glassware, following an approach by Thorn and RCA in 1966. Since Mullard had their own glass plant at Simonstone, Pilkington could look only to Thorn Colour Tubes for home-market sales. No orders were forthcoming until Skelmersdale began production in 1971, and even then Thorn continued (for good technical reasons) to import faceplates rather than buy them from Pilkington. By 1975, £4.7 million into a £7.4 million expansion programme, the annual capacity of the plant was 1,200,000 sets of parts, yet the most optimistic projection of the home market was only 500,000, while exports, neglected during the boom of 1973, were only 100,000 in 1974. The last straw was manufacturers changing the sizes of their tubes at short notice, causing losses to Pilkington through expensive re-tooling costs and unsaleable stock, and late in 1975 the plant closed.

Between them Thorn and Mullard had the capacity to make around 2½ million colour tubes a year, but over the first half of 1975 ran at only half that rate, with no prospect of early improvement. Mullard could afford to stay in the game despite losses of about 10% on current trading because, as a Philips subsidiary, they had a built-in export market. Moreover, they feared that if they dropped tube production there would be a domino effect on other parts of their components business, and even on the rest of the industry. Mullard had given the Japanese their foothold in the crucial 22" segment of the market by importing tubes from them to meet the demand from setmakers during the 1973 boom, but now proposed to challenge them in the small-tube market.[75]

Thorn Colour Tubes, with a trading loss of £4.6 million for 1974–75,[76] were in a weaker position. Skelmersdale had never quite attained its expected performance,[72] and by March 1975 redundancies were under discussion, while unions were expressing fears that it might close altogether.[77] Towards the end of the year the Department of Industry gave Thorn a £1 million grant to keep the plant going, and presided over urgent talks during which the possibility was explored of its conversion from RCA technology to the Philips technology used by Mullard,[78] but no solution emerged; on 5 January 1976 Thorn Colour Tubes announced that they were withdrawing from the business and closing the plant.[76] Ironically, the Government had meanwhile succeeded in persuading the Japanese to increase the export prices of their colour tubes.[69] When Skelmersdale had opened four-and-a-half years previously it had been seen as a symbol of industrial revitalization — a successful company investing in advanced technology to make a product of high added value. Its failure showed how unforgiving the international market had become. Investment of £18 million was lost, including £3–4 million of Government grants and loans, together with 1,400 jobs in an area of high unemployment.

Sir Jules retires

In August 1976, at the age of 77, Sir Jules Thorn retired from the Chairmanship of Thorn Electrical Industries (TEI), having ceased to be Managing Director in 1969. He had built up the group from nothing over a period of more than 40 years, throughout which time he had entrusted its technical direction to the same man, Alfred ('Freddie') Deutsch, recruited from Vienna's tramways in 1928. Deutsch's placidity was the ideal foil to Thorn's mercurial temperament, and such was his gentlemanliness that although it fell to him to act as the group's 'hatchet man', to be sacked by Freddie Deutsch was said to be a privilege. By 1970 TEI had a turnover of £300m and in terms of stock-market valuation was among Britain's top 15 companies, but Thorn had long feared its becoming top-heavy, like AEI,[79] and had kept the reins largely in his own hands. His hatred of extravagance was legendary. He never stinted investment in the best and newest plant, but occupied a modest office, paid himself less than some of his senior employees, and when times were hard would come in to work in a Ford Popular. Such gestures, dismissed by the cynical as play-acting to disarm criticism of shabby offices and low salaries all round, were part of Thorn's wide vocabulary of non-verbal communication. Walking round the factory he would bend down to pick up a resistor off the floor, then hand it to an aide in implied criticism of such waste; if he saw a member of staff coming in late, he would quietly consult his fob watch.

The key to Thorn retaining personal control of the group despite its ever-growing size was his encyclopaedic and constantly updated knowledge of all its activities. Briefed by Deutsch on relevant technical aspects, he subjected everyone to a barrage of searching questions on every possible occasion, thereby ensuring that he didn't hear just one side of an issue. These interrogations were often very tough, for he expected you to argue with him — that was how he got at the truth — yet didn't like to lose the argument. However, he had a genuine warmth and kindliness, and if you knew your job and dealt with him straightforwardly your merits would be appreciated and rewarded. Thorn's approachability extended to all ranks. "Everything all right, Gladys? How's the girl?" he would ask one of 100 part-timers on the production line, remembering that her daughter had been ill. Such contacts contributed to the Ferguson factory's excellent labour relations, not least through the signals Thorn picked up from Gladys, indicating whether she and her fellow-workers were contented and productive. An executive who joined the group shortly before Thorn's retirement recalls his only interview with the great man. Extremely frightened, he had to break it to Thorn that since many consumer-electronics products were now being handled by outlets other than radio dealers, he proposed to appoint Woolworths a Ferguson retailer. Sir Jules delivered the expected diatribe against this insult, grudgingly consented, then melted into total affability.[80]

An early Philips cassette recorder, 1964. The compact cassette greatly simplified the operation of tape recorders and the storage of tape. Cassette machines achieved acceptable performance, later to reach high-fidelity standards, with lower tape speed and narrower tape than reel-to-reel recorders. To popularize the format, Philips freely licensed it to other manufacturers, and soon lost their pre-eminence

opposite: *A page from a house publication of the Coronet company in Hong Kong, 1975. At the top are a sketch of the new building to which Coronet were to be transferred, and a picture of it under construction*

Audio update

In the last chapter we left the radio receiver business seriously threatened by cheap transistor sets from the Far East, which in 1964 accounted for about 50% of the market numerically though only 20% in terms of value.[35] Several years previously C O Stanley had wondered whether Pye should establish their own factory out there, but his pursuit of the idea was rather haphazard. He sent out to Hong Kong a member of his export sales department, Norman Butler, first to advise on the idea's merit and then, when he reported favourably, to implement it. Butler had no manufacturing experience and spoke no Chinese, so he asked Pye's agent in Hong Kong for advice, and was put in contact with an American airline pilot who had decided to dispose of the small radio factory he had for some years been running as a sideline. It was in this manner that Pye acquired 'Coronet Industries Ltd', a primitive 'sweatshop' by European standards, with a workforce of about 100 but no professional-level staff, exporting cheap radios to the United States. Butler was left to fend for himself. He managed to keep the factory going, and to augment its American orders with some from UK importers, quite unconnected with Pye, who sold the sets though mail order and various other outlets under such names as 'Kensington'. When Pye finally decided to have Coronet make a set for sale under the Pye name, in about 1964, they chose an existing model that was judged no longer economical for UK manufacture; a few parts not available in Hong Kong were sent out, but most were sourced locally. The set was rather difficult and labour-intensive to make, and by making a great fuss Butler at last succeeded in having an engineer sent out.

第一版　　（非賣品）　1975　一九七五年十一月

飛利浦工業大廈

圖為地盤一角進行中之工程。

能如期達成。
情形推算，務而興，依工程部內所屬赤模式施工建築行程進度，立於此於方式本式計地數本式順
策亦由上期之利大廈之地之飛利浦已展的計地數本必展的立程赤極工
上期提及飛利浦之大廈開始興建。本廠、廠房、卒建工程部採用滑模作業已顯工

橋

訪客

這兩個月來有不少飛利浦及英國「派一」公司要員到訪本廠執行董事
部初仕先生（Mr. L. J. Wijns）有新近到港、九月間飛利浦考察董事局的
副董事霍頓先生（Mr. Forkun）「派」廠部到廠除考察業務外英國及飛利浦技術顧問
員曹倫先生（Mr. J. T. Griffiths）「派」派來本廠參觀本啊絡十先生
人員基利先生（Mr. M. Gollini）「派」公司的行程於十月間一行
董事其樂網士（Sir John Stewart-Clark）又有英國領橋「派」公司的執行
到廠除接觸視察之飛利浦董事局的行程於十月間來廠參觀本啊絡十公
董事基利先生同來本廠

圖片說明：
右上：霍敦先
務志生發利基利先生生垂青
生生陪同參觀製作部經理喬倫先生與何信德先生
基利先生在本廠討論有關頻繁
先生製作部主任垂詢頻繁。右下：左上：派「下線產品左生與右下左線
務基利先生製作情形。左生左線產品與基

郊遊大會·幸運抽獎

本廠七五年度郊遊大會，原定於九月十九
日舉行，目的地為鴨脷洲。但因颱風襲港，
天氣惡劣的關係，救難遊會就緒亦遇風惡當
一天宣佈取消。該日全廠放假，各人均於日前
大嘆天

。後品獎取領於攝兒運幸獎閒入及空、戈、頭

別君、由張林榮君、自動熱熙君、電子瓦韓英分
程中，進料粉查部由古蘇仙君取得，生產部至伍榮
物則，然郊遊會雖未能如期舉行，惟事
不造美。

名貴獎品四十餘份，得獎者無不雀躍分
攝影機各種名貴獎品、自動沖晒機、電子瓦韓英分
常豐富，由各部頭林君及錄的甲蘇彬君森君
君獎得之其他大小抽獎，惟是次
萬分有各種
萬分！

。況情獎抽運幸之行舉堂飯於

急救訓練班

。攝所部程工展發觀參生先仕榮

員共四冊人，分由各部生產部為多，自本廠內
生學習部頭多，其中尤以女性居多，其中尤
利用工餘心理。而以女性居多，其中尤
習班附設特別利用心理。而以女性居多
老師帶來的人體模型，到急救的原理與實習
一番理所當然女以人體模型，一番實習，老
實力。

「急救訓練班」已於九月十八日開
課，上已上，「傷口包紮」
「人工呼吸系統血液循環系統方法等．．．．
「教傷心理論」之各節課程裁稿激之感至此
實用，手應各種忙亂時有趣味、習作業有實
還項目認真談至，至於認真感各項目
等．．．．

Shortly afterwards Butler was sent off to Australia when John Stanley sent out what his father termed a "fire-in-the-belly boy" to take over Coronet, but was re-instated when this appointment proved disastrous. After gaining control of Pye in 1967 Philips took Coronet in hand, and before Butler retired in 1973 had re-equipped the factory, strengthened its staffing and introduced quality control. Its workforce never much exceeded 200, however, and Coronet, by this time making more for Philips than for Pye, were subsequently transferred to a large factory built in the New Territory, near the enormous housing projects where their workers lived.[81,82,83]

Radiograms fared much better than transistor radios against foreign competition; their bulk made them expensive to ship, and the home industry was better able to tailor cabinets to British taste. Production peaked, at 8% of the industry's total turnover,[84] in 1964, when stereo record reproduction, vhf radio and transistor circuitry were still sufficiently recent features to accelerate the replacement of old models. Home-produced radiograms also benefited from the competitiveness of British record-playing mechanisms, which in 1966 achieved export sales amounting to 18% of the receiver industry's total turnover.[85]

After 1970 both the radiogram and the portable record-player were rapidly displaced by what were variously described as 'audio separates', 'unit audio' and 'stereo systems'. Reel-to-reel tape recorders had been widely available since the early-1950s but had never appealed to the mass market, and although the compact cassette was introduced by Philips in 1963 it was not until 1970 that sales of recorders, all of them imported, began to rise dramatically. The scope of broadcasting was widened when the BBC introduced stereophony, using the American 'Zenith-G.E.' system, in 1966 and the following year launched both Radio 1 and Britain's first local radio stations since the 1920s. The first commercial local stations followed in 1973, under the control of the Independent Broadcasting Authority (IBA), successor to the ITA. From 1974 onwards stereo systems became 'music centres' through incorporating cassette recorders, and teenagers became law-breakers through copying 'pop' records. In 1976, BREMA estimated that roughly half of this market was held by its members.[86] Audio products required less sophisticated manufacturing plant than television sets, and they tended to be made in smaller factories acquired through the industry's various mergers and closures.

The high-fidelity industry

The quest for 'perfect reproduction' goes back at least to the 1930s, but until the 1950s the limitations of medium-wave radio and 78rpm records meant that the quality attainable from the best contemporary microphones, amplifiers and loudspeakers could be heard only under 'closed-circuit' conditions close to a radio or recording studio. Television sound gave no more than a tantalizing hint of what VHF radio could achieve. There was thus no basis for a high-fidelity industry. The situation was transformed by the advent of the long-playing record and of VHF/FM broadcasting, and specialist firms were established to exploit it; initially, many enthusiasts still built their own amplifiers, tuners and speaker enclosures, buying only pick-ups, turntables and loudspeaker units. A British tradition of high fidelity began to evolve, characterized by a preference for the natural over the spectacular, a significant influence being the plastic-cone loudspeakers several companies made under licence from the BBC.

In 1965 some thirty equipment manufacturers banded together to form the Federation of British Audio (FBA), partly to give an industry composed in the main of small firms the advantages of a larger organization for such purposes as exhibiting at overseas trade fairs. The industry has continued to prosper, and in 1980 the FBA (now comprising 58 companies) became a special member of BREMA; ironically, it was an exceptionally black year for the audio products of BREMA's other members.[87] High fidelity is a rich man's hobby, and with exports accounting for well over 50% of sales the names of FBA companies tend to be better known in America, Germany and Japan than they are in Britain. The FBA is nevertheless aware that resting on one's laurels is as dangerous in high fidelity as in any other business, and in mid-1990, with the aid of a grant from the Department of Trade & Industry, is completing a feasibility study for a research project.[88] This would have the aim of leap-frogging the technology of the immediate future to establish a leading position in the market of ten or fifteen years hence.

Inward Investment

Japanese competition took on a new dimension in 1974, when Sony opened a television assembly plant at Bridgend, in Wales, and Matsushita announced plans to build one near Cardiff. The object of such plants was, of course, to gain access to the EEC, and they were regarded by Britain's partners in the community as 'Trojan Horses'. Their acceptability depended very much upon the extent to which they used European components, and Britain gave notice at EIAJ/RIC talks in 1976 that products using less than 50% by value of British components could not be regarded as British-made,[89] and thus would count towards the total volume of Japanese imports agreed between the two industries. None of this had any legal basis, for the relevant EEC regulation conferred origin so long as an added value of 45% of the ex-works invoice price was achieved in the Community or the named country of manufacture.[90] Nevertheless, Sony were already playing along in the interests of good relations, having announced soon after opening that they hoped to be using 50% British components within a year, although each UK component-supplier would first have to have its products cleared by Sony engineers in Japan.[91]

Early in 1977 it became known that Hitachi, with the British Government's encouragement, planned to open a factory in Washington new town. But by then it was indisputable that Britain had over-capacity in both setmaking and components, and there were vigorous protests from the unions and from the Radio Industry Council. When Hitachi demonstrated their wares at a trade show in London, 200 workers from the components industry picketed the hall and distributed leaflets asserting that if the company got a foothold in Britain it would cost 5,000 jobs.[92]

In their private deliberations the RIC made the same point with devastating candour. Thorn, they stated, bought far more of their components from British manufacturers than from the Far East "notwithstanding that Far Eastern components were found to be more reliable. Reliability of British-made sets could be improved by using more Far Eastern components and this would certainly be

Sony's factory at Bridgend. When Trinitron receivers were first produced here, in 1974, 90% of their components were Japanese-sourced. The teletext models produced in 1989 were 90% European-sourced

encouraged, to the detriment of the British components industry, if further competition from UK-based Japanese companies were allowed."[61] Strong representations were made to the Government, and Hitachi were obliged to withdraw their proposal.[93]

However, a working party of the National Economic Development Office (NEDO) prepared guidelines, which were accepted by Government, welcoming inward investment by Japanese companies provided that they either took over existing capacity or engaged in joint ventures with existing manufacturers. NEDO was encouraged in this positive attitude by an international study that it had commissioned from a strategy consulting group, comparing the UK industry with that of various other countries and yielding some alarming statistics.[94] The direct labour cost of a set made in the UK was almost double that of one made in Japan, although the Japanese hourly rate of pay was 72% higher, because the Japanese set took 1.9 man hours to make and the British one 6.1 man hours. This was partly because the Japanese set contained 30% fewer components, which was attributed to a greater use of integrated circuits, and partly because at least 65% of those components were inserted automatically, as against a maximum of 15% in the UK. For automation to be fully cost-effective, it was asserted, the plant needed a throughput of around half a million sets a year, attained by all the Japanese plants considered but by no British ones. The consulting group also stated that the quality of components entering Japanese plants was an order of magnitude superior to those entering UK plants.

The Joint Ventures

When NEDO published these findings in February 1979 they noted with approval that two British setmakers had just entered into joint ventures with Japanese companies, and predicted that, being underpinned by Japanese technology, these would do much to improve the consumer electronics sector's overall performance. The two ventures were respectively to be known as Rank Toshiba and GEC-Hitachi.

Rank Toshiba

In the spring of 1978 Rank Radio International sent a travelling exhibition to major cities, with the object of re-establishing the Murphy brand name through independent dealers

Rank Radio International mounted an export campaign in Holland in 1978, hoping that their colour sets, good value for money if rather 'basic' by European standards, would appeal to the younger generation who had not yet developed brand loyalty to Philips

Rank Bush Murphy had entered the 1970s a successful medium-sized operation with a prestigious dealer-network, well-resourced research and development facilities, and a profusion of sites: the main factory at Ernesettle, Plymouth, had three satellites in the West Country, audio products were made at Skegness, the maintenance depot was at Ware, management and labs moved to Ernesettle from Chiswick only in the mid-1970s. The Rank Organisation was accounted a good and caring employer up to middle-management level[95] but sufficiently hard on senior executives for those sacked to have formed a thriving club, 'Rank Outsiders'.[39] In 1972 the name of the company was changed to Rank Radio International (RRI), and a determined effort was made to build up exports, but this had barely begun when the home market collapsed and the company moved into a succession of loss-making years, despite increasing its share of the colour television market from under 6% in 1976 to 10% in 1978.[96] In December 1977 the Managing Director was interviewed for the house magazine.[97] He frankly admitted that export sales were disappointing, profit margins too low and component stocks too high, and that too often products didn't work properly when unpacked by dealers. What he could not admit was that RRI was acknowledged to be no longer viable, and that Bernard Rogers, his Director of Engineering, was currently in Japan assessing the prospects for a tie-up with Toshiba. Rogers was taken to their television plant and was awed by the extent to which it was automated, right down to the adjustment of dust-cores, with scarcely a soul to be seen. RRI's target capacity of around 350,000 sets a year was just about high enough to justify full automation, and Rogers returned home to recommend pursuit of the idea, although he had doubts about its implementation and left as the new company was being set up.[5]

Rank Toshiba was formed as a £10 million company in November 1978, Rank retaining 70% ownership and Toshiba acquiring their 30% by injecting £3 million in cash, mainly to modernize the plant. The venture received £1.9 million of Government sponsorship, for it would save almost 3,000 jobs in an area of high unemployment.[98] Colour-set production was planned to reach 350,000 sets a year by 1981, using a Toshiba-designed chassis; of these, 200,000 would be sold by RRI, now purely a selling company, under the existing brand-names Bush, Murphy and (for export) Rank Arena, while the rest would be sold by Toshiba's marketing companies.[96] Management remained the responsibility of Rank, but Toshiba provided engineering expertise, and the Managing Director of Toshiba's UK marketing company doubled as Chairman of Rank Toshiba.

Within two years, in September 1980, Rank announced that they were terminating the venture,[99] and Rank Toshiba ceased trading in March 1981.[100] The expected economies of scale had never materialized, for production never exceeded 270,000 sets a year. In part this was because the strength of the pound undermined exports, which figured substantially in the company's plans. A more fundamental reason, however, was that because of the separate marketing arrangements the planned rationalization of the product range never took place, and by the end of the joint venture the company was producing 62 different models.[101] RRI wanted a chassis based on the Mullard 30AX tube and, with substantial interest in the rental market, set great store by ease of servicing. Toshiba aimed to produce sets that would not need servicing.[95,102] Finally, the whole venture retained too many of the features that had brought the previous company to the brink of failure: uneconomic vertical integration, acceptance of indifferent quality standards from suppliers, a workforce represented by 7 unions, and poor co-operation between departments.[103]

The Rank Organisation were anxious to minimize the loss of employment caused by closure, while Toshiba wished to maintain a presence in the UK, and saw sufficient potential in Ernesettle, and particularly in its senior managers, to risk a salvage operation. Early in the run-down period of the joint venture they appointed its Managing Director, Geoffrey Deith, and its Personnel Director, David Smith, to set up a new company which would re-commence manufacture, initially with a workforce of only 300, as against the 2,600 latterly employed at Rank Toshiba's four factories, of which three would now close. The appointment of four more senior managers soon followed, and the team of six began to plan the new company, Toshiba Consumer Products (TCP) and to recruit its staff, almost entirely from former employees of Rank Toshiba. Since so few were needed and all were known to them the management had a unique opportunity to pick people who promised well for the new project, on the principle of "attitude first, skill second".[104]

So radically did TCP differ from a typical British company, while conforming to some popular notions of a Japanese one, that it is easy to assume that Toshiba imposed on it a Japanese approach to management and industrial relations. Such a view would, however, be quite unfair both to Toshiba and to the people involved in setting up the new company. Five of the top-management team were British, the sixth being the Japanese Engineering Director, and two of the people who greatly influenced the company's distinctive culture, Managing Director Geoffrey Deith and EEPTU official Roy Sanderson, were putting into practice ideas that they had developed in entirely British contexts. Toshiba, once convinced that the potential was there, trusted the British to realize the company in their own way,[105] departing from their usual practice by appointing a non-Japanese Managing Director.[106] The distinctively Japanese contribution to TCP was to lie more in quality control and the relationship with suppliers. Quality checks would be made the responsibility of the operators instead of having patrolling inspectors. Similarly, there would be no 'goods inward' inspection, but neither would there be any tolerance of quality defects in components.

In a few short months, the top-management team thrashed out every aspect of the new company — from its underlying philosophy, through its structure, to such small but important details as overtime entitlement and the most cost-effective way of regulating telephone calls. Moreover, Geoffrey Deith insisted that Rank Toshiba was run down in an orderly fashion, so that virtually all planning for the new company took place out of normal working hours. In the six weeks between closing the old company and opening the new one, on 4 May 1981, plant was transferred from Redruth, several areas of Ernesettle were revamped, and the Rank assembly line dismantled. To underline the new company's 'single status' policy, Rank Toshiba's six dining areas, ranging from works canteen to directors' dining room, were replaced by a single restaurant for all staff, pitched at 'the top end of motorway catering'.[107] As a further means of reminding the re-employed girl, sitting at the same bench and doing the same job, that she was nevertheless working for a new and totally different company, the colour of the factory floor was changed.[95]

TCP was (and is) managed through a Company Advisory Board (COAB) drawn from staff at all levels, and described by Roy Sanderson as "a dramatic advance on the usual phoney system of consultation found in British industry."[100] Two key features were that there were no pre-meetings, which prevented decisions being taken in advance for mere rubber-stamping at the meeting, and that COAB was given full information, even if confidential.[108] One union, the EEPTU, was given exclusive bargaining rights, though staff were allowed to belong to other unions. In the joint venture, EEPTU had 80% of the workforce as members,[109] making it the natural choice for a single-union agreement, and it was Toshiba's good fortune that the EEPTU had a tradition of non-militancy. The company's 'no-strike' agreement with the union

The first set produced for sale by Toshiba Consumer Products, May 1981, and the first meeting of the Company Advisory Board. A round table was considered essential, to avoid any feeling of there being two 'sides'

attracted much media attention but was less significant than the procedures designed to ensure that it was never put to the test. Any problem not resolved by COAB was to be negotiated directly between the union's full-time official and the Managing Director, and only if they failed to reach agreement would the matter go to arbitration. However, the arbitrator would not be allowed to recommend a compromise, but would be obliged to find for one side or the other; the object of this so-called 'pendulum' arbitration was to encourage both parties to submit moderate proposals. It is a matter of pride that to date it has never been necessary to invoke this procedure, let alone the 'no-strike' agreement.

To appreciate the significance of this new regime of labour

relations it is worth glancing back at the pre-war scene, when people queued outside factories for jobs and 'personnel management' was a euphemism for 'hiring and firing'. In slack periods a foreman would be instructed to lose so many workers in a given category and would simply walk round the factory tapping people on the shoulder and telling them to collect their cards. Working practices were also harsh, and several people's reminiscences [110, 111, 112] have included unhappy recollections of the Bedeaux system of work study, described by one of them as "industrial slavery"; this was in fact a technique of some subtlety, designed to approach the ideal of equal reward for equal effort, but during the depression was widely used as a weapon against the workers.[113]

Geoffrey Deith, whose enthusiasm and charismatic personality had been vital to TCP's creation, returned to the Rank Organisation in 1981, leaving a company whose performance testifies to the validity of its approach. By 1984, the percentage of products not 'right first time' off the line had fallen from 40% to 7%, absenteeism was down to a third of what it had been in Rank Toshiba, and output per person per year was up from 93 receivers to 250.[114]

GEC-Hitachi

In common with other setmakers, GEC found themselves in the late-1970s with serious over-capacity, having recently rebuilt and expanded their factory at Hirwaun. They were suffering unacceptable losses, and rather than close the factory Sir Arnold Weinstock sought a co-operative venture with Hitachi, who had just been refused permission to establish their own television-receiver factory in the UK; GEC would gain extra load for their factory, while Hitachi would obtain their desired foothold in the EEC. An agreement was signed in November 1978 and shortly afterwards GEC-Hitachi began business as a 50/50 joint venture, under GEC management but with Hitachi controlling its technology. As had been planned for Rank Toshiba, the parent companies would continue to market separately under their own brand names using a common Japanese-designed chassis. The proportion of European parts was scheduled to increase progressively, but this became a source of friction between the two parties. Hitachi required twelve months' notice of any proposal to substitute a European component, which then had to be submitted to lengthy tests, so the chassis was often superseded before the change could be made. This situation tended to perpetuate the basic inequity that although the factory continued to operate at a loss Hitachi were making profits on the imported tubes and other components, whereas GEC were not.

Contention also arose from the separate marketing operations. Hitachi maintained that GEC were spending too little on advertising, and thus failing to make their proper contribution to loading the factory. The factory itself was acknowledged to be badly managed, with poor discipline and industrial relations, and high absenteeism. The venture, in fact, was a worse failure than Rank Toshiba, yet it lasted for over five years. Lord Weinstock, as he became in 1980, proposed a closer linkage that would include product-development and sales, but Hitachi declined on what he regarded as the unconvincing grounds that their marketing company had some outside shareholders. He offered to buy them out, but again they declined. Finally he bowed to the inevitable and sold out to them in

Eric Hammond, General Secretary of the EEPTU, plants a tree at Hitachi Consumer Products (UK) Ltd, Hirwaun, in April 1985

A celebration at Hitachi, 1987

March 1984, though continuing to market television sets under the GEC name for a year or two longer, reluctant to cut all links with the industry in which he had begun his managerial career.[30]

It was generally held that Hitachi's best chance of success lay in following Toshiba's example by closing Hirwaun and making a totally fresh start, but to have done so would have involved them in considerable financial penalties, because of Government benefits received in connection with the joint venture. They therefore decided to maintain continuity, though making redundant 500 of the 1,300 employees inherited at take-over.

Carrying out the radical changes to be made demanded, and received, both resolution and tact. The management, ten of whom were Japanese, prepared a 40-page document *A New Future at Hirwaun*, which set out in detail the way in which they proposed the company should be run, and this was explained to all employees at numerous meetings. The regime it described was very similar to that already operating successfully at Toshiba Consumer Products, giving negotiating rights to one union only, again the EEPTU. Hitachi had been warned from many quarters that they would never succeed in removing negotiating rights from the other five unions with members at Hirwaun, and some full-time officials did try to initiate industrial action, but their senior shop-stewards on site refused to co-operate. After negotiation with the EEPTU an amended agreement was drawn up and again explained to employees at meetings, though this time only to the 85% of them who were EEPTU members, the other unions having advised their members not to attend. Finally, EEPTU members were balloted, and 87% voted to accept the agreement. The plant then had its two-week summer shutdown, and 800 'company members' returned to the brave new world of a single-status establishment.

Hirwaun was a much harder nut to crack than Ernesettle, because continuity of employment made it more difficult to shed old habits, relationships and attitudes, while the plant had been notoriously undisciplined[115] and the joint venture soured by mistrust. Moreover, South Wales is an area imbued with Labour Movement traditions difficult to reconcile with the ethos of a Japanese company, or for that matter of a British union like EEPTU.[105] But although the pay-negotiating machinery failed on one occasion to prevent a brief unofficial sit-in in the company's single-status restaurant,[116] the transformation has nonetheless been impressive. Within two years absence was down from around 13% to 3.5% and operator efficiencies up by 30%. The best day's output ever achieved by GEC-Hitachi was in 1981, when 2,200 employees produced 1,750 television sets. By 1986 Hitachi, with 1,000 members, was regularly producing 2,400 sets a day, in addition to 500 hi-fi units and 500 video recorders.[117]

Farmers or hunters?
It was not to be joint ventures but the establishment of wholly owned plants by Japanese companies (and by one Taiwanese company) that would transform the UK consumer-electronics industry in the 1980s. In October 1979 Mitsubishi began producing colour receivers at a factory in Haddington, East Lothian, which they had taken over when the Norwegian company, Tandberg, were obliged by financial problems in Norway to terminate their UK operation. This brought the number of Japanese companies operating here to five (including the two ailing joint ventures), and the unhappier implications of their presence were painfully brought home to the UK delegates at the 1979 RIC/EIAJ inter-industry talks, which took place at Stratford-upon-Avon in November. When Lord Thorneycroft expressed the hope that the establishment of Japanese plants in the UK would not only contribute to exports, but lead to a reduction in imports from Japan, Mr Yoshii

said that while such import substitution might well happen naturally in the long term, it was not something that the EIAJ would consciously try to achieve, nor even a question they had really considered. Their objective was to become accepted as members of the industrial community in Japan's centres of demand — to become "farmers instead of hunters".

There followed a discussion on components, depressing and chastening for the British delegates. An 'inwards mission' mounted to further the sale of UK components to the Japanese industry, both in Japan and in the UK, had been a total failure. While conceding that it had probably been foredoomed, Lord Thorneycroft pointed out that if there were no prospects of success the whole question of Anglo–Japanese trade and EEC–Japanese trade would come under scrutiny. The Japanese protested that they were eager to source their UK plants locally, but the British complained that the concentration of design in Japan led to products being designed around Japanese technology and components, leaving UK component-makers forlornly trying to catch up from two years behind; this syndrome, it may be recalled, was currently souring the relationship between GEC and Hitachi. Further difficulties arose from the relatively small scale of Japanese manufacture in the UK; when Japanese setmakers tried to involve UK component makers in early discussions on products, they were not always given top priority by the companies' senior managers, who in turn knew that the quantities required would be too small to allow them to quote competitively with Japanese companies supplying the setmakers world-wide. But the key question remained that of quality, and in his closing remarks Lord Thorneycroft admitted that European components were lower in quality and higher in price than Japanese. There was little comfort to be found in Mr Yoshii's response:

> "He fully understood that UK component manufacturers wished to secure a world market for their products. However, they must try harder themselves and not simply rely on the Japanese industry to help them. The EIAJ were prepared to help, but UK suppliers must come up to world standards; therefore the major effort needed to be made by the UK component manufacturers and not the Japanese companies."

The talks' final session concerned the EEC and found the Japanese delegates much more compliant, happy to be reassured that BREMA would look after the interests of its Japanese members in exactly the same way as those of indigenous manufacturers.[118] Given the delicacy of all the matters discussed, it is understandable that BREMA's Annual Report should record that delegates went to *Julius Caesar* and visited Warwick Castle, but say next to nothing about the talks themselves.[119]

A question of quality

Early warning that Japanese television receivers were more reliable than British ones reached Ferguson in the early-1970s from their rental associates, who used them in the smaller screen sizes.[14] A Ferguson engineer visiting JVC's television factory in Japan found the production methods very similar to those at Gosport but was amazed to see that there were no fault finders at the end of the lines because there were virtually no faults. Whenever a faulty component was found, it was sent to the laboratory for investigation; at Gosport it would just have been thrown in a bucket.[33] A year or two later, Currys' buyer bluntly told a senior Thorn executive that when a salesman sold a Hitachi set he never saw it again, whereas the customer who bought a Ferguson on Saturday afternoon would be back on Monday morning because it had gone wrong.[39] In 1974, Ferguson's management launched a determined three-pronged attack on poor quality and reliability, embracing design, manufacture and components.

They started from a position well behind not only the Japanese, but their chief UK rivals, Philips, who had been developing an increasingly professional approach to the subject since the 1950s. From the mid-1960s Croydon collaborated with the group's continental factories in evolving techniques for detecting and repairing faults as they occurred on the production line rather than relying on final inspection. Moreover, each fault found was allotted to one of, typically,120 categories for which the cost had been estimated, allowing rational assessment of whether any proposed remedy would be cost-effective. Analysis of faults occurring during manufacture gave some indication of how reliable the sets were likely to be, but sets were also life-tested, and by mathematical analysis it could be accurately predicted from how many sets failed during a week's life-testing (supplemented by longer testing of smaller samples) how many would fail during a year's service. All Philips European video factories were kept informed of each others' performance, and analysis was followed by determined action. By 1978, the Philips G11 colour receiver had become slightly more reliable than a typical Japanese set.[120]

The Japanese had not always set the standard. When Akio Morita, co-founder of Sony, first visited the United States and Europe, in 1953, he discovered that to the American consumer 'Made in Japan' meant 'cheap and nasty', and he was overawed by American and German industry. However, he was inspired by Philips — if one small, agricultural country where people rode bicycles could produce such a company, so could another![121] At the same time two American consultants were sowing the seeds of a 'quality revolution' in Japan. Twenty-five years later, in 1978, one of the consultants, J M Juran, published an article contrasting Japanese and Western quality as exemplified by the colour television receiver, and the following year extracts from it were circulated within the British industry by the Consumer Sector Working Party of the National Economic Development Office.[122] Western sets were failing in service at five times the rate of Japanese ones, and faults detected at the factory of a leading American manufacturer had been running at 150–180 faults per 100 sets produced; this figure had fallen to 3 or 4 after the company came under Japanese management, while in Japan 0.5 was typical.

UK setmakers knew that the quality of components they were currently using gave them no hope of achieving Japanese standards in their receivers. A relatively simple formula connects the number of faults per 100 sets coming off the line, the certainty of detecting those faults, and the probability that a set delivered from the factory will work; it shows that achieving good delivered quality from indifferent production demands an unrealistically high standard of inspection.[123] In any case, there is little point in investing in automation if many of the sets come off the line needing labour-intensive fault-finding and repair. The intense competitiveness of the rental-dominated UK receiver industry had not bred a healthy components industry.

Setmakers had established a tradition of bargaining with a supplier for the lowest possible price, and of dropping him without hesitation if a competitor offered a fractionally cheaper product or if he ran into technical problems; the Japanese tradition was to build up a stable relationship with a supplier and when necessary help him to remain competitive. There was also vertical integration in both countries, but Japanese setmakers' component divisions were bigger than their British counterparts, enjoyed more autonomy and possessed more technological clout.[33]

The order of improvement needed was reflected in the terms used to define component quality. British and American setmakers dealt in Acceptable Quality Levels (AQLs), defined as the percentage of faulty components that could be delivered without incurring any penalty; the Japanese dealt in Parts Per Million (PPM). An essential stage in the transition from AQL to PPM was co-operation between setmakers and component-makers in finding out first how, and then why, components were failing. Accordingly, in 1977 two individuals agreed to undertake such a project: Bernard Rogers, Rank Radio International's Director of Engineering, and Brian Johnson, Mullard's Quality Manager. Every failed Mullard semiconductor and IC from RRI's production was returned to Mullard with full details of the circuit in which it had been used and the nature of its failure; this collaboration between Mullard and the Ernesettle factory continued under the Rank-Toshiba and Toshiba Consumer Products regimes. Concurrently, Mullard analysed their own rejects and the failed components from Philips' life-tested receivers, and gave detailed advice to set-designers.

A spectacular improvement in the quality level of Mullard semiconductors was quickly achieved by these techniques,[124] and was echoed by other improvements throughout the components industry. In 1982 Bernard Rogers undertook for the Consumer Sector Working Party a study on the comparative quality of a wide variety of British and imported components,[125] and the following year was able to report that British electronic components had shown such a significant improvement that their reliability was not discernibly different from that of the best overseas competitors, although the quality of plastic moulded components continued to give cause for concern.[126]

It was not only in the matter of quality that suppliers had to learn new ways over these crucial few years. Toshiba Consumer Products offered guaranteed weekly orders with no cancellations, prompt payment, and technical assistance when required, but in return expected to receive exactly what they wanted, exactly when they wanted it. An incredulous supplier reported "If they want 2,000 on a specific day and we send 1,999 they immediately ring and ask for one to be sent by Red Star."[127]

Television Technology Advances
Reducing the component-count
The pursuit of higher quality was assisted by advances that made receivers cheaper and more reliable as well as improving their performance. Mention has already been made of self-converging tubes and of the progressive replacement of discrete components by ICs. A further major advance came in the late-1970s, when the receiver's intermediate-frequency tuned circuits, all requiring critical adjustment, could be replaced by a single device needing no

adjustment: the surface acoustic wave (SAW) filter, originally devised for use in radar. Its application to television was demonstrated in laboratories around 1970, and pioneering work was done by Bush in association with Plessey, but as then manufactured it was far too expensive for use in a consumer product.[5,128] Subsequently the use of a different material enabled SAW filters to be made more cheaply, and with mass production the price fell to a few tens of pence.

A consequence of such advances was that between 1970 and 1984 the total number of components in a typical Philips colour receiver fell from 900 to 400, and the number of semiconductors from 40 to 20.[129] This trend made it attractive to build an entire television chassis on a single printed circuit board (PCB), thereby eliminating the profusion of plug-and-socket interconnections between modules, which were not merely expensive but became one of the main sources of unreliability as other components became more reliable. Japanese manufacturers used fewer components than British[94], and Toshiba were already producing a single-PCB chassis in 1977[5] without benefit of an SAW filter, but the first British set of this type was Ferguson's TX9 chassis, launched in 1978, which did have such a filter. Sets were serviced by replacing the entire board under an exchange scheme; the faulty board was returned to the factory, where it was repaired, checked, and re-aligned back to its original specification on a secondary production line.

Ferguson back a winner
The TX9 chassis was for 90° tubes, and was immediately followed by the TX10 for 110° tubes. Because the larger scanning angle demanded more and bigger components, the TX10's PCB was cut in two after manufacture to fit it into the cabinet, so it was not strictly a 'single-PCB' chassis. This distinction was of some relevance to Ferguson's application for a Queen's Award for Technological Achievement. No-one in the company had even thought of applying for one until the Director of Engineering, Doug Topping, happened to hear on his car radio that the closing date for the 1981 awards was just two weeks away. On an impulse he telephoned for an application form, which turned out to be more like a book, and just managed to meet the deadline after gathering all the information called for. The thrust of the application was that condensing the chassis onto a single PCB reduced size and cost while improving reliability, and Topping decided that since the TX9 made this point better he would cite it exclusively, despite the TX10's association with the more modern and up-market 110° receiver.[33]

Whether the TX10 would have won an award cannot be known, but the TX9 did, thereby enhancing the commercial success already being enjoyed by both chassis. They achieved outstanding picture quality, at a time when Ferguson receivers had for some years been rather outclassed by the Philips G8 and G11 series, and this fact was exploited in a £3 million advertising campaign built around one of the industry's most memorable slogans, worthy to stand alongside "I'm going home to my Philco" and "Fine sets these Fergusons". André Previn declared with quiet conviction that the receivers gave "probably the best picture of all time", with the result that the public started asking for them by name.[30,139]

By the early-1980s, manufacturers' policy on brand names had been thrown into reverse. Twenty years previously, one consequence of the industry's consolidation had been that retailers could offer an impressive variety of brand names, even if many of them used the same chassis. But from the early-1970s British manufacturers found it increasingly difficult to persuade dealers to stock their subsidiary brands when Japanese companies were offering good margins on genuinely different products,[39] which they promoted more lavishly than their current sales could have supported, in order to break into the British market.[33] Accordingly manufacturers 'demised' once-famous names like Ekco and Ultra, and concentrated their advertising budgets on a single name.[18] By the time Thorn Consumer Electronics became Thorn EMI Ferguson, following the Thorn Group's acquisition of EMI in 1979, they were using neither of the two names they had acquired from EMI in 1957; Marconiphone had been dropped, and HMV sold off to an independent manufacturer, Fidelity Radio. There has been one notable exception to this trend. Philips, who had acquired a 60% shareholding in Pye in 1967, completely took over the company's radio and television interests in 1977, but continued to use the Pye brand-name. Early in 1990 they announced that they would confine it to the low-price end of the market and keep the Philips name exclusively for more expensive products with the emphasis on higher specifications and new technology.[131]

Teletext: a technological bonus

Engineers do not rest until they have the whole of a broadcast signal under intensive cultivation, and in the early-1970s both the BBC and the IBA turned their attention to the lines above the top of the picture, hitherto left blank so as to give the receiver's vertical scan enough time to fly back and re-start. Receiver design had improved since the 625-line standard was formulated, and it was possible to use one or more of these lines to carry digital data signals without detriment to the picture. By 1973 both authorities had demonstrated systems in which such signals conveyed a number of 'pages' of written information, any one of which the viewer could choose to be stored, decoded and displayed, either in place of the normal picture or superimposed on it.[132] But between these demonstrations and today's teletext there was a long road to be travelled.

Having been developed independently, the BBC's 'Ceefax' and the IBA's 'Oracle' were incompatible, so BREMA organized a technical working group to derive a common system, and Sir Jules Thorn gave his assurance that his company would make no receivers until this was done.[2] When a preferred system had duly been specified as "teletext", and experimental services instituted by the broadcasters, there remained the problem of producing receivers at an affordable price. This required dedicated large-scale integrated circuits (LSIs) to be developed; by using 'off the shelf' ICs, Rank Radio International scored a world first in 1977 by marketing a receiver having teletext built in, but it cost over £700.[133] The following year, still ahead of their competitors and making one last innovation before going out of setmaking, RRI produced a much cheaper teletext set fitted with a decoder module using the first dedicated LSIs, designed by Texas Instruments (TI). By marketing this module at a time when a number of teletext parameters were still being finalized, TI were taking a calculated risk in order to be first into the new market. Mullard, by contrast, held fire until they judged (correctly) that a plateau of development had been reached, then produced an LSI that superseded

TI's and put them in an unassailable position commercially, so that although TI did come up with a second-generation LSI they soon decided to drop out of teletext.[5]

The development of teletext receivers was also aided by the timely availability of SAW filters. For the pulses of digital data to be reproduced accurately enough to display uncorrupted text, the receiver's intermediate-frequency filtering must be better than is necessary simply to give an acceptable picture. Although tuned circuits could be designed to yield the necessary performance under laboratory conditions, manufacturers experienced some difficulty in consistently attaining it on the production line.[14] The performance of a SAW filter is of the necessary excellence and is achieved with total consistency, since it is determined by the dimensions of the device's acoustic pathways. Over the years more lines of teletext data were progressively inserted into transmissions, thereby enabling the number of pages available to be increased without making the waiting time for a given page unacceptable, while engineers carried out tests (and kept an eye on rental companies' service calls!) to ensure that older receivers did not react badly to signals they had never been designed to tolerate.[2]

Although teletext worked well, and the broadcasters compiled useful 'magazines' for it, early indications were that the public did not see it as justifying the premium, typically about 20%, that it added to the cost of a receiver. However, as a British contribution to information technology it was seen by the Government as deserving encouragement, particularly as the hope was that its growth would be paralleled by domestic take-up of what was then called 'viewdata' and is now known as 'videotex': data distribution through telephone lines, with provision for interactive terminals, sharing much of teletext's technology. This hope was not to be fulfilled, for at the end of 1986 there were only 31,000 domestic users[134] — around 4% of the number that it was suggested in 1982 would be needed by that date.[135] In June 1981 teletext receivers were granted preferential treatment regarding the deposits required for rental and hire-purchase,[136] and although this advantage ended in July 1982 when all rental and hire-purchase controls were removed, another was already in operation. In 1980 it had been announced that the capital allowance for rental receivers (which, it may be recalled, Arnold Weinstock had regarded in the 1960s as being too indefensible to last long) was to be phased out,[137] but from 1982 to 1984 the allowance was retained for teletext receivers only;[138,139] as a result, sets with teletext cost hardly any more to rent than those without it, and accounted for most of Ferguson's production.[14]

This timely 'pump-priming' reflected great personal interest and commitment on the part of the Minister of State for Information Technology, Kenneth Baker, who also promoted teletext vigorously abroad. In 1982 there was an offtake of almost half a million teletext sets, and by the end of 1985 there were over 3 million in use.[140] As the number of sets increased, broadcasters provided more programmes with teletext subtitles for the hard of hearing. In 1986 receivers were introduced in which additional circuitry offered 'Fastext' — easy and rapid access to four pages chosen by the magazine's editor as likely choices to follow the page currently on the screen — and by 1989 teletext was provided in two-thirds of large-screen sets and in almost 40% of colour receivers overall. Moreover, although it is open to any country to manufacture them, import penetration in teletext receivers has typically been around 10%, as against 30–40% for colour television sets as a whole.[141]

Broadcasting authorities, Government and industry have co-operated to ensure that, having invented teletext, Britain did not lose its leadership. Before the end of the 1970s the system was being broadened to cover foreign alphabets, and by 1984 the UK technology had an export record that justified its being named World System Teletext (WST).[142] Although viewdata/videotex had not had the expected impact in the home, it had become internationally established in professional applications, and WST's compatibility with European videotex standards secured its widespread adoption as systems were set up by television stations in many parts of the world; in 1985 it was used in 98% of the world's installed capacity of teletext,[143] and UK semiconductor companies, notably Philips Components (as Mullard were renamed in 1988), have built up a healthy export business in dedicated LSIs, both for the origination of teletext signals and for use in receivers.

See what you like when you like
Broadcasters had used videotape recording since the late-1950s, but because it was necessary to use rotating heads in order to record video frequencies the machines were large, complex and extremely expensive. Simpler machines of lower performance were produced during the 1960s for industrial and educational use, but towards the end of the decade the prospects of a domestic videotape machine recording off-air (which would of course have to be colour-capable) were still considered so remote that a film-based system for playing back pre-recorded material was developed in America. Known as Electronic Video Recording (EVR), it was made under licence in several countries, including the UK, where an electron-beam recording plant capable of turning out a million films a year was built, while Rank Bush Murphy made and marketed the associated player.[144] Although EVR had originally been intended for domestic use it did not succeed in that role in America,[145] and when it was launched in the UK in 1971 the emphasis was on educational and promotional applications. It worked reasonably well, but sank without trace as videotape machines appeared that were comparably priced and capable of recording off-air. The Philips N1500 was launched in 1972 at £315, equivalent to well over £1,500 in 1990, and thus made negligible impact on the domestic market, although it was quite widely bought by schools, as was its successor, the N1700. But it was two Japanese-designed systems, independently developed in the mid-1970s, that finally made the domestic video recorder commercially viable: JVC's VHS ('Video Home System'), and Sony's Betamax. They were incompatible, though both used half-inch tape.

The video recorder was a most attractive addition to the distributor's range of products: a high-priced item adding a new dimension to television yet not threatening any existing product with obsolescence. Moreover, the British public's liking for the programmes broadcast to them caused large numbers of people to acquire machines to record them, thereby promoting the sale and hire of pre-recorded tapes, which in turn made possessing a machine even more desirable. Although receiver rental had declined significantly as receivers had become more reliable, the public perceived the video

From a publicity brochure for the EVR machine, marketed in the UK by Rank Bush Murphy as the Rank Teleplayer, c. 1971

The electron-beam recording plant built at Basildon by the EVR Partnership to make films for the system

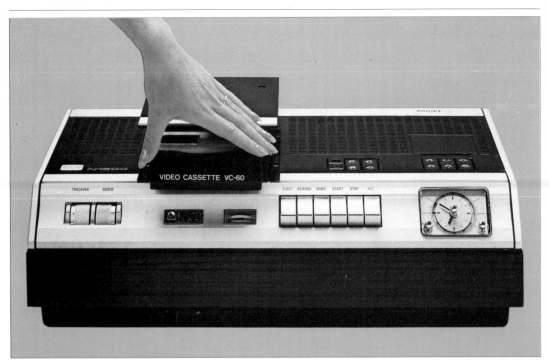

recorder as a product to rent rather than buy; it was unfamiliar, might prove unreliable and expensive to repair, and could quickly become obsolete, particularly as there were two competing formats. As the manufacturer with the largest stake in rental, Thorn lost no time in arranging with JVC to market VHS machines under the Ferguson name, and did so from mid-1978, albeit only in small quantities until the pre-Christmas season of 1979;[14] this astute move complemented the introduction of the TX chassis, and gave a further boost to Ferguson's fortunes.

In June 1980 Philips belatedly launched a third format, known as V2000, which was somewhat more advanced technically than the other two, in that during playback a servo system kept the video head accurately centred on the recorded track. This feature made it possible to use narrower tracks, which in turn allowed the recording to be accommodated on only half the tape's width; the cassette could therefore be turned over like an audio cassette, giving twice the playing time of the other systems. Some two years before launching V2000 Philips had tried to persuade Thorn, Thomson, Telefunken and Grundig to adopt it, in the hope of establishing it as an industry standard. Shortly before the Thorn/JVC deal was finalized, Philips invited Ferguson's top management over to Eindhoven and gave them a good dressing down for being in consultation with a Japanese company. This did not help an already weak case. The V2000 was still in the future, and the Ferguson team suspected (correctly as it turned out) that it would not be ready by the predicted date; VHS was already up and running. Moreover, Philips were only prepared to offer machines identical to those they would sell under their own name, whereas JVC would supply Ferguson with visually distinctive models. In the event, only Grundig joined the V2000 camp.

The existence of three broadly similar but incompatible formats was an unstable situation, understandably unpopular with the retail and rental trades, and particularly galling to those concerned with the

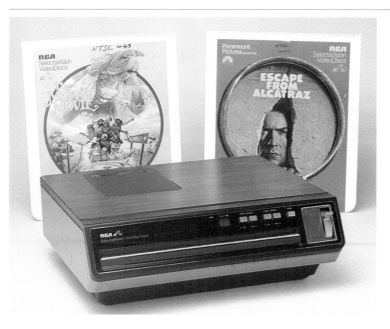

After many years of research into the possibility of video discs three incompatible systems came to fruition, and were marketed around 1980. Only one — Laser Vision — has survived

The RCA video disc player, of 1978, picked up the signal by a capacitive pickup, which mechanically tracked a groove, as in a gramophone. Ferguson assessed this system but did not adopt it

The Ferguson VHD disc player, of the early-1980s, used technology developed by JVC. As with the RCA system the pickup was capacitive, but in this player it was tracked electronically

The Philips LaserVision disc player of 1980 used a laser to scan the disc, and could pick out individual pictures, making it suitable for many applications besides showing pre-recorded films

sale and hire of pre-recorded tapes. As the latecomer, with the lowest market penetration, V2000 was the obvious candidate for elimination. Although the format had helped Ferguson by keeping their main competitor out of the VHS market, they helped the process along with advertisements in the trade press listing the huge number of brands using VHS worldwide, the handful of Japanese brands tied to Betamax, and the two lone adherents of V2000.[39] Philips finally conceded defeat in June 1984 by launching their first VHS machines, and dropped V2000 shortly afterwards. Sony have retained Betamax, albeit at a very low level of production, but also make VHS machines, and since 1983 have mainly been associated with their own 8mm format, whose small cassette is particularly suitable for use in videotape recorders integral with cameras ('camcorders').

These manœuvres took place during an explosive growth in the possession of video recorders, which on a per capita basis soon became higher in the UK than anywhere else in the world.[146] In 1980 total disposals were only 350,000; two years later they topped two million,[147] and by the end of 1986 there was a recorder in 49% of households;[148] the advent of Channel 4, in 1982, had made it fractionally more likely that the viewer would find a recorder useful in

The principle of LaserVision

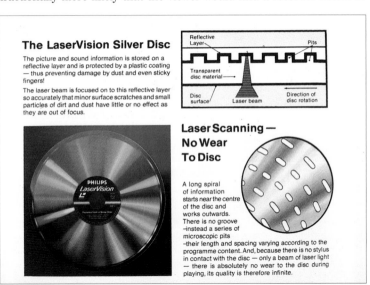

The LaserVision Silver Disc

The picture and sound information is stored on a reflective layer and is protected by a plastic coating — thus preventing damage by dust and even sticky fingers!

The laser beam is focused on to this reflective layer so accurately that minor surface scratches and small particles of dirt and dust have little or no effect as they are out of focus.

Reflective Layer — Pits — Transparent disc material — Disc surface — Laser beam — Direction of disc rotation

Laser Scanning — No Wear To Disc

A long spiral of information starts near the centre of the disc and works outwards. There is no groove –instead a series of microscopic pits –their length and spacing varying according to the programme content. And, because there is no stylus in contact with the disc — only a beam of laser light — there is absolutely no wear to the disc during playing, its quality is therefore infinite.

The optical system

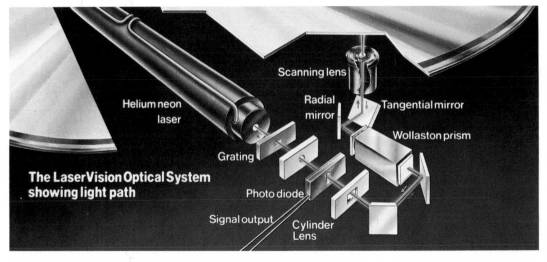

The LaserVision Optical System showing light path

Helium neon laser — Scanning lens — Radial mirror — Tangential mirror — Wollaston prism — Grating — Photo diode — Signal output — Cylinder Lens

resolving clashes between attractive programmes. Initially, all the recorders were imported, but in 1981 Thorn set up a joint venture with JVC and Telefunken to manufacture them in Europe. The consortium was known as 'J2T' (the name being left unchanged when Telefunken was taken over by Thomson) and had two factories, one in Berlin and the other in Newhaven, where Thorn EMI had previously made audio products. Assembly at Newhaven began in October 1982, entirely from imported parts, and in just over two years J2T produced their millionth recorder,[149] by which time there were three other plants making recorders in Britain.[150]

The Philips LaserVision disc, launched in 1980, can justifiably be termed a technological triumph. It produced considerably better pictures than domestic videotape and offered rapid access to any point in the recording, while the prices of both discs and players were competitive with tape. However, the system's restriction to pre-recorded discs prevented it from becoming established on the domestic market, because people could buy or hire pre-recorded videotapes for the machines they already used for recording programmes off the air. Notwithstanding this commercial setback, LaserVision's technology was soon to have a profound impact on sound recording, and in 1990 is poised to re-emerge in video as 'Laser Disc'.

Stereo sound for television
In the early-1970s the BBC had begun to distribute television sound around the network in digital form, by housing the pulses within the video signal's synchronizing pulses and removing them before

A LaserVision disc

transmission. In 1983, they began investigating the possibility of adding digital stereo sound to television, using elements both of this technology and of that subsequently devised for satellite television broadcasting. The project went extremely well, and by 1986 it was established that the necessary signal could be radiated from television transmitters without upsetting existing receivers. In order to spread the cost of developing the necessary ICs it was desirable to involve other countries, and it was found that the proposed system, known as NICAM, required little modification to be used by Scandinavian countries, who were particularly interested in using its two sound channels for dual-language applications.[151]

Ferguson's Bradford laboratory and Texas Instruments Ltd tackled the design of components for decoders,[5] and by 1987 products were designed and the system confirmed as totally satisfactory.[152] It then transpired that the BBC could not afford to install the system it had so successfully designed, and it was announced that ITV and Channel 4 would inaugurate a preliminary service, initially in London and Yorkshire only, in September 1989.[153] However, as the date approached it became evident that neither Channel 4 nor the ITV companies had enough suitable stereo programmes to give anything that could properly be called a service, and the launch was played right down in order to prevent accusations that the public were being persuaded to buy NICAM receivers under false pretences.[154] So effectively was this done that when two months later the Chief Executive of Channel 4 was asked at a conference for his opinion on "the lost opportunity of NICAM" he replied "What is NICAM?"[155] But despite this inauspicious start, it is estimated that by the end of 1990 half a million NICAM receivers, distributed between television sets and video recorders, will have entered the market, and that ITV and Channel 4 will have achieved 75% national coverage; the BBC expects to begin transmission with about 70% coverage in the autumn of 1991.[156]

Out of intensive care

A decade on from the unhappy Stratford-upon-Avon talks of 1979, and with six more Far-Eastern companies in membership of BREMA, how far have events justified the apprehensions then expressed? The extent to which imports from Japan have been reduced through Japanese manufacture in the UK has turned out to be of less concern than the growth of imports from other, less co-operative countries in the Far East. Perhaps inevitably, the products made in the UK by Far-Eastern-owned companies are still largely designed abroad, but the companies have made considerable progress in extending the functions of their plants beyond those of assembly and testing, and many more components are being sourced locally. Both these benefits are being achieved partly through vertical integration. Sony began manufacturing Trinitron tubes at Bridgend in 1982, made a million of them by 1987, and in 1989 announced plans to invest a further £36 million in tube manufacture.[157] After establishing colour-receiver manufacture in East Lothian, Mitsubishi opened a video-recorder factory at Livingston, West Lothian, and later decided to undertake precision mechanical manufacture there; this was so successful that in 1988 a second factory was brought on stream to house deck-assembly and drum-assembly lines.[158]

Many of the plants owned by Far-Eastern companies include

The Rt Hon Peter Walker, Secretary of State for Wales, tours Aiwa's production floor after expansion of their factory at Crumlin, Gwent, in 1989

The auto-insertion area at Aiwa

specialized units that deal with particular aspects of the parent companies' needs. JVC's plant at East Kilbride was opened only in 1988, but has from the outset had an Engineering department concerned with innovations in television technology, particularly in the field of picture quality.[159] The Taiwanese company, Tatung, upgraded the R & D laboratory that they acquired when they took over the old Decca television factory at Bridgnorth, Shropshire, in 1981, and maintained a substantial R & D unit when they moved to Telford in 1984. In 1990 Sharp founded a laboratory in Magdalen College's Oxford Science Park, specializing in Optoelectronics and Information Technology; this £10 million investment is the company's first fundamental research operation outside Japan.

In the early-1980s agreements between the EEC and Japan's Ministry of International Trade & Industry (MITI) put the UK and continental Europe on a common footing, since when 'local sourcing' by Far-Eastern-owned UK plants has meant 'European' rather than

One of Mitsubishi's two video-recorder factories at Livingston, West Lothian, 1989

Ceremonial broaching of sake barrel at the opening of Mitsubishi's second Livingston factory, 1988. Left to right:
Mr S Yatsuzuka, General Manager, Livingston video recorder plant; Mr R Watt, Chairman Livingston Development Corporation; Sir Peter Parker, Chairman Mitsubishi Electric (UK) Ltd; Mr S Miyagawa, Deputy General Manager, Kyoto Works, Japan

HRH The Princess of Wales, escorted by Mr A Toda, Managing Director of NEC Technologies (UK) Ltd, at the opening of the company's new plant at Telford, Shropshire, on 2 November 1987

Published by courtesy of Star Journal Studios, Telford

Video recorders in production at NEC's factory in 1988. In October 1989 production of video recorders ceased in order to allow the plant to increase its production of computer monitors

Published by courtesy of Star Journal Studios, Telford

Video recorder production at Sharp's factory at Wrexham, 1988. The plant opened in 1985, and in 1988 was doubled in area to 350,000 sq ft

Video recorder production lines, showing lifts. These are used both for transferring products between conveyors without impeding gangways and, as here, for transferring them to and from overhead 'ageing' lines running above the conveyors at a height of several metres

Printed circuit board assembly/test area

Performance measurement equipment

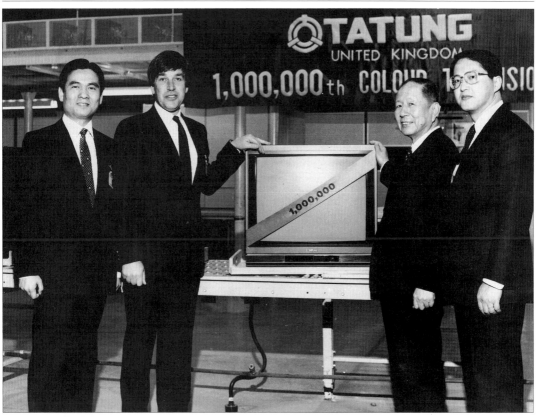

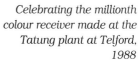

Celebrating the millionth colour receiver made at the Tatung plant at Telford, 1988

Colour receivers at the Tatung plant, c. 1988

In 1989 Matsushita established at Bracknell, Berks, Panasonic's European headquarters

Mr Y Koyama, Managing Director of Matsushita (UK) Ltd, receiving the Queen's Award for Export from Mrs Susan Williams, OBE, Her Majesty's Lord Lieutenant for South Glamorgan, in July 1989, at the company's Cardiff factory. The award was for two classes of product: colour television receivers & microwave ovens

Engineering (left) and (right) Quality Assurance areas at JVC's plant in East Kilbride, near Glasgow. These pictures were taken during the start-up period after the plant opened in April 1988, and show a higher proportion of Japanese staff than are currently employed there

'British'. But by whatever name, its increase has been dramatic, and reflects the extent to which the Japanese approach to quality has taken root in Europe. In 1976 when Matsushita, manufacturers of Panasonic and Technics products, opened their first UK factory, the Government had urged them to use as many British components as possible and the company had already sent a selection, including colour tubes, to Japan for quality testing; 90% of them were rejected.[71] In 1989, the local-content value of Panasonic colour receivers was over 70%.[160] The UK now has component-makers who meet world standards, through elimination of the weaker companies, through great efforts on the part of the survivors, and latterly through inward investment, mostly by Japanese companies.[90] Early in the decade Mullard, the leading UK supplier to the consumer electronics industry, went to considerable lengths to adapt to the conditions of the 1980s. They established an effective presence in Tokyo, opening a permanent office there staffed by Japanese, and in 1983 launched an ongoing quality-training programme with a weekend course led by J M Juran.[161]

Japanese companies, well aware that Britain is not Japan, have tactfully minimized the culture-shock brought about by their taking over much of the British consumer-electronics industry. Some aspects of their ethos, inseparable from their high performance, are not negotiable: the preoccupation with quality, the expectation of loyalty to the company and the reciprocal concern for the workers' welfare. But they have not insisted on their production-line workers totally abstaining from conversation as their counterparts in Japan do, and although many have single-union deals of the type negotiated by Toshiba and Hitachi, Mitsubishi in Lothian[105] and NEC in Telford[162] have fallen in with the local tradition of non-union plants. Many companies have become benefactors to British institutions, ranging from Sharp (with UK headquarters in Manchester) sponsoring Manchester United, to Matsushita's donations to the University of Birmingham's Shakespeare Institute. Matsushita are also dedicated to staff training schemes, and almost 10% of their European workforce have travelled to Japan for training.[163]

Withdrawal on the European Front
Philips
When Philips took over Pye in 1976, a detailed comparison was made between their respective television receivers, with a view to rationalizing UK production, and on grounds of component-count, cost and performance the Philips G11 chassis was adopted. Throughout the 1970s the British market was sufficiently different from the continental to justify Philips in maintaining a range of television receivers distinct from those designed in Eindhoven; this was partly a matter of styling, partly of the British viewer's indifference to expensive refinements. But the need for economies of scale to meet Japanese competition, and the convergence of design caused by the growing use of ICs and SAW filters, made a pan-European approach inevitable, with a different design philosophy. In Britain, for example, the aim had been to make the most cost-effective basic model, which accounted for the bulk of the trade, without too much regard for the cost of deriving from it the relatively few high-specification variants required; on the continent, where high-specification models were the norm, the basic model was designed for economical upgrading, even

The Mullard colour-tube factory at Durham, which opened in December 1972

Examining shadow mask for defects, 1989

Placing the faceplate on the cone prior to fusing the two together, 1989. Care is needed in this operation to ensure that the spreading of 'frit' paste between the two is uniformly compressed

Close-up of a black-matrix screen, 1989. The contrast of colour tubes is enhanced if the phosphor is inlaid into a black matrix. At Durham in 1989 this technique was applied only to high-resolution 14″ monitor tubes, which continued to use dots rather than stripes

The automated production line for applying the black matrix

'Mullard' became 'Philips Components' in 1988

Pye's Lowestoft factory in 1969

though that made its own cost rather higher. Philips Electronics designed no more complete receivers, but retained a Research and Development role, their Mitcham laboratories being one of the parent group's four international 'Centres of Competence', each specializing in particular aspects of television.[123]

In 1980 the industry's colour television deliveries were nearly 2 million, slightly up on 1979, despite high interest rates and rising unemployment. Philips were nevertheless running well below capacity at both their television factories and making heavy losses. They announced in October that they were to concentrate television-set manufacture at Croydon, and close the Pye factory at Lowestoft, which in its heyday in the early-1970s had employed 2,800 people full time but was currently down to 1,100. Sanyo re-opened the factory in 1982 with a workforce of just 65, subsequently increased to 400. The Croydon plant was entirely refurbished and reorganized, being described late in 1984 as "a full member of the network of Philips European CTV factories", with a workforce of 1,200 and an annual capacity of 500,000 colour receivers.[164] Within a year, staged redundancies began, and the plant was down to 500 workers when it was closed in December 1988, declared to be unable to achieve the necessary economies of scale.[165] Production was transferred to the Philips factory at Bruges, whose capacity was increased accordingly.

Philips Components, as Mullard were re-named in 1988, continue as major manufacturers in the field of consumer electronics. Specialized ICs, some of them designed at Mitcham, are made at Southampton, and the colour tube factory at Durham, supplied from

Assembly line at Pye's Lowestoft works, 1978

"Pye factory reaches end of road" was the headline over this story in the Eastern Daily Press *on 14 October 1980*

HOPES WITH NEW FIRMS

Mr. Terry Sullivan.

Mr. Eric Goreham.

Though still stunned by the sudden announcement that the Pye TV factory at Lowestoft is to close with the loss of 1100 jobs, unions and management were yesterday looking to the future of the site.

It is apparent that, as far as the Philips group is concerned, the factory, which was opened in 1951 and is one of the biggest employers in the town, has now reached the end of the road.

Facing "serious losses," Philips see no possibility of keeping it open. The factory will shut down over the next 18 months. The first jobs will go in March.

Any future which the 28-acre site may hold seems to lie with new firms coming in. The factory, with a variety of different sized units, lends itself to becoming what one shop steward described as "an industrial estate."

The idea of a salvage plan based on new firms has been mooted by the town's MP and Minister of Employment, Mr. Jim Prior — and by the plant manager, Mr. Terry Sullivan.

Dreaded

This will be one aspect of the problem which will be discussed when union leaders and shop stewards meet at the factory this morning.

Yesterday was Black Monday for the 1100 workers who finally heard the news they had dreaded for months — their jobs were gone. TV construction is to be concentrated on the group's Croydon factory.

Union officials described the closure as "a disaster" and "terrible

news" — and gave notice that they will fight to save their jobs.

Mr. Prior saw it as a "cruel blow," and revealed that the company had asked for cash help under the Industry Act — but the amount needed was too great.

There will be severance and money-in-lieu payments to those thrown out of work. A 40-year-old employee on £80 a week and with ten years' service will receive just over £2000. Examples given by Pye range up to £6240 for a 50-year-old on £120 a week with 20 years' service.

Mr. Sullivan told the "EDP" that he was terribly aware of the impact which the closure would have on the employees and the town in general. The decision to close was taken at a board meeting towards the end of last week, but the future of the factory had been under consideration for about two years.

As far as Philips was concerned, he said, this was the end of the road. There was no way — no new product they could put in — to save it.

"I feel that the best hope for the site, and for the town," he said, "is for parts of it to be taken by small new firms."

The site covers 29 acres and includes a number of separate buildings giving about 30,000 square metres of floor space.

"It does lend itself to development by a number of small firms — and perhaps that is the best hope," he said.

Stunned

As far as the transfer of some workers to the Croydon plant was concerned, Mr. Sullivan said that it was hoped that some jobs would be available. "We do have 18 months in which to try to help everyone to our utmost, and we shall certainly be doing that," he said.

Mr. Eric Goreham, senior shop steward at Pye, was close to tears as he told an "EDP" reporter: "We are all still stunned. We feared it might happen, but we all felt that it couldn't really come to this."

Whole families, he said, would be hit by the closure. "There are

Grim-faced workers cycle from the Pye factory yesterday.

Eastern Daily Press, Saturday, August 28, 1982

Within two years the headline was "MORE TV JOBS IS PRIOR HOPE", when Sanyo re-opened the old Pye factory. There was a single-union deal with the EEPTU whose National Officer, Roy Sanderson, is here seen with local MP Jim Prior

Sanyo at Lowestoft, 1983

CHASSIS ALIGNMENT

Simonstone and Blackburn, has a workforce of over 1,200 and operates on a 5-day week of 24-hour days; it exports 60% of its output and is a major supplier of tubes to the UK's Japanese setmakers, always excepting Sony. It would, however, be rash to regard any plant's future as assured in the internationally organized world of consumer electronics in the 1990s. When Philips revealed grossly reduced profits for the first quarter of 1990, the figures for consumer electronics remained healthy but two ominous conclusions were drawn. While staying in semiconductors was vital to the company's continuing as a leader in consumer electronics, the cost of doing so threatened to become insupportable.[166] And although sales of colour tubes continued to rise, their profitability was undermined by price erosion.[167] One day in the autumn of 1989 the display in the Durham factory's entrance hall welcoming the day's visitors listed seven Chinese names. The factory was being studied as a preliminary to the opening of a similar one in China.[168]

Ferguson[3.39]

The TX9 and TX10 chassis set Ferguson on a successful course in the early-1980s, while the company's link with JVC through the 'J2T' video-recorder conglomerate led to their designing and manufacturing for JVC large-screen television sets tailored to the European market. This contract was important symbolically as well economically — a British company producing receivers up to Japanese standards. Since becoming quality-conscious in the mid-1970s, Ferguson had not only put their own house in order but had made it clear to component-suppliers that they too must meet world standards, and had driven the point home by increasing the proportion of Japanese components in their sets.

Concurrently, however, Ferguson had serious commercial problems. In 1984 it was decided to allow Thorn EMI's rental business, hitherto tied to Ferguson sets, to buy on the open market, and demand immediately fell by 120,000 sets a year, or around 15% of current output. Cushioning against market fluctuations was reduced, and the volume of production fell dangerously. By this time Ferguson's video recorders were carrying their television receivers, and the industry's 29% drop in video-recorder offtake in 1984 contributed to the company's 1984–85 loss of £25 million. The policy of moving 'up-market' that had been successfully pursued for the past five years was abandoned, and production was concentrated upon basic models. To improve productivity the Enfield and Gosport factories were modernized and reorganized, and the work-force was cut from 6,000 to 4,300, but these changes could not overcome Ferguson's underlying weakness. Although they were the UK brand-leaders in television, with a market share of over 10%, they were exporting less than 10% of their output, and by the end of 1987 would lose the JVC contract in anticipation of that company opening their own UK factory. As Thorn EMI's Managing Director put it, they were "a national business in a global market",[169] and it became evident that they could survive only as part of an international group.

In June 1987, after negotiations lasting barely two weeks, Thorn EMI sold Ferguson for £90 million to the French company Thomson Grand Public — the other T in J2T. Thomson had already bought a number of continental setmakers, and were making 2.8 million colour sets a year; this was about four times Ferguson's current rate

Equipment built by Ferguson to refute a claim by the French company CFT to have invented a basic principle of the PAL system, and thus to be owed tens of millions of pounds in royalties by British setmakers. The equipment was used in the High Court trial in 1983, in which CFT's claim was dismissed, and again in the Court of Appeal in 1985. CFT's appeal was also dismissed, and costs awarded to Thorn-EMI Ferguson

A Ferguson receiver of 1984, identical to those that they made to JVC specification for sale in Europe bearing the JVC logo

A chassis-alignment station at Ferguson's Gosport factory. The right-hand screen gives the operator his instructions, which do not allow him to proceed to any stage of alignment until the preceding stage is within limits

A Ferguson satellite-reception package marketed for the Astra satellite in 1989, comprising a 60cm dish and an upgradable receiver with remote control

Small-screen receivers undergoing final checking prior to boxing, at Ferguson's Gosport factory, 1989. Visible at high level in the background are the sets on a mobile soak-test

432

excluding sets being made for JVC. The purchase gave them access to the UK market, the largest in Europe, and put them towards the top of the world league. Thomson cut Ferguson back from a size that was consistent with their profitable past but was no longer relevant. Two years after the purchase they announced that the Enfield factory, by this time producing only electronic sub-assemblies, would close at the end of 1989, with the loss of 750 jobs; Gosport was planned to have a work-force of 1,300. The closure was precipitated by unexpectedly poor sales, but technological progress was also a factor. Enfield had done pioneering work on using printed circuit boards in television sets, and had built a large plant to make them, but fewer and smaller components meant fewer and smaller boards, and PCB production was no longer economic at an output of around three-quarters of a million sets a year; at the end of 1988 it was transferred to a plant in Germany with four times the capacity. In the 1970s and early-1980s the labs at Enfield had had no fewer than 280 people working on television development and product support. With the factory closed and product support transferred to Gosport, the labs housed only the 40 engineers of Ferguson's development department, now constituting the UK team of Thomson's international Research & Development company. The laboratory at Bradford had contributed in the early-1980s to two major British developments in television engineering: MAC (referred to later) and NICAM. By the time of the takeover its staff had been cut back to less than half, and it has subsequently been reconstituted as a small, independent company.

Fidelity[170]

The sale of Ferguson in 1987 left only one British-owned manufacturer of colour television sets: Fidelity, specializing in low-priced 14" models, and in 1986 producing 260,000 sets at its factory in Acton.[169] The company had been founded after the war, and had been successful right through the 1950s and 60s with low-price radios, radiograms and record-players. They had subsequently moved over to television, and survived as unspectacular but seemingly quite successful setmakers until 1984, when they were bought for £14 million by a large manufacturing group, Caparo; however, the declared profits of £1.4 million on which the purchase was based were later alleged to be fictional. Caparo put in a dynamic Chief Executive, Richard Hanna, to turn the company round, and he tackled their indifferent quality performance as well as making determined efforts to move the product range up-market.

The venture was foredoomed, however, for external circumstances made the 14" receiver irredeemably unprofitable before new products could replace it as the company's bread-and-butter. In 1984 a 14" Korean receiver came into the UK at around £110, but by 1987 the strengthening of the pound against the dollar had lowered that figure to £72; an anti-dumping duty of 10% was finally imposed on Korea in April 1990. The last straw, however, was competition from Chinese receivers, imported at less than the cost of their components on the world market. Although China's exports to the UK are nominally restricted to an annual quota of 20,000 it has not proved possible to prevent receivers from crossing the almost transparent border into Hong Kong, whence they enjoy free entry into the UK. In 1988 imports from Hong Kong accounted for roughly a quarter of the small-screen market, or over half a million sets,[54] and in March 1989 14" colour television sets were being retailed at £99.[171] Fidelity's losses were threatening the profitability of the whole Caparo group, and in May 1988 the brand name and trade mark were sold to Amstrad for £3.1 million; the factory closed at the end of July.

Some New Products of the 1980s

In terms of turnover, colour television sets remain the consumer electronics industry's major product, with retail sales totalling around £1,100 million in 1989, closely followed by video recorders at £724 million. However, the 1980s have seen the emergence of several important new products, pride of place belonging to one that actively involves the consumer, and typically costs two or three times as much as a large-screen colour receiver.

The camcorder
The combined television camera and videotape recorder ('camcorder') was developed in the 1970s for professional use, and initially was confined to news-gathering applications where topicality was considered to justify the transmission of pictures not quite up to broadcast quality. The first domestic versions appeared in the early-1980s, and have developed in performance and sophistication at a rate that has inspired the suggestion that they should be marked with a 'sell by' date. In mid-1990, models in the low- and medium-price range record either on the normal VHS format, often with a special compact version of the cassette, or on the 8mm format developed by Sony primarily for this application and now also used by other manufacturers. However, these formats no longer do full justice to the pictures produced by the better cameras, and higher-specification versions of both have been developed: S-VHS and Hi8. Camcorders using these formats currently start at around £1,000. Suitably coupled to a high-quality television receiver, they can replay pictures which, being exempt from the limitations of PAL coding, are in some respects better than anything received off-air. Moreover, the re-recording necessary for editing tapes does not produce serious loss of quality. In 1989 total sales more than doubled on 1988, to reach 280,000, and although this was in part due to Amstrad's remaindering an obsolescent £499 model at £299, 12% of the camcorders sold by electrical shops cost over £1,200.[172]

As a consumer-electronics product identified with the pursuit of a hobby rather than with mere passive entertainment, the camcorder is greatly appreciated by the industry. Like the amateur photographer, or for that matter the wireless experimenter of the 1920s, the camcorder enthusiast may be expected to move up to more-ambitious equipment as his skill increases, and to be an insatiable buyer of accessories. Thus the normal process of price erosion as technological progress puts each desirable feature into cheaper models is offset by the appearance of new refinements in the dearer ones. As computerization becomes more sophisticated it tends less towards wresting control from the user, thereby spoiling his fun, and more towards helping him to make the most of whatever skills he possesses.

Two considerations slightly tarnish the industry's perception of the camcorder. Britain has taken no part in its development, and her factories can for the present expect to be involved only at a relatively mundane level. Neither do the traditional outlets for radio and television products have a monopoly of sales. The camcorder neatly complements photographic cameras, and with its high unit price is already making a substantial contribution to the turnover of many camera shops. The author's local camera-centre reports that its camcorder sales are mostly to people who are not photographic enthusiasts, suggesting that the public are not sure which category of shop is more natural to the product.

The personal stereo
The compact cassette had been around for over fifteen years before its compactness was exploited in 1980 by the 'Walkman' — one of that select band of proprietary names that the public pays the compliment of using generically. The appeal of a miniature, non-recording tape player feeding stereo to headphones seems obvious enough in retrospect, but in fact Sony launched it very tentatively, and three months passed before sales took off. Several strands of thought may have contributed to its development. Sony's Chairman and co-founder, Akio Morita, says that he thought it would relieve youngsters, who seemed unable to live without constant music, of the need to walk about carrying heavy, anti-social ghetto-blasters. His co-founder, Masaru Ibuka, is said to have wanted better in-flight sound than airlines provided. It has also been suggested that Sony's Tape Recorder division, having just lost radio-cassette machines to Radio division, felt that honour required them to come up with a new product.

Much has been made of the Walkman's relationship to the Japanese psyche, from comparing it with bonsai as expressing fascination with the miniature, to considering it as a means of meeting the need for personal space. However, it must also meet more universal desires to account for total sales, over ten years, of fifty million Sony machines and three times that number by other makers. Are there, one wonders, other equally simple and equally world-beating consumer-electronic products waiting to be developed?[173]

The compact disc
Consumer electronics has seen many instances of rivalry leading to incompatibility: Baird vs Marconi-EMI, International-octal vs Mazda-octal valves, $33^1/_3$ vs 45 rpm, PAL vs SECAM, VHS vs Betamax vs V2000 and (yet to be related) Sky vs BSB. Enlightened self-interest leading competitors to pool resources and evolve something beyond their individual capabilities is much rarer, although America produced two notable instances in the 1950s, with the NTSC colour system and Zenith-GE stereo.

The audio compact disc (CD), launched in Britain early in 1983, was therefore remarkable for being a joint development, by Philips and Sony, as well as for its outstanding performance. Philips had learned from the commercial failure of the V2000 videotape format and the domestic market's indifference to the LaserVision disc the unwisdom of undertaking a major development without ensuring that it became a world standard. Now, in the adaptation of LaserVision's technology to the recording of digitally encoded stereo sound, Sony helped Philips to produce a commercially attractive format, and persuaded other Japanese companies to back it.[18] The CD combines unprecedented fidelity with freedom from wear, high immunity to damage, and immediate access to any part of the recording. In 1983 it was seen as an exotic product on the further shores of high fidelity, and only

33,000 players were sold in 1984. By 1986 the figure was 500,000, establishing the CD player as the consumer-electronics industry's fastest-growing market of the post-war era,[174] and in 1989 reached 1.6 million. Aiwa, Sharp and members of the FBA manufacture players in the UK.

Broadcasting in the Space Age

At the end of the 1980s Britain took her first steps into a fundamentally new mode of broadcasting, with implications far beyond its modest initial impact. Television relays via geostationary satellites 36,000km above the equator became routinely available in the mid-1960s, but the signals reaching the earth were so weak that they had to be focused into elaborate low-noise amplifiers by dishes tens of metres across. By the late-1970s, technology had improved to the point where much smaller dishes could be used, and satellites were seen to offer a means of revitalizing cable television. The excellent coverage achieved by the BBC and the IBA had largely destroyed cable's original role of bringing television to poorly served built-up areas, and attempts to revive it by adding local programmes had not been notably successful. Now, however, the prospect arose of local cable companies distributing a selection of channels beamed down from one or more satellites, and the Cable and Broadcasting Act (1984) provided for the award of franchises to such companies.

The late-1970s provided the further prospect of high-power satellites sending down signals strong enough to be picked up by dishes only a metre or less across, feeding individual domestic receivers. Such 'Direct Broadcasting by Satellite', or DBS, can provide national coverage for a number of programmes in addition to those from terrestrial UHF transmitters and opens up the prospect of higher standards of definition. It has the further advantage over terrestrial transmission that a new DBS service becomes immediately available in all parts of the country including remote rural areas, always excepting the very few locations where line of sight to the satellite is blocked by intervening hills or buildings. Realization of these heady possibilities was, however, to be seriously compromised for want of effective overall control, prompting BREMA to describe the situation in 1988 as an "appalling shambles".[175]

Preparing the ground

By 1979 the French and German authorities were planning DBS services, while BREMA was expressing regret that there had as yet been no UK participation. However, by 1982 the IBA had devised a radically new form of colour transmission for DBS, a Government report had recommended its adoption by the UK, and the BBC was expected to begin broadcasting two satellite channels in 1986.

The IBA recognized that because transmissions from satellites used FM, they were not well adapted to carry PAL signals. The system they devised and demonstrated in 1982, known as 'MAC' (Mulitiplexed Analogue Components) uses digital synchronizing and sound signals, while the brightness and colouring signals for each scanning line are time-compressed, allowing them to be transmitted one after the other; at the receiver, they are restored to normal duration and brought back into time-coincidence. MAC is significantly less noisy than PAL when transmitted by satellite, and is free from two defects inherent in PAL and arising from interaction between its colouring and brightness signals: a fuzzing of edges where there is a large change of colour, and the liability of striped fabrics to be overlaid with swirls of spurious colour. There is also ample accommodation for digital sound and data signals, again separated in time from the picture signals. Finally, MAC has potential for subsequent upgrading to higher definition. Until there are television sets with built-in MAC receivers, satellite aerials are connected to 'set-top' receivers. For sets able to accept this receiver's video-frequency output, all MAC's advantages are available; otherwise the signal is re-coded to PAL and fed to the set's aerial socket.

MAC was not the first use of time compression in television; patent searches subsequently revealed that Walter Bruch, the inventor of PAL, had in 1970 filed a patent for a similar signal with conventional synchronization for use in video recording, and the Japanese broadcasting organization NHK are known to have experimented with time compression for satellite broadcasting in the 1970s.[176]

Although MAC received official approval in 1982 it was still a long way off being a commercially viable system, requiring the development of advanced ICs for receivers. The decision was taken to seek a common European standard rather than develop the system purely for British use, and to achieve agreement it was necessary to make fundamental changes, not necessarily for the better, in the specification of the digital sound and data signal. These international negotiations delayed progress, for until agreement was reached semiconductor manufacturers would not go ahead with the development of ICs. By 1983 it was evident that DBS was not going to start up in 1986 as originally planned,[177] and in Britain there was an additional source of delay. The economics of DBS were proving unattractive to the BBC, and in 1985 they finally abandoned their attempts to establish a service.[178] Then in December 1986, the IBA awarded a fifteen-year franchise to a substantially backed group, British Satellite Broadcasting (BSB), which was to inaugurate a three-channel service at the end of 1989.[179] Meanwhile 'D2-MAC', compatible with cable systems, had been adopted by France and Germany, who planned to start DBS in 1987. In that year Britain adopted 'D-MAC', similar to D2-MAC in concept but with twice the data capacity.[180]

Market forces take over

So far DBS promised to follow British broadcasting's traditional way of introducing new developments, with a satisfactory, durable solution reached after Government, broadcasters and industry had painstakingly assessed all the possibilities amidst mounting condemnation of the resultant delay. Harmony was only mildly disturbed when BREMA discovered, in July 1987, that BSB were adopting a higher profile on technological matters than was thought appropriate to their primary role as programme providers. The company intended to specify their receivers fully instead of leaving the design to setmakers and their semiconductor suppliers, and for the first three years would restrict manufacture to just three setmakers, as yet not chosen. A few months later a BREMA delegation visited Luxembourg to discuss with a European satellite consortium their plans for carrying a number of channels for UK viewers on their 'Astra' satellite, to be launched late in 1988, almost a year before BSB's scheduled debut. Astra was in fact a communication satellite not a DBS one, being medium-power rather than high-power, using frequencies outside the DBS band, and orbiting at longitude 19°E instead of at 31°W as recommended for DBS satellites serving the UK. But these niceties were in no way going to impede the project, and BREMA encouraged all manufacturers to provide receivers for Astra.[181]

However, by spring 1988 it was evident that DBS was in danger of running into anarchy. The operators of Astra were prepared to transmit whatever coding system the programme providers chose to provide. Receiver ICs for continental Europe's D2-MAC system were becoming available but would not receive the D-MAC system, to which BSB were committed; ICs suitable for both variants were under development but would not be available in time for the Astra launch.[182] Programme providers for nine English-language channels were then announced. Initally four but eventually six would be operated by 'Sky', owned by Rupert Murdoch's News International, while W H Smith would have two channels, and there would be a 24-hour music channel, MTV. Devastatingly, but hardly surprisingly, the programme providers elected not to wait for MAC technology, but simply to transmit PAL signals, although W H Smith hoped to transfer to D-MAC once decoders for that system were freely available.

This decision put paid to any hope that DBS would be introduced in an orderly way. For the first time in Britain, the technology of broadcast signals was to be settled by having rival organizations adopt incompatible systems then slog it out in the market place. Few viewers could be expected to use both satellites, since only an expensive motorized aerial could avoid the need for two aerial systems, while many first-generation receivers would be restricted to either Sky or BSB. With the example of the rival video-recording formats freshly in mind, the industry inclined to the belief that there was only room for one system, and users of Astra would enjoy a great advantage by being first in the field. In August 1988 Sky were looking forward to broadcasting early in 1989; BSB were not scheduled to do so until September 1989, and had got only as far as choosing, from the sixty who had expressed interest, the three manufacturers whom they would allow to have the necessary ICs to make D-MAC receivers: Ferguson, Salora (a European brand of ITT) and Tatung;[183] six months later they were to add Philips to the list. The restriction thus imposed by BSB on the supply of D-MAC ICs did not apply to manufacturers wishing to incorporate a D-MAC receiver in a television set, but the commercial unattractiveness of such a product made this a purely theoretical distinction.

Sky set out their stall

When Sky began broadcasting, in February 1989, the public had yet to be convinced that DBS, from whatever source, was worth having. It would cost at least £250 to buy and install the equipment, and after a free trial period there would be a monthly charge of around £10 to watch the recent films that were one of DBS's chief attractions; details of the encryption and decoding technology needed to implement this 'subscription' feature had not yet been released. Indications from cable television were not encouraging, with only 272,000 subscribers at the end of 1988, representing 18% of homes passed.[184] Feature films apart, Sky and cable television both offered programmes of lower average cost and quality than those available on Britain's four terrestrial channels. But although the programmes were cheap, the high transmission cost of DBS required a rapid rate of growth to keep initial losses within bounds, and cried out for a concerted campaign by programme providers, setmakers and retailers. Instead, BSB understandably did their utmost to persuade the public to wait until their own launch, in order to prevent Sky from establishing an unassailable lead during their temporary monopoly. Research commissioned by BSB established that, with the honourable exception of the *Financial Times*, newspapers associated with either of the two parties were biased in their coverage of DBS,[185] Sky benefiting the more because of News International's strong position.

Many early Sky installations consisted of a £199 package marketed by Amstrad, who were mainly associated with computers. The company had been one of the original members of the BSB consortium, but had transferred their allegiance to Sky when it became evident that with MAC circuitry it was not going to be possible to meet BSB's original target price of £200.[186] Sales were initially slow. Sky had predicted that there would be 1.2 million satellite homes by the end of 1989,[187] but claimed only 50,000 nationwide after three months of operation.

Rupert Murdoch found small independent retailers "very good and supportive" but was contemptuous of multiples, with "an underpaid kid behind the counter ready to sell a toaster",[188] and soon began to involve himself in distribution, initially by promotions through his newspapers. *Today* announced that it was to give away 10,000 Amstrad packages, a month's free trial was available to 100,000 *Sun* readers, and *News of the World* offered 20,000 vouchers worth £100 against purchase of a package. Despite his poor opinion of their abilities Murdoch carried out these promotions through multiples, generating resentment amongst independents,[189] though it was conceded that by getting dishes onto walls he was doing much-needed pump-priming. The *Today* offer produced 180,000 applications, each bearing useful data on the applicant's circumstances,[190] and most of those who failed to win were subsequently offered, as a test-marketing exercise, a rental deal which, from the introduction of encryption in February 1990, would include subscription to the movie channel. A month later, Sky made the deal universally available, at an all-in weekly charge of £4.49 (plus a £35 returnable deposit), insisting that it was a subscription package not a rental one, but criticizing rental companies Granada and Thorn for having failed to get behind satellite television;[191] rental had indeed been unattractive, because to rent a receiver the viewer had first to buy a dish and have it installed, at a typical total cost of £150.[192] To make entry to satellite viewing even easier, Sky offered the prospective subscriber two weeks' free trial before he signed up. By the end of 1989 there were half a million dishes installed, and more ambitious Astra receivers were coming onto the market; Panasonic's £450 kit featured full remote control, stereo sound, and a wealth of on-screen information including a noise-level bar-graph to assist alignment of the dish.

BSB's brief challenge

BSB were still several months short of operation. The company's own 'Marcopolo' satellite had been launched in August, but it had been decided in June that the service could not begin until Spring 1990, principally because ITT were late with one of the ICs for the receiver. Nine months previously Grundig UK had predicted this would happen;[193] now, the resignation was announced of BSB's Deputy Chief

Executive responsible for technology. But concurrently shareholders showed their confidence in BSB by injecting extra capital, and the IBA announced that it had granted the company two extra channels, making a total of five. This, however, brought its own problems, for it meant that four of the channels would have to be transmitted at half power until a second Marcopolo satellite was launched some time after broadcasting began. This in turn meant that BSB would have to use bigger receiver-aerials than planned, although these would still be smaller than those needed for Sky, since Marcopolo was a high-power satellite and Astra only a medium-power one.

The company had decided at an early stage to exploit their ability to use a small aerial by abandoning the conventional parabolic dish in favour of a flat, square array of 144 individual aerial-elements connected to the low-noise amplifier by paths of carefully matched length. Even before its feasibility as a mass-produced low-cost item was established, this 'squarial', measuring only 25cm x 25cm, was a central feature of BSB's advertising. Apart from being less obtrusive than a dish aerial and less vulnerable to bad weather it also had a wider beam-width and was correspondingly easier to install. But perhaps the most crucial aspect of the squarial's compactness was a legal one. The Department of the Environment allowed a household to mount, without planning permission, a single satellite aerial not more than 90cm in diameter. BSB had hoped that this restriction would not affect their access to homes already receiving Astra, because the squarial would be judged *de minimis* — i.e. too small to matter. But to deal with half-power transmission the squarial had to be increased to 40cm x 40cm, and the *de minimis* argument was less tenable; late in 1990 this issue was still unresolved.

When BSB finally began broadcasting on 29 April 1990, they had spent £400 million — twice as much as Sky's total after a year of operation — and a further £900 million was available. They made a point of leaving distribution strictly to the established trade, intervening only through a 'launch club', which gave benefits valued at £170 to viewers who signed up early and paid a small deposit. There was more equipment in the shops than there had been for the opening of Sky, if less than had been hoped for, and Philips were already producing 8,000 receivers a week.[194] Initial disposals were very similar to those Sky had achieved; after two months there were 34,000 receivers in operation, their aerials split between squarials and small parabolic dishes. Sky dishes, however, numbered almost a million by the autumn. BSB's own studios had been equipped to allow the full benefit of D-MAC to be realized, but did not originate by any means all of the programmes transmitted. As a foretaste of D-MAC's technical potentialities wide-screen films were transmitted in 16:9 aspect ratio, in readiness for the wide-screen television sets expected to reach the British market in late-1990, but with additional signals that caused the receiver to select at each moment the most effective portion of the picture for display on conventional sets with 4:3 screens.

Subsequent events have probably made such refinements irrelevant. It had been anticipated that Sky and BSB would compete for several years before one or the other prevailed,[195] but in the face of continuing losses the two companies announced in November 1990 that they were to merge, as British Sky Broadcasting. If the merger receives governmental approval, early indications are that the new company's five channels will eventually be transmitted only on an

Astra satellite, using PAL. Such a development, by undermining Europe's commitment to MAC technology, would greatly reduce the likelihood of an evolutionary change to high-definition television.

The View from 1990

Statistics published in 1987 showed that since 1972 the prices of a 3500S Rover car and of a man's haircut had both increased by about 750%, those of a glass of beer and a visit to the cinema by over 400%, and that of an electric iron by nearly 200%. The price of a 22" colour television set had fallen by 4%, to £248.[196] Insofar as this fact reflects the great technological progress achieved over fifteen years it can only be welcomed, but to an industry that has for decades maintained that margins were unhealthily low its message is depressing. More cheering are the 1989 figures showing that the average price of a large-screen receiver was £408, and that a third of the colour sets sold were bought for reasons other than the failure of an existing one, indicating both a trend towards multiple ownership and a desire to possess a modern-looking receiver. Nine out of ten large-screen receivers sold, and a small but increasing proportion of the small-screen ones, had the 'flatter, squarer tube' (FST) which has come to make its predecessors look decidedly old-fashioned. This 'fashion' aspect is welcomed as a sign that the British consumer may at last be getting away from wanting the cheapest possible receiver — a national trait attributable to the popularity of rental, which does not engender the same pride of possession as ownership does.

The FST also produces better pictures than its predecessors, with less liability to distracting reflections from lamps or windows, and often a 'black matrix' screen that preserves high contrast at restfully low brightness levels. However, of recent years the basic function of receiving and displaying a good picture has become so routine a matter that the technological thrust has been more in the direction of features such as teletext, on-screen displays and sophisticated remote controls. Television sound, for so long a Cinderella, has a powerful fairy-godmother in NICAM, which provides a further opportunity for marketing more expensive models. Radio receivers, too, show promise of outgrowing mere sound reproduction, with car radios already programmable to maintain uninterrupted vhf reception throughout a long journey, and the prospect of portable radios displaying details of the programme from inaudible transmitted pulses.

It is only by maintaining a leading position in providing such high-added-value features that the continuing manufacture of consumer-electronics products in developed countries can be assured; as Fidelity learned to their cost, straightforward small-screen colour receivers have already gone the way of cheap transistor radios. Over the last fifteen years Britain's setmaking and semiconductor industries have contributed to, and benefited from, the development of three major new technologies originated by her broadcasting organizations: teletext, MAC and NICAM. As broadcasting becomes more dominated by market forces through the operation of the forthcoming Broadcasting Act, it cannot be taken for granted that there will still be resources available for initiating such long-term R & D projects. The industry may thus lose a unique entrée to the high-added-value end of consumer electronics. The British industry's lack of involvement in the development of the domestic video recorder in the late-1970s meant that manufacture in the UK started late, and in the 1989 trade figures there was still a £49 million deficit in video recorders to set against the surplus of £58 million in colour receivers; reference has already been made to the prospect that a similar situation will arise over camcorders. More encouragingly, Philips and Thomson are jointly to invest £2 billion in the development of 1250-line high-definition technology conceived to evolve compatibly with the 625-line standard; it was, after all, a receiver manufacturer that gave the world the then high-definition of 405 lines in 1936.

Quite apart from its technology, the British consumer-electronics plant of to-day has little in common with its predecessor of even twenty years ago. Government financial incentives have completed the industry's dispersion from the Home Counties, while few of the plants owned by Far-Eastern companies are devoted exclusively to consumer electronics. What mainly keeps people on their toes is no longer the fear that the company down the road may drive them out of business with a better product; it is that the parent company may see their plant in Belgium or Germany as a better place in which to make the same product. In consumer electronics, happily, such merciless spotlighting of national differences tends to act in Britain's favour. The British industry's constructive attitude towards the challenge from Japan in the early-1970s has led to the UK becoming a favoured location for Far-Eastern companies' European plants, while the enlightened labour relations established in them stand as an example to other industries.

Besides its 'global players', the industry has room for companies of any size that establish for themselves a distinctive niche in the market. The niche is the manufacturer's natural habitat in the subjective world of high fidelity, where the customer expects even a loudspeaker amplifier to have a personality. To occupy one in the workaday realm of portable radios might be thought impossible had Roberts Radio, Britain's sole surviving indigenous setmaker, not been doing it so successfully for so long. Royal Warrants aside, that old adage of acoustic architects "wood is good" has no doubt contributed, as has the company's recent emphasis on push-button models to deal with the growing number of VHF stations.

In retailing, the increasing complexity of consumer electronics puts a premium on personal service and after-sales back-up, both traditional strong points of the independent dealer. This sector has become much more professional, more modern in its approach to marketing, and more competitive through its members' adoption of single-unit buying in the tradition of Spar grocers. As a result, its long-term decline has been arrested.[18] The strength of the multiples is nevertheless formidable. In May 1990 the Monopolies and Mergers Commission prohibited the Kingfisher group's proposed takeover of Dixons not only because Dixons and Comet, Kingfisher's electrical outlet, together commanded a share of between 21% and 26% of the market, but because in the fast-growing sector of 'out-of-town' shopping their share was 80%.[197]

Looking back

Today, a customer in a multiple store will casually buy a clock radio or a personal cassette player, perhaps even a portable colour receiver, adding to an inventory of consumer-electronic possessions he would need time to recall completely. In 1930, when only about a third of households had a wireless set, buying one was a matter of some moment, carefully gone into and possibly occasioning a visit to the Radio Show at London or Manchester. Today's matter-of-fact attitude is the result not just of affluence but of technology beyond the layman's imagining, so that as the artefacts have grown more wondrous they have ceased to excite wonder. Once, a voice from ten miles away on a crystal set was a scientific miracle; colour television from a satellite is already taken for granted.

In retrospect, the industry involved in this transformation looks to have been careering down a seventy-year slalom. Before the war it combined explosive growth with a dizzying pace of progress that in fifteen years took its products from ebonite panels and R valves to television sets and all-wave superhets. After the hectic war-years and the shortages that followed, television sustained a decade of prosperity until harsh realities asserted themselves around 1960, when 'stop/go' policies came into conjunction with over-capacity. In the early-1970s the same thing happened again, ending the brief interlude of euphoria brought by colour, but this time to an industry whose home market was no longer protected by an obsolescent line-standard. Radio manufacture, meanwhile, had largely succumbed to its own even harsher reality: that with the coming of the transistor a cheap plastic portable from Hong Kong was well fitted to radio's diminished role of providing background entertainment. The old order of things was finally ended by a new world of integrated circuits and automation, which made even Britain's biggest companies too small to stand alone. Now, leaner but fitter, Britain's setmakers are in good shape to face the 1990s.

It would have been understandable for an industry with such a history to be preoccupied with its own affairs — sometimes with its own survival — and indifferent to broadcasting's wider issues. Yet the infant industry's very first action was to set up the British Broadcasting Company — a definitive example of what can be achieved by collaboration between what we should now call the public and private sectors. A dozen years later, one of its companies was playing a leading role in developing the broadcasting end of high-definition television. Acting first through the RMA and then through BREMA, Britain's setmakers have continued this tradition of constructive collaboration with the broadcasters while remaining competitors. They have contributed greatly to the orderly introduction of new stages in technical development, and have consistently supported the concept of public service in broadcasting.

A BREMA Council Meeting of 1990. In 1979 the Association amended its
name, becoming the British Radio & Electronic Equipment Manufacturers'
Association, but retained its original initials

References

1   P S Carnt & G B Townsend, *Colour Television* (London, Iliffe Books Ltd, 1961) p. 2
2   Keith Jones, private conversations, 1989 & 1990
3   TAC/TSC Minutes of 72nd meeting, held 21 October 1965
4   Alfred Priestley, private conversation, 1988
5   Bernard Rogers, private conversation, 1990
6   TAC/TSC Committee Paper 371, September 1965
7   TAC/TSC Minutes of 71st meeting, held 17 August 1965
8   TAC/TSC Minutes of 74th meeting, held 2 December 1965
9   BREMA Annual Report for 1967, p. 6
10   Ibid., p. 17
11   BREMA Annual Report for 1968, p. 5
12   BREMA Annual Report for 1969, p. 5
13   Roy Browning, private conversation, 1990
14   Sid Jones, private conversations 1980 & 1990
15   *Financial Times*, 28 June 1968
16   Pye of Cambridge Ltd, Annual Report 1965–66
17   *Music Trades Review*, May 1966
18   John O'Neill, private conversation, 1989
19   *Financial Times*, 11 November 1966, p. 24
20   *Daily Telegraph*, 3 October 1969
21   Robert Jones & Oliver Mariott, *Anatomy of a Merger* (London, Jonathan Cape, 1970) p. 223
22   *Financial Times*, 14 December 1976
23   M J Lipman, Memoirs of a Socialist Business Man (Lipman Trust, c.1976) p. 182
24   Robert Jones & Oliver Marriott, op. cit., p. 270
25   Ibid., p. 266
26   E Brian Munt, *A Short History of Ediswan, Brimar and Mazda* (Unpublished, 1989)
27   Tom Ludlow, private conversation, 1989
28   Monopolies Commission, *Thorn Electrical Industries Ltd and Radio Rentals Ltd: A report on the proposed merger* (HMSO, 1968) para 22
29   Ibid., para 28
30   Lord Weinstock, private conversation, 1990
31   Monopolies Commission report, para 141
32   *Electronics Weekly*, 14 February 1968
3   Doug Topping, private conversations, 1989 & 1990
34   Monopolies Commission, op. cit., para 230
35   BREMA Annual Report for 1964, pp. 5–7
36   BREMA Annual Report for 1966, p. 7
37   Percy Adams, private conversation, 1988
38   *Comet: The story behind the name* (Comet Group plc, unpublished, c.1988)
39   David Hewitt, private conversation, 1990
40   Harry Lerner, *Currys: The first 100 years* (Cambridge, Woodhead-Faulkner, 1984) p. 75
41   Belling-Lee Golden Jubilee booklet, 1972: Gordon Bussey Collection
42   BREMA Annual Report for 1969, p.10
43   BREMA Annual Report for 1971, statistical supplement p.iv
44   BREMA Annual Report for 1970, p. 5

45   BREMA Annual Report for 1973, p. 12
46   Information supplied by J C MacKellar
47   *Financial Times*, 5 October 1973
48   BREMA Annual Report for 1973, p. 11
49   BREMA Annual Report for 1973, p. 7
50   BREMA Annual Report for 1974, p. 7
51   BREMA Annual Report for 1972, p. 6
52   Letter, Peter Shore to Sir Arnold Weinstock, 8 May 1974: BREMA archives
53   Letter, H K Jolly to Frank Chapple, 5 September 1974: BREMA archives
54   Oliver Sutton, private conversation, 1990
55   Letter, Yoshii to Thorneycroft, 27 December 1974: BREMA archives
56   BREMA Annual Report for 1976, p. 8
57   Dick Purdy, private conversation, 1990
58   Nick Lyons, *The Sony Vision* (New York, Crown Publishers Inc, 1976) p. 170
59   BREMA Annual Report for 1965, p. 7
60   BREMA Annual Report for 1973, p. 6
61   Minutes of RIC emergency meeting, 15 March 1977: BREMA Archives
62   BREMA Annual Report for 1977, p. 8
63   BREMA Annual Report for 1974, p. 8
64   Nick Lyons, op. cit., pp. 131–46
65   Gerald Wells, private conversation, 1990
66   Monopolies Commission, op. cit, para 57
67   *Sunday Telegraph*, 11 January 1976
68   Mike Bowers, private conversation, 1990
69   *The Economist*, 10 January 1976, p. 67
70   BREMA Annual Report for 1975, p. 8
71   *The Engineer*, 25 September 1975, pp. 20–22 & 70
72   Wally Wright, private conversation, 1990
73   BREMA Annual Report for 1975, Statistical Supplement
74   Sunday Telegraph, 11 January 1976
75   Jack Akerman, quoted in unidentified press cutting of January 1976: BREMA Archives
76   Thorn Colour Tubes Press Release, 5 January 1976
77   *Electrical & Electronic Trader*, 14 March 1975
78   *Financial Times*, 16 January 1976
79   *Financial Times*, 25 November, 1970
80   Reg Gray, Keith Jones, Sid Jones, Jim Ross, Jack Wilson, private conversations, 1989
81   Norman Butler, private conversation, 1990
82   Norman Leaks, private correspondence, 1990
83   Jimmie Griffiths, private conversation, 1990
84   BREMA Annual Report for 1964, Statistical Supplement p. iii
85   BREMA Annual Report for 1967, Statistical Supplement pp. iii & ix
86   BREMA Annual Report for 1976, p. 7
87   BREMA Annual Report for 1980, p. 9
88   Henry Skinner, private conversation, 1990
89   BREMA Annual Report for 1976, p. 9
90   Dennis Harvey, private conversation and correspondence, 1990
91   *Daily Telegraph*, 10 June 1974
92   *New Scientist*, 3 December 1981
93   BREMA Annual Report for 1977, p. 5
94   Memorandum, *Industrial Strategy: Electronic Consumer Goods* SWP: NEDO, February 1979
95   Dennis Swadling, private conversation, 1990
96   House Magazine *The Bridge*, December 1978, p. 7: Gordon Bussey Collection
97   House Magazine *The Bridge*, December 1977, p. 4: Gordon Bussey Collection

98   *The Guardian,* 3 April 1981
99   Malcolm Trevor, *Toshiba's New British Company* (London, Policy Studies Institute,1988) p. 13
100   *Daily Telegraph,* 3 April 1981
101   Malcolm Trevor, op. cit., p. 32
102   Ibid., p. 15
103   Ibid., p. 206
104   Ibid., p. 54
105   Roy Sanderson, private conversation, 1990
106   Malcolm Trevor, op. cit., p. 235
107   Ibid., pp. 77-8
108   Ibid., pp.126-7
109   Ibid., p. 39
110   W S Percival, private conversation, 1989
111   Bob Meens, private conversations, 1989-90
112   Notes of interview with Dr J D Stephenson, 1982: Mullard Archives
113   Dennis A Whitmore, *Work Study and Related Management Services* (London, Heinemann, 1968) p. 6
114   Malcolm Trevor, op. cit., p. 224
115   Ibid., p. 120
116   Ibid., p. 229
117   *Personnel Management,* October 1986, pp. 42–7:Tony Pegge, *Hitachi two years on*
118   Record of RIC/EIAJ meeting held at Stratford-upon-Avon, 5 & 6 November 1979: BREMA Archives
119   BREMA Annual Report for 1979, p.11
120   Sid Perry, personal correspondence, 1990
121   Nick Lyons, op. cit., pp. 56 & 60-1
122   *Quality Progress,* December 1978: J M Juran, *Japanese and Western Quality - A Contrast* (Quoted in NEDO document EDC/ELEC(79)CONS 16: BREMA Archives)
123   John McKellar, private conversation, 1989
124   Brian Johnson, private conversation, 1990
125   BREMA Annual Report for 1982, p. 13
126   BREMA Annual Report for 1983, p. 13
127   Malcolm Trevor, op. cit., pp. 147-8, 152
128   Sid Westwood, private conversation, 1990
129   Peter Mothersole, *The Evolution of the Domestic Television Receiver* (London, Royal Television Society, 1988) p. 23
130   Jim Ross, private conversation, 1979
131   *Electrical & Radio Trading,* 22 March 1990, p. 3
132   BREMA Annual Report for 1973, p. 15
133   House Magazine *The Bridge,* December 1977, p. 6: Gordon Bussey Collection
134   BREMA Annual Report for 1986, p. 16
135   BREMA Annual Report for 1982, p. 15
136   BREMA Annual Report for 1981, p. 7
137   BREMA Annual Report for 1980, p. 11
138   BREMA Annual Report for 1982, p. 11
139   BREMA Annual Report for 1983, p. 11–12
140   BREMA Annual Report for 1985, p. 9
141   *The UK Market for Domestic Television Sets 1967–1988* (Economics & Statistics Dept,BREMA, 1989)
142   BREMA Annual Report for 1984, p. 26
143   BREMA Annual Report for 1985, p. 14
144   Sales brochure *The Rank Teleplayer makes a far-reaching idea*

become reality, 1971: Gordon Bussey Collection

145   Nick Lyons, op. cit.,p. 209

146   BREMA Annual Report for 1982, p. 5

147   BREMA Annual Report for 1985, p. 26

148   BREMA Annual Report for 1986, p. 25

149   BREMA Annual Report for 1984, p. 19

150   BREMA Annual Report for 1983, p. 5

151   BREMA Annual Report for 1986, p. 31

152   BREMA Annual Report for 1987, p. 23

153   BREMA Annual Report for 1988, p. 22

154   *Electrical & Radio Trading*, 31 August 1989, pp. 4 & 19

155   *Electrical & Radio Trading*, 23 November 1989, p. 9

156   BREMA Annual Report for 1989, p. 16

157   Information supplied by Sony Manufacturing Company UK, Bridgend

158   Information from forthcoming Corporate Brochure, supplied by Mitsubishi Electric UK Ltd, Dec 1989

159   Brochure *Building the Future Together* (JVC (UK) Ltd, 1988)

160   Press Release, Panasonic News Centre, Europe, 21 April 1989

161   Malcolm Trevor, op. cit., p. 149

162   David Jones, private conversation, 1990

163   Brochure *Panasonic & Europe* (Matsushita Electrical Industrial Co Ltd, 1989)

164   Philips Croydon internal document: Gordon Bussey Collection

165   *Electrical Retailing*, October 1988, p. 10

166   *Sunday Times*, 20 May 1990, p. D9

167   Philips Electronics Press release, 3 May 1990

168   Keith Geddes, personal recollection

169   *Financial Times*, 19 June 1987

170   *Zen and the Art of TV Manufacture* (Equinox, Channel 4) 7 August 1988

171   *Electrical & Radio Trading*, 20 April 1989, p. 9

172   *Electrical & Radio Trading*, 29 March 1990, p. 12

173   *Design Classics: The Sony Walkman* (BBC2) 19 June 1990

174   BREMA Annual Report for 1986, p. 27

175   BREMA Annual Report for 1988, p. 14

176   Walter Anderson, private correspondence, 1990

177   BREMA Annual Report for 1983, p. 15

178   BREMA Annual Report for 1985, p. 17

179   BREMA Annual Report for 1986, p. 16

180   BREMA Annual Report for 1987, p. 22

181   Ibid., pp. 14–15

182   *Electrical & Radio Trading*, 12 May 1988, p. 33

183   *Electrical & Radio Trading*, 4 August 1988, p. 5

184   BREMA Annual Report for 1988, p. 16

185   *Electrical & Radio Trading*, 11 May 1989

186   *Electrical & Radio Trading*, 4 August 1988, p. 7

187   *Electrical & Radio Trading*, 17 August 1989, p. 3

188   *The Money Programme* (BBC2) 4 February 1990

189   *Electrical & Radio Trading*, 6 July 1989, p. 4

190   Ibid., p. 3

191   *Electrical & Radio Trading*, 7 September 1989, p. 4

192   *Electrical & Radio Trading*, 11 May 1989, p. 2

193   *Electrical & Radio Trading*, 22 September 1988, p.7

194   *Electrical & Radio Trading*, 19 April 1990, p. 27

195   Bronwen Maddox of Kleinwort Benson, Reference 188

196   BREMA Annual Report for 1987, p. 20

197   *The Guardian*, 24 May 1990

BIBLIOGRAPHY

W. J. Baker,	*A History of the Marconi Company*
	Methuen & Co. Ltd. (1970)
Asa Briggs,	*The History of Broadcasting in the United Kingdom*
	Oxford University Press, 4 vols.
	Vol. I The Birth of Broadcasting (1961)
	Vol. II The Golden Age of Wireless (1965)
	Vol. III The War of Words (1970)
	Vol. IV Sound and Vision (1979)
Asa Briggs,	*The BBC: The First Fifty Years*
	Oxford University Press (1985)
Susan Briggs,	*Those Radio Times*
	Weidenfeld and Nicolson (1981)
R W Burns,	*British Television: The formative years*
	Peter Peregrinus Ltd in association with the Science Museum London (1986)
Gordon Bussey,	see entries *Dictionary of Business Biography*
	Butterworths 5 vols.
	Vol. I E. K. Cole (1985)
	Vol. IV H.J. Pye (1985)
	Vol. IV W.G. Pye (1985)
Gordon Bussey,	*The Story of Pye Wireless*
	Pye Limited (1979), revised editions 1983,1986
Gordon Bussey,	*Vintage Crystal Sets 1922 - 1927*
	IPC Electrical-Electronic Press Ltd (1976)
Gordon Bussey,	*Wireless: The Crucial Decade 1924 - 34*
	Peter Peregrinus Ltd (1990)
Anthony Constable,	*Early Wireless*
	Midas Books (1980)
Keith Geddes,	*Broadcasting in Britain*
	Science Museum (1972)
Keith Geddes &	*The History of Roberts Radio*
Gordon Bussey	Roberts Radio Co. Ltd. (1988)
Keith Geddes &	*Television: the first fifty years*
Gordon Bussey	National Museum of Photography, Film & Television (1986)
Jonathan Hill,	*The Cat's Whisker*
	50 Years of Wireless design
	Oresko Books Ltd (1978)
Jonathan Hill,	*Radio! Radio!*
	Sunrise Press (1986)
Joan Long,	*A First Class Job!*
	Frank Murphy - radio pioneer
	The author (1985)
Peter L Mothersole,	*The Evolution of the Domestic Television Receiver*
	Royal Television Society (1988)
R.F. Pocock,	*The Early British Radio Industry*
	Manchester University Press (1988)
Thomas Singleton,	*The Story of Scophony*
	Royal Television Society (1988)
Tim Wander,	*2MT Writtle*
	The Birth of British Broadcasting
	Capella Publications (1988)
Norman Wymer,	*Guglielmo Marconi*
	GEC-Marconi Electronics Limited (c.1980)